CONTENTS

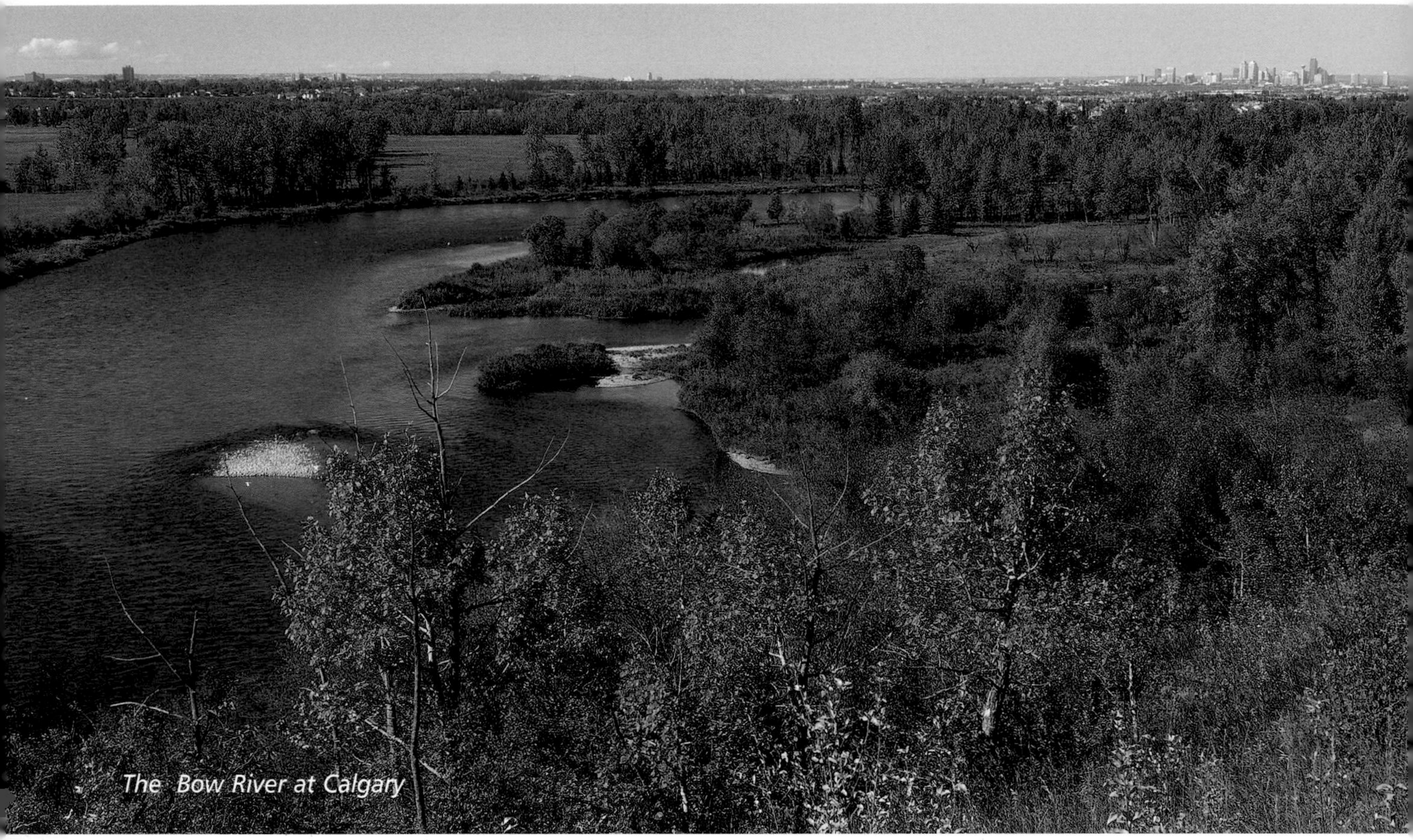

The Bow River at Calgary

From the Mountains to the Sea
The State of The Saskatchewan River Basin
2009

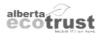

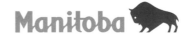

Includes bibliographical references.

ISBN 978-0-9730693-7-2

Printed in Canada

Saskatchewan Watershed Authority · The Calgary Foundation · Ducks Unlimited Canada, Conserving Canada's Wetlands · Alberta Environment · Environment Canada / Environnement Canada · alberta ecotrust · Manitoba

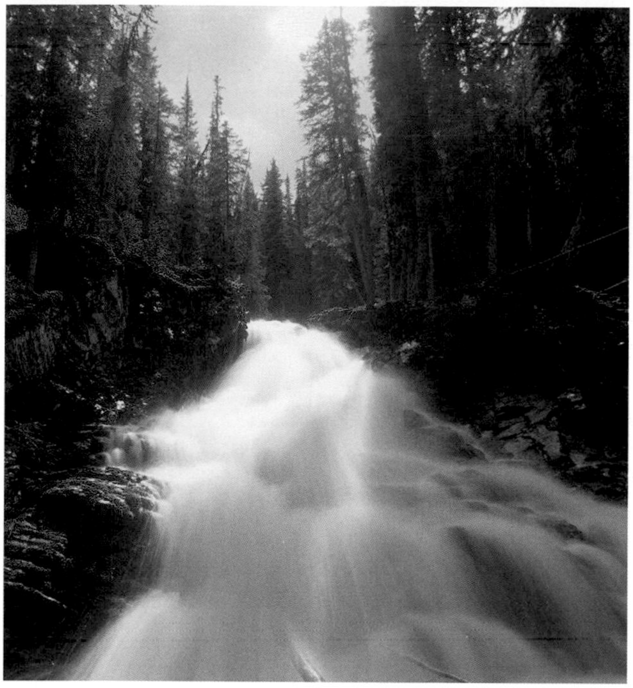

CHAPTER ONE
INTRODUCTION

Bighorn River, Alberta – a tributary of the North Saskatchewan River.

CHAPTER ONE
INTRODUCTION

The waters of the Saskatchewan River basin rise in the eastern slopes of the Rocky Mountains and flow across the Prairie Provinces to Lake Winnipeg, a vast inland sea. Most of the flow in the Saskatchewan River originates in the mountains, with the rest contributed by prairie runoff. The basin's terrain ranges from high alpine to foothills to rolling prairie to boreal plain. The lower basin features the largest freshwater delta in North America. Approximately three million people live in the basin, 95 percent of them in urban centres in Alberta and Saskatchewan. Not surprisingly, those three million people have profoundly altered the landscape of the basin.

PURPOSE OF THE REPORT

This report aims to fulfill, at least in part, the goal that those who make decisions and recommendations concerning the waters and associated resources within the Saskatchewan River basin do so with an understanding of the entire basin. One of the objectives is to reveal the overall condition of the basin by assembling existing information so that interested groups can review it easily. In this way, the report will contribute to integrated water resources management in the basin.

The report pays particular attention to hydrology, water use, water quality, and biodiversity aspects of the basin. It uses currently available data and information. No new data were obtained for this project, although some of the interpretations of existing data are new. As far as possible, information from all basin jurisdictions is brought to a common language and terminology.

Water management in the Saskatchewan River basin is complex. To foster a better appreciation of the agencies and organizations with responsibility for water management, the report identifies and describes water-related institutional arrangements in the basin.

The basin is subject to a number of water demands and water stresses, particularly evident in the South Saskatchewan sub-basin, where some 500 000 ha of irrigated agriculture consume significant quantities of water each year. These demands and stresses have led to a number of collaborative processes and formal arrangements unique to the Saskatchewan River basin. All three provinces in the watershed are in the process of developing water strategies to address issues in their respective portions of the basin. As well as this, the Prairie Provinces Water Board (PPWB) provides a means by which provincial water managers and federal representatives may equitably share the waters of transboundary streams, such as the Saskatchewan River. Because of shared experience and geography, there is a long history of partnership and collaboration in water management in the basin.

Since 1993, the Partners FOR the Saskatchewan River Basin has promoted stewardship and sustainability, delivering more than 20 major educational and informational projects. Partners FOR the Saskatchewan River Basin continues to strive for excellence, maintaining that the primary client is the River. On June 23, 2006 the Board of Directors agreed to prepare a State of the Basin Report for the Saskatchewan River basin. This project was made possible through the generous financial support of Alberta Environment, the Saskatchewan Watershed Authority, Manitoba Water Stewardship, Ducks Unlimited Canada, the Calgary Foundation, the Alberta EcoTrust, and Environment Canada.

INTEGRATED WATER RESOURCES MANAGEMENT

The origins of Integrated Water Resources Management (IWRM) lie in the increased environmental awareness of the early 1970s. Prior to that time, the dominant role of water managers and policy makers was to provide a sufficient supply of water at the appropriate time to meet reasonably foreseeable human needs. Unfettered flowing water was described as 'waste water' and dams as 'water conservation structures.' As populations grew and the economy developed, the necessity to accommodate the many overlapping and sometimes

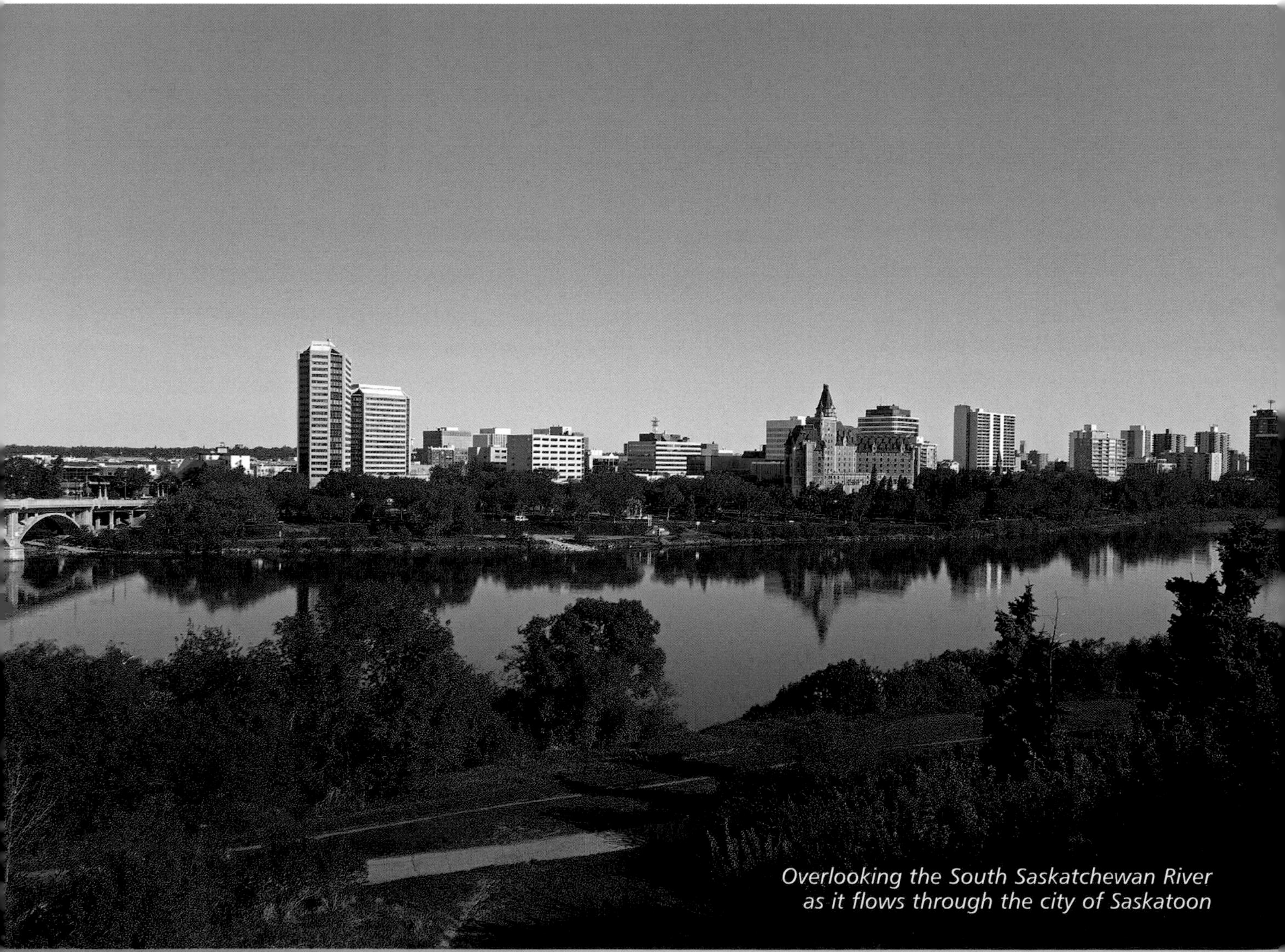

Overlooking the South Saskatchewan River as it flows through the city of Saskatoon

conflicting needs of various land and water uses became more evident. This resulted in efforts to balance human and ecosystem needs through inclusion of environmental considerations in water resources management activities. Indicators of increased environmental awareness include creation of departments of the environment, both nationally and provincially, and the holding of the United Nations Conference on Human Development in 1972.

In the 1980s, the call for environmentally sustainable economic development became more pronounced. A report of the World Commission on Environment and Development stressed the link between environmental and economic concerns and popularized the term 'sustainable development.'[1] The report called for holistic approaches to environmental management to ensure both human progress and human survival. More recently, at the Johannesburg Summit in 2002, the nations of the world agreed to 'develop integrated water resources management and water efficiency plans.' If sustainable development is considered as a goal, then IWRM is a process for achieving that goal.

Many definitions of IWRM can be found, but they all imply managing water resources to achieve publicly acceptable multiple objectives, including environmental, social and economic objectives. This requires not only interdisciplinary approaches to water management, but also attention to institutional arrangements, public engagement and capacity building. Integration in IWRM means more than simple coordination. It implies a holistic yet strategic approach. Sound science is a cornerstone of IWRM. This report uses the concepts of the Global Water Partnership: that is, IWRM is 'a process that promotes the coordinated development and management of water, land and related resources, in order to maximize the resultant economic and social welfare in an equitable manner without compromising the sustainability of vital ecosystems.'

The river basin is usually seen as the most appropriate spatial unit for IWRM, as the basin can encompass both natural processes and human uses. Other considerations include the hydrologic regime, ecological integrity, economic value of water, consideration of both structural and non-structural responses to water problems, inclusion of risk and uncertainty in project assessment, and public involvement.[2] IWRM, therefore, requires a process that integrates social, economic, environmental, and technical matters now, and in the future.

STRUCTURE OF REPORT

This report begins with an overview chapter that includes a discussion of the environmental indicators used later in the report. The next chapter reviews institutional arrangements currently in place, followed by a chapter describing the basin's water towers. This is the name given to the mountain and foothills region that produces most of the water flowing in the basin. There are then several chapters containing more detailed reviews of the major sub-basins of the basin. The report ends with a chapter concerning Lake Winnipeg, and a chapter reviewing key vulnerabilities facing the entire basin.

This report gives a snapshot of the Saskatchewan River basin based on information sources available in 2008. Key sources are identified throughout. Because of the basin's physical size and complexity, a report such as this can only be a summary. Interested readers can pursue the identified sources for more detailed information.

The report does not make recommendations. Based on the snapshot presented, readers are invited to draw their own conclusions concerning actions required for sustainable water management in their own portion of the basin. The Partners FOR the Saskatchewan River Basin will be holding meetings and discussions to identify possible next steps.

HOW TO USE THIS REPORT

This report may be read from start to finish, but other approaches can be used. A reader seeking a broad impression of the Saskatchewan River basin should read Chapter 2, which gives an overview, Chapter 3, which discusses institutional arrangements in the basin, and Chapter 12, which reviews vulnerabilities and threats to the basin as a whole. Readers seeking more information should read Chapter 4 and Chapter 11, which discuss the importance of the water towers and of Lake Winnipeg to the entire basin. Finally, readers having an interest in a specific part of the basin should read the appropriate sub-basin chapter. As we are all upstream of other water users, please read the chapter that discusses the part of the basin immediately downstream of your chapter.

ENDNOTES

[1] World Commission on Environment and Development 1987. *Our Common Future.* Oxford University Press. Oxford, UK.

[2] Kreutzweiser, R.D. 1995. "Water Resource Management: Canadian Perspectives and the Great Lakes Water Levels Issue". In *Resource and Environmental Management in Canada,* edited by Bruce Mitchell. Oxford University Press. Oxford, UK.

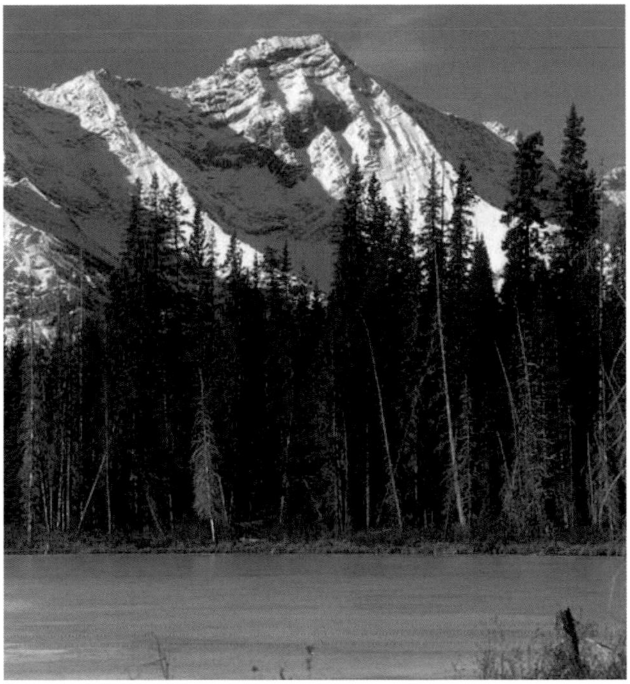

CHAPTER TWO
BASIN OVERVIEW

CHAPTER TWO
BASIN OVERVIEW

Originating on the eastern slopes of the Rocky Mountains of Alberta and Montana, the Saskatchewan River basin extends from the continental divide through Alberta, Saskatchewan and Manitoba to Lake Winnipeg, the 11th largest freshwater lake in the world, by surface area. The name Saskatchewan is taken from the Cree Indian word, kisiskâciwanisîpiy, *meaning swift-flowing river.*

Saskatchewan River Basin by Province and State

Montana	1760 km^2
British Columbia	28 km^2
Alberta	209 560 km^2
Saskatchewan	172 118 km^2
Manitoba	23 398 km^2

Although it is part of the larger Saskatchewan-Nelson system, which flows into Hudson Bay, the Saskatchewan River system itself is the fourth longest in North America. The river travels about 1940 kilometres from the Rocky Mountains to Lake Winnipeg. It drains a surface area of some 405 864 km^2 – almost the size of France. The basin is shown on the inside cover of this report.

The terms basin or drainage basin and watershed tend to be used interchangeably in North America, while a similar term, catchment, is rarely used. Technically, the watershed represents the height of land between basins from which water is shed in two direction: that is, it is the basin boundary. A sub-basin is simply a drainage subdivision within the Saskatchewan River basin.

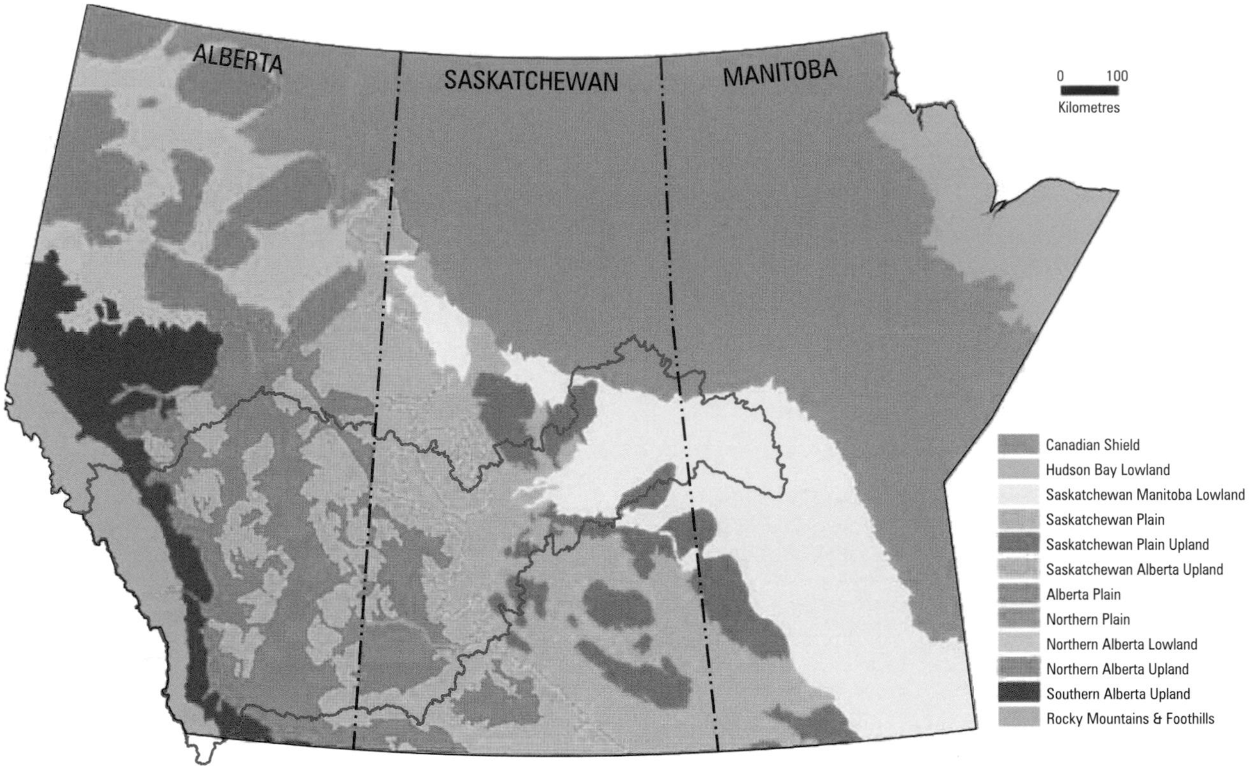

Figure 2.1. Physiographic Regions of the Prairie Provinces.[3]

LANDFORM AND LAND COVER

The Saskatchewan River basin extends from the continental divide across a vast interior plain to the Canadian Shield. The higher elevations are characterized by mountain peaks over 3000 m in height. Dramatic cliffs and rock faces support some low-growing plants on warmer exposures. Somewhat lower elevations contain open stands of alpine fir, while yet lower elevations are covered by stands of fir, pine and white spruce. The Alberta foothills, characterized by a series of ridges parallel to the mountain range, form a transition zone to the plains. In the lower river valleys, aspen and poplar forests occur on alluvial fans and terraces, while grasslands dominate the warmest, driest exposures.[1]

The interior plain descends in three steps: the Alberta plain, having an elevation of over 750 m; through the Saskatchewan plain, having an elevation of 450 to 650 m; to the Manitoba lowland, where elevations are less than 300 m (Figure 2.1). The Cypress Hills in southern Alberta and Saskatchewan and the Porcupine Hills near Pincher Creek, Alberta are the only parts of the basin not glaciated in the last ice age. The undulating, hummocky plain that we see today is composed of 50 to 300 m thick deposits of glacial drift from earlier ice ages. Brown and dark brown soils are dominant and the natural landcover of the plains is mixed grasses with limited aspen woodlands in the northern fringe. In the southern parts of the basin, trees and shrubs are found only in the river valleys where there is enough moisture to support riparian forests. The deciduous and mixed-wood forests of the northern plains give way to coniferous forest in the lower basin.[2]

Short-grass and tall-grass prairie covered much of the Saskatchewan River basin prior to European settlement. Deciduous and mixed-wood forest dominated the northern plains. Small potholes and other wetlands dotted the landscape. Human activity has now transformed this landscape. Figure 2.2 depicts the current landcover of the basin.

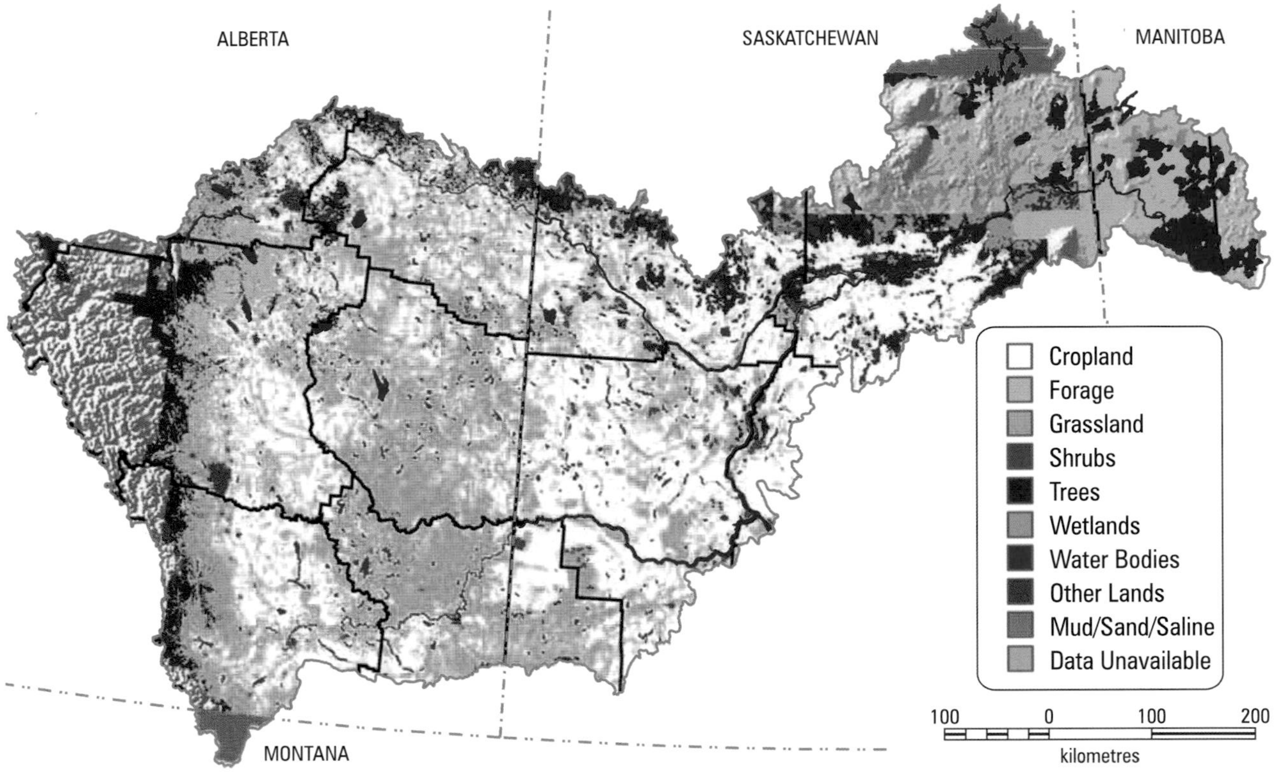

Figure 2.2. Landcover of the Saskatchewan River Basin (source, PFRA)

Wetlands are any lands that are permanently or temporarily covered or saturated with water. Plant growth in wetlands is adapted to saturated soils. Water may collect on the land surface long enough to promote soil development and, subsequently, support the types of plants and animal communities adapted to saturated conditions. The water table is near the surface and water less than two metres deep may cover the land for much of the growing season.

Wetlands are classified according to five general classes: bog, fen, swamp, marsh, and shallow open water.[4] Some wetlands are classified as peatlands with subclasses of bog, fen or swamp. Non-peat wetlands are known as mineral wetlands, with subclasses of swamp, marsh or shallow water.

Wetlands vary in size. Wetlands may contain saline water or freshwater. Water movement may be from the wetland to groundwater or the reverse. More than 70 percent of prairie wetlands have been altered or lost since European settlement, primarily to assist agricultural development.[5]

An examination of wetland changes in the Saskatchewan River basin in Alberta over the last 50 years indicates that 66 percent of the wetland area has been drained or altered to the point where little wetland ecosystem function remains. The analysis uses high-resolution aerial photography. Wetland loss in the Saskatchewan portion of the basin is likely similar. The remaining intact wetlands continue to play an important role in the basin. Wetlands are critical habitat for many species. They retain nutrients and contaminants and help control erosion. They also help re-charge groundwater systems.

Ecologically distinct areas can be classified based on geology, landform, soils, vegetative cover, climate, hydrology, wildlife and human factors. The classification hierarchy consists of ecozones, which are further subdivided into ecoregions and ecodistricts. The boundary between two ecozones is

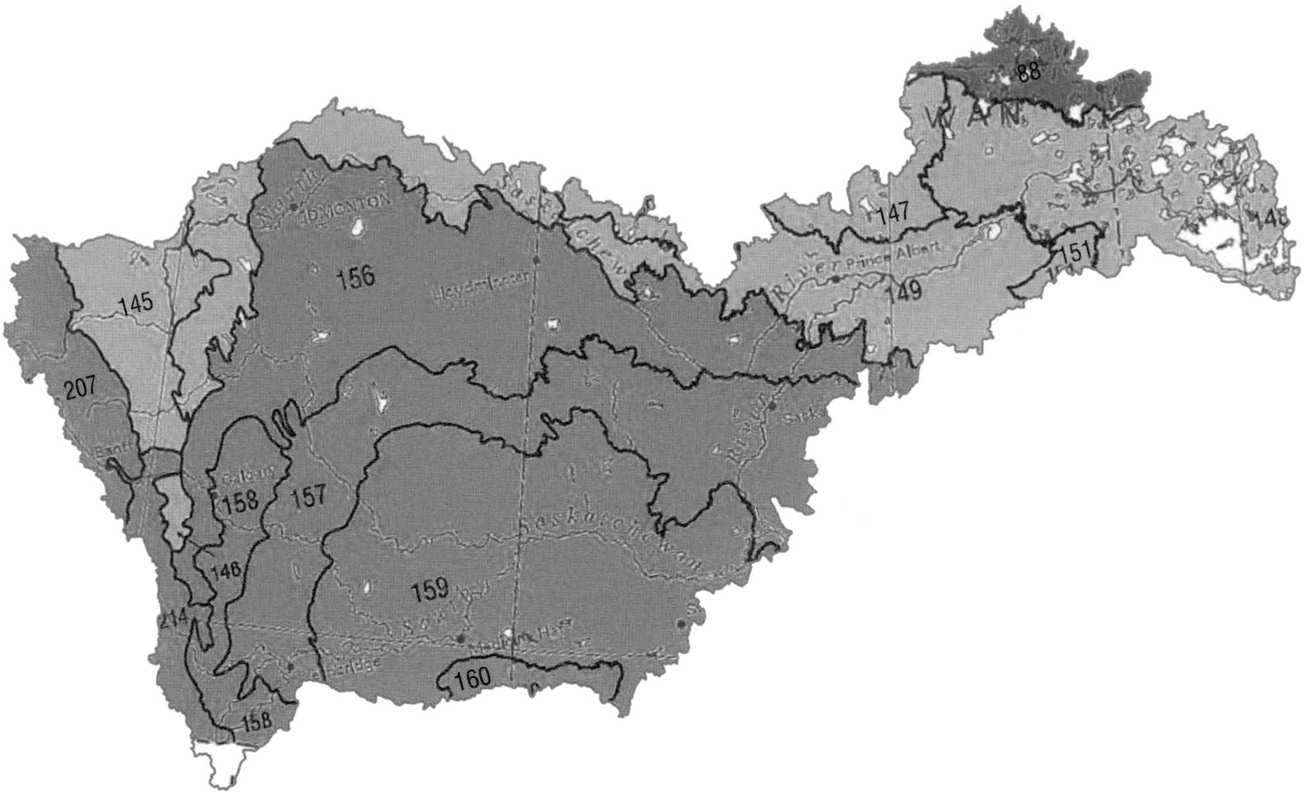

Figure 2.3. Ecozones of the Saskatchewan River Basin (source, Ecological Stratification Working Group).

Ecozone	Ecoregion Number and Description	
Montane Cordillera	214	eastern continental ranges
	207	northern continental ranges
Prairie	156	aspen parkland
	157	moist mixed grassland
	158	fescue grassland
	159	mixed grassland
	160	cypress upland
Boreal Plain	145-6	western Alberta upland
	148	mid-boreal lowland
	149	boreal transition
	151-2	mid-boreal uplands
Boreal Shield	88	Churchill River upland

known as an ecotone. A federal-provincial-territorial process in 1996 identified 13 Canadian ecozones.[6] (Alberta has now classified natural regions and subregions that are similar, but not identical, to the national ecozones and ecodistricts.) Although dominated by the prairie ecozone, the basin contains portions of three other ecozones: the montane cordillera, the boreal plain and the boreal shield (see box and Figure 2.3). The montane cordillera is the Rocky Mountain portion of the basin. Together with the foothills portion of the boreal plain, this part of the basin is identified as the 'water towers' – the source of much of the water that flows in the basin. The boreal plain ecozone generally forms a transition from the prairie to the boreal shield. Moving northward and eastward, shrublands, birch, aspen and poplar grove woodlands give way to spruce, pine and tamarack forests. Wetlands, including peatlands with organic soils, cover a significant portion of the ecozone. A very small northern portion of the basin at the Saskatchewan-Manitoba boundary lies in the boreal shield ecozone. This rolling landscape features exposed bedrock and closed stands of spruce and fir.

CLIMATE

The Saskatchewan River basin experiences the cold continental climate that is typical of the North American central plains. Winters are long and cold, but sunny, while summers are short and warm. Winter temperatures, particularly in southern Alberta, can be raised quickly by chinook winds, dry westerly winds sweeping down the slopes of the Rockies.

Precipitation is most significant in the mountains with average annual precipitation ranging up to 1500 mm. The prairie ecozone is particularly dry, even semi-arid in the south, with precipitation ranging from 300 mm in the rain-shadow of the mountains to as much as 500 mm. In the plains portion of the basin, precipitation increases progressively from southwest to northeast. Most of the annual precipitation falls as rain in the spring and summer. These rains replenish soil moisture and sustain crop production. Runoff in the basin, however, is largely dependent on spring snow-melt on the plains and melting of the winter snowpack in the mountains. Evaporation over much of the basin exceeds precipitation, leading to moisture deficits.

HYDROLOGY

Most of the water that flows in the Saskatchewan River originates in the water towers of the Rocky Mountains. Indeed, the Saskatchewan River's two principal tributaries, the North Saskatchewan and South Saskatchewan rivers, can be termed 'exotic' rivers as these rivers serve simply as large conveyance channels taking Rocky Mountain water across the plains. The North Saskatchewan River originates at the Saskatchewan Glacier in the Columbia Icefields. Headwaters tributaries include the Cline, Brazeau, Ram, and Clearwater rivers. The South Saskatchewan River is fed by three major tributaries: the Red Deer, Bow and Oldman rivers. Tributaries entering the main channels from the plains include the Battle River, which joins the North Saskatchewan River near Battleford, and Swift Current Creek, which joins the South Saskatchewan River near Swift Current. There are several lower basin tributaries including the Carrot and Sturgeon-Weir rivers, which join the Saskatchewan River near the Manitoba boundary.

The mountain headwaters of the Saskatchewan River have high gradients that decrease as the channel moves downstream. The North Saskatchewan River, for example, has an average gradient of 2 to 3 m/km upstream of Rocky Mountain House. This slope decreases to 0.4 m/km at Edmonton and 0.15 m/km in Saskatchewan. The braided channel in the mountains gives way to a single entrenched channel in the foothills. At Edmonton, the river meanders through a one-kilometre-wide valley bounded by walls almost 100 metres in height. The streambed in Alberta consists of gravels that become increasingly sandy at the Alberta-Saskatchewan boundary. The South Saskatchewan River is similar in form. The Bow River has a slope of 7 m/km at Banff, while the South Saskatchewan River downstream of Medicine Hat has a slope of 0.5 m/km. The streambed of the South Saskatchewan River is composed of gravel and cobbles in Alberta, becoming gravel, sand and silt in Saskatchewan. An important natural feature of the Saskatchewan River basin is the Saskatchewan River Delta – the largest inland freshwater delta in North America – beginning just west of the Saskatchewan-Manitoba boundary. This 8000 km^2 delta is a wildlife area of national significance. At the downstream part of the delta, the river flows through Cedar Lake, now regulated for hydropower, and on to Lake Winnipeg.[7]

The streams, lakes and wetlands of the Saskatchewan River basin are sustained by snowmelt. Snow accumulating throughout the winter on the eastern slopes of the Rocky Mountains melts in the spring and summer, providing significant river flows in May, June and July. Although this snowmelt runoff can be augmented by spring rains, the available water supply for the basin is largely dependent on the accumulated snowpack. A significant portion of the precipitation that falls in the mountains contributes to groundwater recharge, which, in turn, discharges to

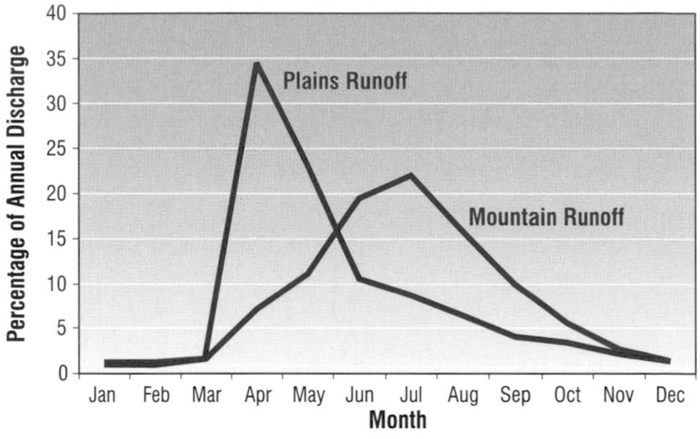

Figure 2.4. Percentage of Annual Runoff by Month for Plains and Mountain Streams.

surface water. Almost 90 percent of the water that flows in the North and South Saskatchewan rivers originates in the mountains. Plains tributaries joining the Saskatchewan River near the Saskatchewan-Manitoba boundary contribute large volumes of runoff. Runoff in the plains in April and May is also governed by spring snowmelt and early spring rains. In southern Alberta and southwestern Saskatchewan, winter snowpacks can be significantly reduced by chinook winds. The plains runoff replenishes local water supplies, including groundwater and wetlands, but may never join the principal streams. The rain that falls on the plains also replenishes groundwater and some wetlands. Figure 2.4 shows the timing and relative quantities of runoff by month for typical prairie and mountain streams. The total volume of runoff from the mountains is much greater, as stated earlier.

In the basin as a whole, 44 percent of the land surface does not contribute surface runoff to the main streams in a median year. In these areas, surface runoff may replenish local impoundments and wetlands. Surface water in a non-contributing area may also recharge groundwater and this groundwater may contribute to the baseflow of a

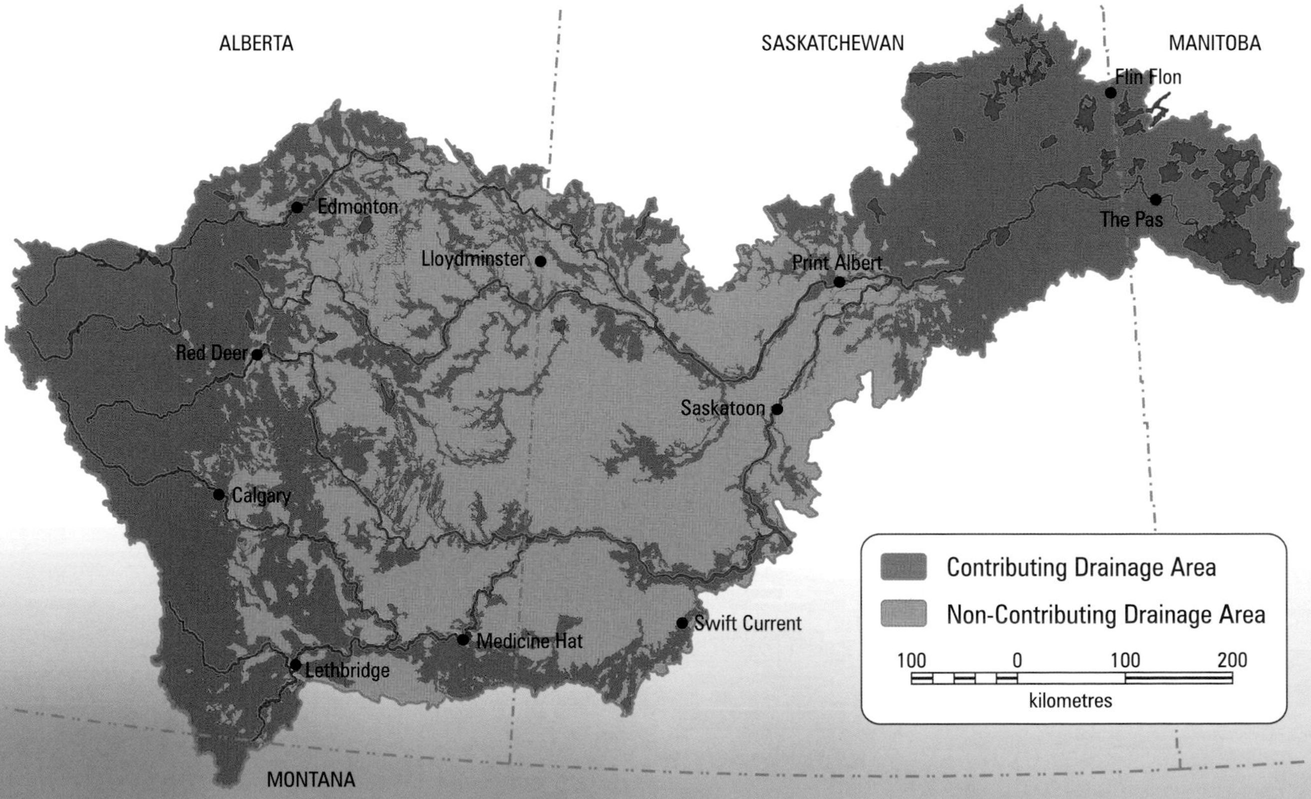

Figure 2.5. Contributing and Non-contributing Drainage (adapted from data, courtesy of PFRA).

nearby stream. In wet years, flow from some non-contributing areas may join the main streams. In other cases, such as for Sounding/Eyehill Creek in the North Saskatchewan River basin, the non-contributing area is a closed basin that does not contribute flow even in an extraordinarily wet year. Figure 2.5 identifies the contributing and non-contributing areas. Most of the non-contributing areas lie in the prairie ecozone. The portion of the drainage basin that contributes to streamflow in a median year is considered the effective drainage area of the basin. Changes to the landscape such as drainage works or road construction may influence the effective drainage area. Because of the small contribution of runoff from the plains, the natural flows of the North and South Saskatchewan rivers may sometimes decrease as they flow eastward.

Water levels and streamflows, as well as lake levels, in the basin are monitored by the federal and provincial governments, under cost-sharing arrangements. Other organizations such as hydroelectric companies may also contribute data. There are 301 streamflow stations in the basin and 86 lake or reservoir-level stations. These stations are operated by Environment Canada's Water Survey of Canada and by co-operating agencies such as Alberta Environment, Saskatchewan Watershed Authority and Manitoba Water Stewardship, under federal-provincial agreements. Data from all the sites and other related information can be obtained on-line from the Water Survey website at www.wsc.ec.gc.ca.

Streamflows in the basin exhibit considerable variability, both within years and between years. This natural variability is shown in Table 2.1. The units of volume used are cubic decametres: that is, thousands of cubic metres. One measure of flow reliability is the relation of the range in flows to the median flow. Mountain-fed streams, like the Bow River, have a much more reliable flow than streams originating on the plains, like the Battle River.

The hydrological indicators used in this report pertain to the reliability of the annual flow, the shape of the flow hydrograph, and the degree to which the flow is regulated.

Although streamflow is the source of most of the water used in the basin, groundwater is an important source of rural water supplies. Both Alberta and Saskatchewan consider groundwater not to be potable if the total dissolved solids (TDS) are more than 400 mg/L. Figure 2.6 displays the

Table 2.1. Natural Variability of Streamflows in the Saskatchewan Basin.

River	Minimum (dam^3)	Median (dam^3)	Average (dam^3)	Maximum (dam^3)	Range as Percent of the Median
Ram River near the Mouth	291 000	420 000	466 000	884 000	141
North Saskatchewan River at Interprovincial Boundary*	4 340 000	6 794 000	7 064 000	12 293 000	117
Battle River at Interprovincial Boundary*	53 200	215 000	273 000	1 281 000	570
Red Deer River near Bindloss*	725 000	1 590 000	1 841 000	5 565 000	305
St. Mary River at the Mouth*	425 000	849 000	882 000	1 625 000	136
Bow River at Banff	884 000	1 247 000	1 240 000	1 620 000	58
South Saskatchewan River at Interprovincial Boundary*	4 612 000	8 661 000	9 055 000	17 509 000	149
Carrot River near Turnberry	826 800	5 049 000	5 826 000	14 010 000	260

** Flows have been naturalized. See discussion in the water management section of this chapter.*

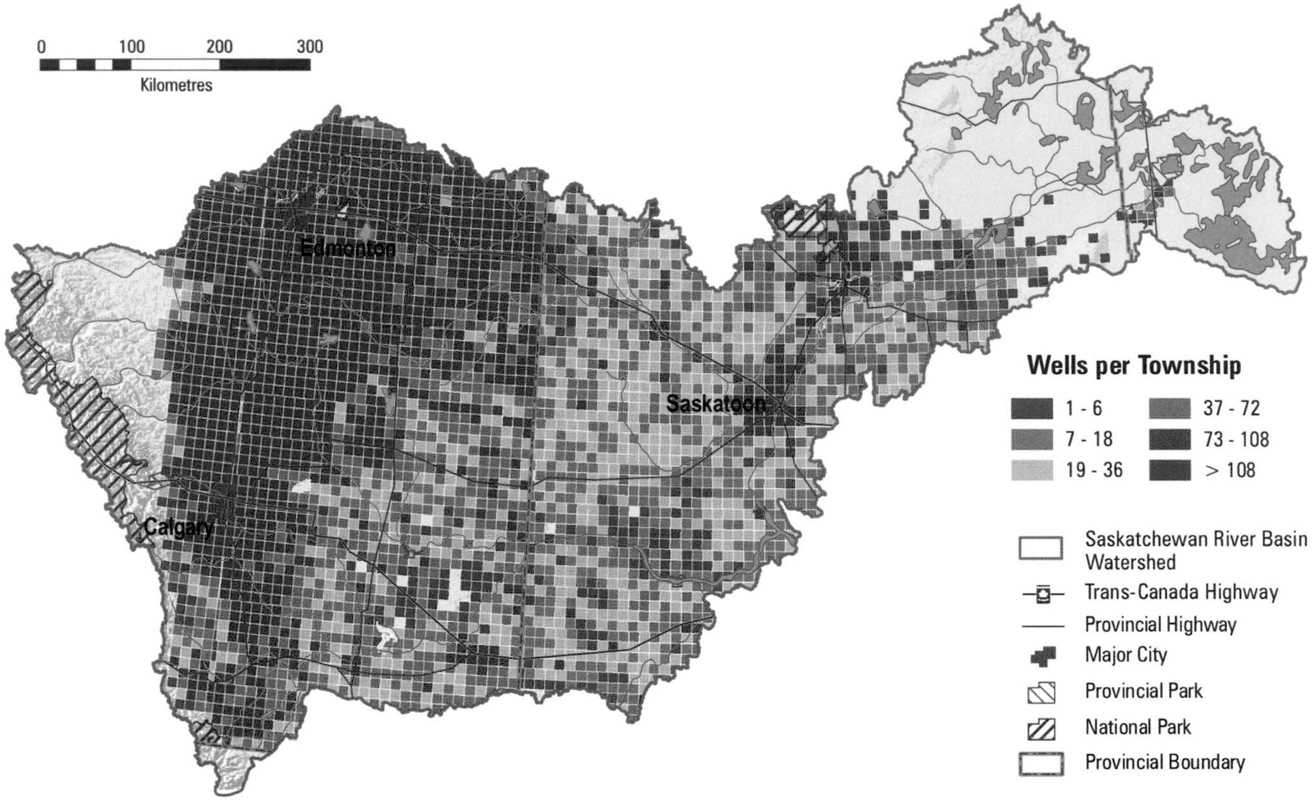

Figure 2.6. Distribution of Potable Groundwater Wells by Township (adapted from data courtesy of PFRA).

number of potable groundwater wells by township for the period 1961 to 1999. The figure includes wells drilled into deep aquifers and those drilled or bored into shallow aquifers: that is, aquifers less than 15 m in depth.[8]

An aquifer is a water-bearing formation sufficiently porous to yield water to a well. Prairie aquifers can be classed as either bedrock or quaternary aquifers. Bedrock aquifers are either porous or fractured enough to yield water, while quaternary aquifers are near-surface sands and gravels, deposited by glacial ice sheets in the last 2.5 million years. These latter aquifers tend to be unconfined and can be recharged from precipitation or surface water. They can, as well, supply water to springs and contribute to streamflow.

HUMAN SETTLEMENT

People have lived in the Saskatchewan River basin for about 11 000 years.[9] By the time English and French fur traders arrived in the basin, the use of horses was well established, as was aboriginal use of the waterways.

The first European to visit the basin was Henry Kelsey, a Hudson's Bay Company fur trader, who was sent in 1690-92 to strengthen trade with the Cree people and to look for minerals and medicinal plants.[10] Guided by returning Cree, he left Fort York on Hudson Bay in June 1690. He established a base at near present-day The Pas and travelled southwest into the Pasquia Hills and upper Assiniboine River basin. During his expedition he met and travelled with Assiniboine and Naywatame people. His journals contain the first descriptions of the plants

Indigenous People of the Basin

When Europeans first visited the Saskatchewan River basin, they did not find an empty land. The basin had been occupied by its original inhabitants for thousands of years. It is generally considered that the Americas were indeed empty land until people arrived using a land bridge from Asia. These original people used both a coastal route and an interior route through present-day Alberta. At the end of the last glaciation, as the Laurentide ice sheet pulled away from the Rocky Mountains, a land corridor opened sufficiently to allow people to move south into the plains. One site on St. Mary Reservoir indicates a hunter society some 11 000 to 11 350 years ago. These early inhabitants are believed to have hunted large, now-extinct mammals such as giant bison. By 8000 years ago a well-developed, bison-hunting society had evolved on the plains. Although people depended on other species of animals and plants as well, the bison not only provided sustenance but also provided shelter, clothing and tools. Plains people distinguish two time periods: the dog days and the horse days. Dogs were the only animals domesticated by the early inhabitants, and were used to carry goods. Horses originating from Spanish colonialists to the south arrived in the basin in the mid-1700s, before the Europeans. They became an essential element of the flourishing hunter-warrior culture of the plains encountered by the first Europeans.

When Europeans first visited the basin, it was occupied by several Indian nations including the Blackfoot, Assiniboine and Cree. The Blackfoot Confederacy was composed of five distinct nations: the Siksikah (Blackfoot), the Kainai (Blood), the Piikani (Peigan), the Sarcee and the Gros Ventre. They occupied almost the entire basin in Alberta. The Plains Cree occupied areas in Alberta, Saskatchewan, Manitoba in the prairie ecozone, while the Woodlands Cree occupied forested areas in northern parts of the basin in the three provinces. The Assiniboine occupied areas in Manitoba and Saskatchewan. For most of the First Nations in the Saskatchewan River basin occupying the prairie ecozone, bison were integral to their culture. Seasonal movement involved following bison in the summer and breaking up into smaller bands for the winter.

The Woodland Cree, residing in forested areas, fished, hunted (e.g. caribou, moose) and trapped and travelled along waterways by birch bark canoe. The woodland people were particularly important to the fur trade as they established themselves as intermediaries between the Hudson's Bay Company and the plains people. Trading was important to aboriginal culture long before the arrival of the Europeans. Goods regularly made their way from the Gulf of Mexico to the plains.

Trade goods, however, were not the only thing to cross the continent. Three enormous smallpox epidemics scourged First Nations in the 1780s, 1830s and 1860s. Many communities lost as many as 75 percent of their people in a matter of weeks. The period of recovery from these epidemics was long and difficult.

and animals of the Canadian prairie but his travels were unknown outside the Hudson's Bay Company for decades, not being reported to the British Parliament until 1749.

In 1741, Louis-Joseph La Vérendrye visited the lower Saskatchewan River and established Fort Bourbon near present-day Grand Rapids.[11] His father's earlier expeditions to the North American central plains took him south of the Saskatchewan River basin. By the mid-1750s, the Saskatchewan River had French posts at present-day The Pas and at the forks of the North and South Saskatchewan rivers (The Forks). Anthony Henday, a Hudson's Bay Company fur trader, passed through this area with a large party of Cree people in 1754-55. His travels took him to the Red Deer and North Saskatchewan rivers and he is generally regarded as the first European to visit

Alberta.[12] Another Hudson's Bay company trader, Samuel Hearne, established Cumberland House in the Saskatchewan River Delta in Saskatchewan in 1774. The village is the oldest continuously-occupied settlement in the basin. For almost another 100 years, the Saskatchewan River basin continued to draw the attention of fur traders, explorers and missionaries.

In 1857-59, John Palliser, following a private visit in 1847, mounted a scientific expedition to the British territory in the west.[13] His travels covered much of the southern Prairies, including the Saskatchewan River basin upstream of The Forks, and parts of southern British Columbia. His detailed reports were an essential source of information for planners of western settlement. Notably, he established the extent of a 'fertile belt' bounded on the south, by what is known today as Palliser's triangle, the semi-arid plains region that was experiencing drought at the time of the expedition. The mid-1800s marked the transition of the Canadian Prairies from a fur trade society to an agricultural society.

The decade of the 1870s brought many changes to the mid-continent.[14] In 1870, the fledgling Canadian government assumed control of western British North America from the Hudson's Bay Company. Following this assumption of sovereignty, and with increasing pressures of European settlement, a series of numbered treaties was negotiated with First Nations in the 1870s. Treaties 4, 5, 6, 7, and 10 negotiated in 1874 to 1877, cover parts of the Saskatchewan River basin. The treaties are nuanced and complex but, in essence, are aimed at defining the relationship between First Nations and the Crown, as represented by the government of Canada.

The late 1800s was a period of burgeoning economic development in western Canada, prompted, in part, by completion of the transcontinental railway in 1885, and the subsequent rush of settlers. Government policies aimed at settling the West led to a population boom in the early part of the 20th century. In succeeding years, this largely rural agricultural population has been transformed into a highly urbanized, industrial and post-industrial society. According to the 2006 census, the total population of the Saskatchewan River basin is about three million. This population is concentrated in the Province of Alberta with 2 412 736 people living in the Edmonton-to-Calgary corridor. Table 2.2 shows population figures for the major centres in the basin, by province. While water demands for irrigation and other agricultural purposes continue, urban residents need water for domestic and industrial purposes. Basin residents and visitors also use the water resources of the basin for many recreational purposes.

The population of urban centres throughout the basin is steadily increasing. Rural populations in much of the Alberta portion of the basin are increasing, while those in Saskatchewan and Manitoba are decreasing.

Table 2.2. Population of Census Metropolitan Areas in the Basin, 2006 Census.

Alberta		Saskatchewan		Manitoba	
Calgary	1 107 200	Saskatoon	202 340	Flin Flon	5594
Edmonton	1 034 945	Prince Albert	34 138	The Pas	5589
Red Deer	82 772	Battlefords	17 377		
Lethbridge	74 637	Swift Current	14 946		
Medicine Hat	56 997	Lloydminster	24 028*		

** Includes population in both Alberta and Saskatchewan.*

WATER MANAGEMENT AND WATER USE

The details of water management in the Saskatchewan River basin are covered extensively in Chapter 3 – Institutional Arrangements. Although natural resources management, including water management, is the constitutional responsibility of provincial governments, water management in the basin involves a web of international, national, provincial, First Nations, regional, and local governments and organizations. Consider, for example, that the St. Mary River and its tributaries in the headwaters of the South Saskatchewan River are subject to the international *Boundary Waters Treaty*. Similarly, streamflows at interprovincial boundaries are subject to the *Master Agreement on Apportionment* between the federal government and the three provincial governments. Federal lands within the provinces, such as national parks, First Nations reserves, and Canadian forces bases also introduce complexity, as do federal responsibilities related to agriculture and fisheries.

Water management in the basin is based on the principle of prior appropriation. That is, water rights are vested in the provincial crown, and the province licenses withdrawal or diversion of a specified quantity of water, subject to certain terms and conditions on a first-come, first-served basis.[15] Early water users, such as irrigators and hydroelectric power developers, could then proceed with major investments knowing that water would be available to support their developments. The full water needs of later licensees may be met only under favourable flow conditions, but the right is established and the risk involved is clear. In practice, during water shortages, water diversions may be reduced in reverse order of licence seniority. Alternatively, rights holders may agree to share water. It should be noted that legislation in the three Prairie Provinces allows for unlicensed domestic or on-farm water use by landowners. This is a vestige of the riparian principle under British common law.

Western Water Law

When settlers first arrived in the West, water users were subject to the riparian doctrine of British common law. That is, water rights belonged to the owner of the land adjacent to the stream. Water used, however, must be returned to the stream substantially unchanged in quantity or quality. The riparian doctrine assumes an abundant supply of water, something that cannot be guaranteed in the semi-arid west. In 1894, *The North-west Irrigation Act* vested all water rights in the federal Crown and introduced the doctrine of prior allocation. That is, the Crown could grant exclusive water rights on a first-come, first-served basis, priority being indicated by the date of application. With secure title to water, settlers could then make the necessary investments in irrigation development. Although there have been some refinements since that time, such as licences for specified periods, the water licensing system in each of the four western provinces is largely based on the doctrine of prior allocation.

Water use is a broad term that includes any use of water for any activity, economic or otherwise. Water use can include withdrawal or diversion of water from a source, or water used in place. Examples of water use in various sectors include: agriculture (for irrigation and watering livestock), municipal services (including urban residential, commercial and industrial use), industrial (primarily mining, oil and gas), energy (thermal and hydro-electric), recreational (boating or golf courses), or environmental (instream flows or sustaining wetlands). Water uses may be considered consumptive or non-consumptive. For example, water used in stock-watering is almost entirely consumed, while water used in cooling thermal power stations is almost entirely returned to the water body. Provincial agencies consider the likely consumption of water for a specific use in their licensing processes. Summing up the quantities of water allocated by water licences will overestimate water consumption in a river basin as many licensees do not use their entire entitlement in a given year.

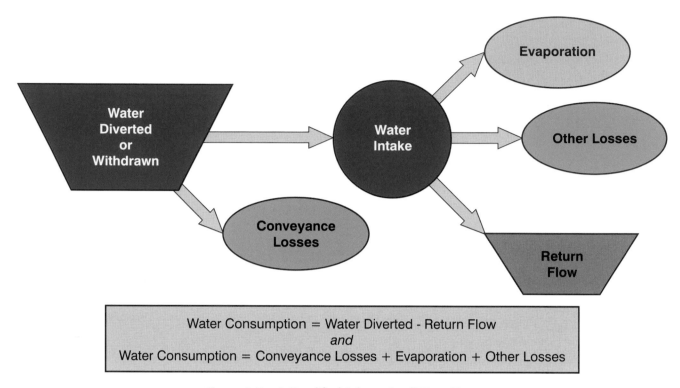

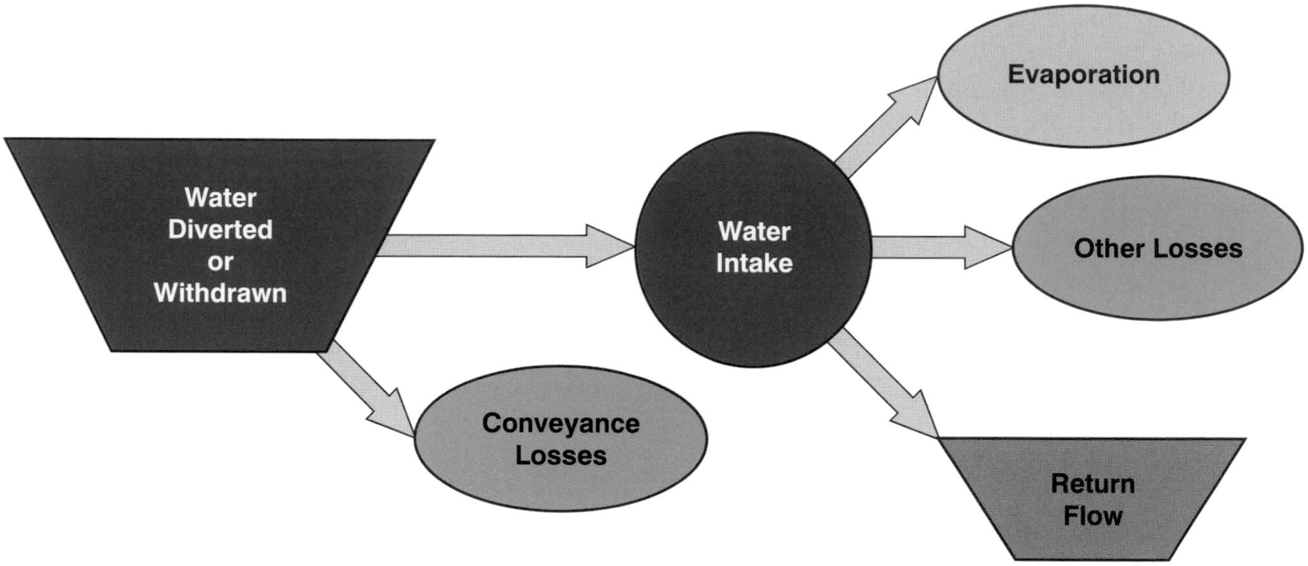

Water Consumption = Water Diverted - Return Flow
and
Water Consumption = Conveyance Losses + Evaporation + Other Losses

Figure 2.7. A Simplified Schematic of Water Use.

The terminology related to water use varies from one agency or practitioner to another. In this report, the term water allocation is used to identify the quantity of water set aside under provincial law for a particular user. The allocation may include a consumptive use component and a return flow that would be available to downstream users. Water withdrawal or water diversion is the quantity of surface or groundwater that a water user removes from the aquatic system. Water consumption is water diverted by a user that does not return to the aquatic system. Water consumption includes losses to seepage or evaporation. Return flow is the difference between water withdrawal and water consumption. These concepts are illustrated in Figure 2.7.

In general, hydroelectric power stations do not affect the annual flow volume, although they do alter the timing of flows received downstream. Water is stored in reservoirs during the spring then released in autumn and winter, as power demands increase. Spring and summer flows, therefore, will be lower than natural, while autumn and winter flows will be higher. These winter increases in flow also play a role in assimilation of effluent from urban centres. On the other hand, irrigation reservoirs tend to store water in the spring then supply it to projects during the summer growing season. Since much of the water is consumed, irrigation reservoirs not only affect the natural hydrograph, but also reduce the annual flow recorded downstream.

Considering the basin as a whole, annual water consumption ranges from 10 to 20 percent of the naturalized flow at The Pas, Manitoba. The naturalized flow of a stream is the flow that would have occurred in the absence of dams, withdrawals, and diversions. The difference between these flows and recorded flows is most notable in the South Saskatchewan River basin, where many reservoirs impound flow for power generation, agricultural water supply, and other water uses. Significant quantities of water are withdrawn for irrigated agriculture. Naturalized flows are calculated at many locations in the basin by adjusting the recorded flow record for withdrawals and additions to the stream, change in storage of reservoirs, and other factors such as reservoir evaporation. As these calculations do not consider the effects of land-use changes such as agricultural development and timber harvesting. It is preferable to call them naturalized rather than natural flows.

Water Licensing

The federal government issued the first water licences in the Saskatchewan River basin in 1894. Following the resource transfer agreements in 1930, the licences are now issued under provincial legislation. The quantity of water allocated under a licence includes the amount expected to be consumed or lost, plus a return flow. Licences for municipal purposes may assume that 20 percent of the withdrawal will be consumed; those for irrigated agriculture assume 75 percent will be consumed.

In Alberta, licences are issued under Alberta's *Water Act*, which came into force in 1999. The Act provides for a statutory right to 1250 m^3/year without licence for household purposes, and for registration of traditional agricultural uses, primarily livestock watering, of up to 6250 m^3/y. (Applications for registering traditional agriculture use had to be completed by the end of 2001.) All other withdrawals must be licensed. The Act requires that new licences must be for a specified period, rather than in perpetuity. It also provides for transfer of water rights, with the province retaining up to 10 percent of the water transferred for environmental uses.

The *Saskatchewan Watershed Authority Act* came into force in 2005. Under the Act, domestic users (household or on-farm) do not require a licence for uses less than 5000 m^3/y, provided there are no constructed diversion works. Like Alberta, new licences are issued for specified periods. There is no provision for transferring licences to other water users.

Manitoba issues licences under *The Water Rights Act* of 1988. Under the Act, domestic users (household or on-farm) do not require a licence for uses less than 25 m^3/day, up to 9125 m^3/y. Licences are issued for periods up to 20 years. There is no provision for transferring licences to other water users.

Water licences are registered by various sectors and sub-sectors. These vary from province to province and reflect the dominant water uses in a jurisdiction. The sectors are shown in Table 2.3. All provinces provide subcategories to indicate agricultural uses, such as irrigation and livestock watering. Specific uses included in Alberta's commercial sector, such as golf courses and market-gardening, are included in various sectors in Saskatchewan and Manitoba. Saskatchewan includes petroleum-related licences in its industrial sector. The 'other' sector in each province has a strong environmental goods and services component, although it can include other purposes. These uses may include lake stabilization, fisheries, and habitat enhancement. In this report, water use sectors will include municipal, livestock watering, irrigation, petroleum, industrial and other.

Table 2.3. Water Use Sectors.

Province	Water Use Sector				
Alberta	Municipal	Agriculture	Commercial	Industrial	Petroleum	Other
Saskatchewan	Municipal	Agriculture		Industrial		Other
Manitoba	Municipal	Agriculture		Industrial		Other

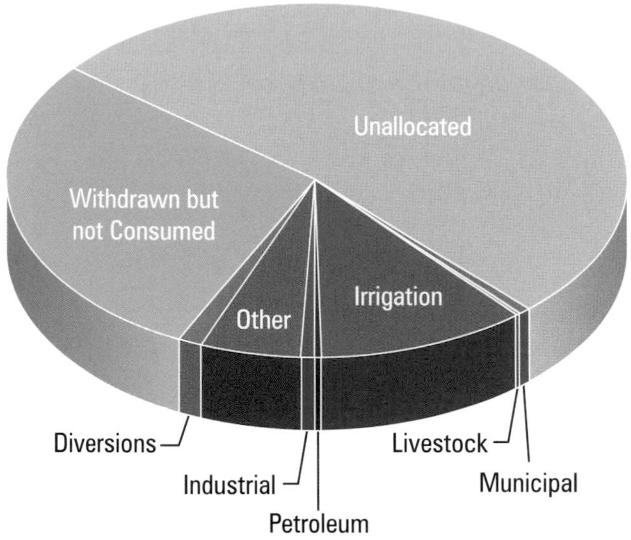

Figure 2.8. Water Withdrawal and Consumption in the Basin in a Median Year.

There are over 20 000 water licences and registered uses in the Saskatchewan River basin. All but several hundred of these are in the South Saskatchewan sub-basin in Alberta. Figure 2.8, which is based on information provided from many sources, presents water allocation and consumption from surface water in the Saskatchewan River basin. Surface water allocations represent about one half of the median annual flow, but a considerable portion of the water withdrawn returns to the ecosystem. Groundwater consumption in the sub-basin represents about 2.5 percent of total consumption.[16] It is evident that irrigated agriculture represents the most significant water use in the basin – most of this use being in the South Saskatchewan River sub-basin. The next largest water consumer is the 'other' sector.

Water consumption in the North Saskatchewan River sub-basin is relatively small. Annual water consumption in that sub-basin is about the same as the annual evaporative loss from Lake Diefenbaker in the South Saskatchewan sub-basin. About seven percent of the water consumed in the North Saskatchewan River sub-basin is groundwater.[17] The contrast between water consumption in the North Saskatchewan and South Saskatchewan rivers can be seen in Figure 2.9.

Water Use Trends

In 1982, the Prairie Provinces Water Board reported on a four-year study of historical and current water uses in the Saskatchewan-Nelson basin.[18] This *Water Demand Study* examined water use in 1978 in the

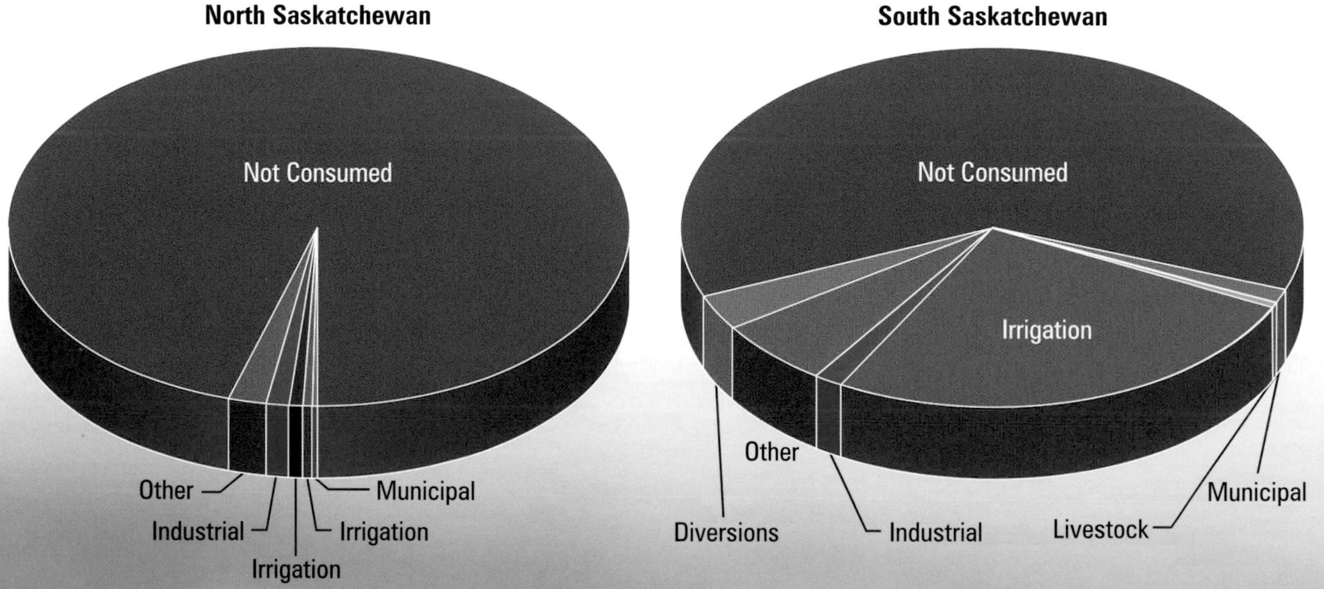

Figure 2.9. Water Consumption in the North and South Saskatchewan Rivers.

following sectors: municipal, industrial, agriculture, power generation, recreation, and environmental. These sectors are further broken down so that, for example, agriculture includes irrigation, livestock watering and rural domestic uses. The study used the concepts of water withdrawal, water consumption, and return flows and provides detailed water-use data both by sub-basin and by province. It therefore forms an important benchmark for considering subsequent water use studies. Since that time, the Province of Alberta has examined current water uses and future water demands, particularly for the South Saskatchewan sub-basin, where irrigation water demands are high.

In general, water consumption in the North Saskatchewan sub-basin currently is about 300 000 dam^3 annually and is driven by industrial demand in Alberta.[19] This demand is primarily for petroleum production and refining. On the other hand, current water consumption in the South Saskatchewan sub-basin is about 3.3 million dam^3 annually. About 70 percent of that water use is for irrigated agriculture in Alberta. As licensed water uses reach 50 percent of the median flow of a stream, concern grows about future water supplies and the sustainability of new water uses. At present, 68, 70 and 18 percent of the median annual flow of Bow, Oldman and Red Deer rivers, respectively, is allocated. The Waterton, Belly and St. Mary rivers – Oldman River tributaries – are particularly highly allocated. These figures do not take into account actual water consumption. The return flows from irrigated lands, for example, is about 17 percent of the water withdrawn. The Bow and Oldman River sub-basins have been closed to new water licences.

Several studies examine future water use in the Saskatchewan River basin in Alberta. Generally these studies take a business-as-usual approach in projecting water use some 20 years into the future. They do not make any assumptions concerning adoption of water conservation measures. On the other hand, the current policy of the Alberta government is to improve water-use intensity. Even then, it is likely that at some future time Alberta will come closer to using its entitlement to water from the South Saskatchewan River under the *Master Agreement on Apportionment*.

This report illustrates current water allocation and water consumption in various sub-basins of the Saskatchewan River basin. The indicators used are based on surface water licences and water consumption in comparison to the median flow. These indicators are reasonably effective for the reliable, mountain-fed streams of the basin. Water allocation and consumption for the less reliable, plains tributaries present additional challenges.

Groundwater withdrawals and consumption in the basin are relatively small. When groundwater use is significant, it is discussed.

Instream Flow Needs

While the water licensing approach has been successful in allocating scarce water resources to meet human needs, it was not designed to sustain aquatic ecosystems. In the early days of western settlement, waters flowing unfettered in a stream were commonly referred to as 'waste waters' and structures were built to 'conserve' water. Modifications of seasonal flow patterns and diversion of water from a natural stream will affect the integrity, structure, and function of aquatic and riparian ecosystems. Water managers now must balance human demands with the requirements for sustainable ecosystems. Determining appropriate instream flow needs is much more complex than simply identifying a minimum flow requirement. Instead, one must examine hydrology, geomorphology, biology, water quality, and the connectivity between physical and biological processes. The resulting instream flow need will mimic the seasonal and annual variations of a natural stream.[20] In the South Saskatchewan sub-basin, Alberta uses instream flow needs based on water quality, fish habitat, riparian vegetation, and maintenance of natural channel processes, as a proxy for ecosystem integrity.

Table 2.4. Water Conservation Objectives, South Saskatchewan Sub-basin in Alberta.

River or Reach	Water Conservation Objective
Red Deer River downstream of Dickson Dam	45 percent of natural flow, or 16 m^3/s, whichever is less. April to October flows can be reduced to 10 m^3/s below Blindman River
Bow River below Bassano Dam	17.1 m^3/s
• Bow River between Bearspaw Dam and Bassano Dam • Oldman River downstream of Oldman River Dam • St. Mary River at the Mouth • Belly River below Diversion • Waterton River at the Mouth	Increase flows by 10 percent of existing instream objective (Bow and Oldman rivers) or 10 percent of existing water conservation objectives of 2.75, 0.93 and 2.27 m^3/s for the St. Mary, Belly and Waterton rivers respectively
All of the South Saskatchewan River	42.5 m^3/s

As a further step, Alberta has recommended water conservation objectives downstream of major dams and diversions for rivers in the South Saskatchewan River sub-basin. These are shown in Table 2.4. The water conservation objective for the South Saskatchewan River, 42.5 m^3/s, is the minimum quantity required for delivery to Saskatchewan under the *Master Agreement on Apportionment* under normal flow conditions.

Saskatchewan has not adopted water conservation flows as such, but is committed to releasing at least 42.5 m^3/s from Gardiner Dam on the South Saskatchewan River and to a summer target flow of 60 to 150 m^3/s. The province is also committed to a 75 m^3/s minimum flow downstream of E.B. Campbell Dam on the Saskatchewan River.

WATER QUALITY

The natural water quality of any stream is influenced by the landscape and geology through which it flows. In the Saskatchewan River basin, the quality of water flowing in streams or contained in lakes and reservoirs is the consequence of both natural processes and human activity. Water may contain dissolved substances such as calcium, sodium, bicarbonate, or chloride, as a result of natural processes. It may also contain plant nutrients, such as nitrogen or phosphorus, as well as trace elements such as selenium, chromium or arsenic. Naturally occurring substances can affect the appearance or taste of water, but may also be harmful to human health and aquatic life, if found in sufficient concentration. Water may also contain dissolved gases such as oxygen.

Human activities such as urban development, irrigation and other farm activities, industrial development, and resource developments related to petrochemicals, mining, and forestry may degrade the quality of natural waters. Land-use change, of itself, may also affect water quality. The biological quality of water can be changed by the introduction of bacteria normally found in the intestinal tract of humans or animals, or by water-borne pathogens such as *Giardia lamblia* or *Cryptosporidium parvum*. In recent years, concern has increased about pharmaceuticals and personal care products in aquatic systems.

The waters of the Saskatchewan River basin tend to be naturally hard, particularly with calcium and bicarbonate, and that hardness increases as we move downstream. The mountain-fed streams of the basin also tend to be naturally nutrient poor, but municipal-treated sewage effluents, storm water runoff, and agricultural runoff significantly increase levels to concentrations greater than natural levels. The waters become turbid during spring runoff and summer rainstorms.

One general descriptor of water quality in a basin is its trophic status. This classification, based on biological productivity, has been applied to lakes for many years, and, more recently, has been applied to streams. Trophic classification represents a continuum of biological production ranging from oligotrophic to mesotrophic to eutrophic to hypereutrophic. Oligotrophic systems exhibit very little biological production; the water tends to be clear and well-oxygenated. Mesotrophic waters may be moderately clear, but oxygen may be depleted in the deepest parts of lakes. Eutrophic systems may contain high densities of plants and algae. Lakes may produce algae blooms and be low in oxygen. Hypereutrophic lakes will contain significant persistent algal blooms. Oxygen depletion can lead to fish kills. Alberta has classified the trophic status of its lakes based on total phosphorus and phytoplankton chlorophyll *a*. Total nitrogen and Secchi depth (a measure of water transparency) criteria have also been added. Similar classifications based on nutrient and algal biomass have been proposed for streams.[21] Trophic status will be used as an indicator of water quality in this report.

In recent years, incidents leading to serious illnesses and even fatalities arising from poor management of a few municipal water treatment systems in Canada have led to increased public concern over safety of drinking water. In March and April 2001 the city of North Battleford experienced an outbreak of gastrointestinal illness that affected 5800 to 7100 people in the Battlefords area, and hundreds elsewhere. *Cryptosporidium* had entered the water treatment system through the raw water supply to the North Saskatchewan River and broken through the system. A Commission of Inquiry made many recommendations concerning source water protection and water treatment.[22] The North Battleford incident and other incidents in Canada and elsewhere have led to increased attention on source water protection, water treatment plant upgrades, and certification of system operators.

Good quality water, however, has many other uses, including food production, sustaining aquatic life, and contact recreation, such as swimming or boating. The known uses of a body of water are employed as the basis for determining water quality objectives. These uses may include contact and non-contact recreation, protection of aquatic life, irrigation, and livestock watering. Commonly used objectives developed for the Prairie Provinces Water Board are shown in Table 2.5. Objectives used within the three Prairie Provinces are similar; thus water quality, as determined by sampling and testing, can be compared to these objectives.

Table 2.5. Water Quality Objectives.

Water Quality Parameter	Objective
Chloride - Dissolved	100 mg/L
Sodium - Dissolved	100 mg/L
Sulphate - Dissolved	500 mg/L
Total Dissolved Solids	500 mg/L
Arsenic - Total	0.05 mg/L
Chromium - Total	0.011 mg/L
Mercury in Fish	0.5 μg/g
Nitrogen - Total Ammonia	Based on pH and Temperature
Nitrogen - Nitrate/Nitrite	10.0 mg/L
Coliforms - Fecal	100/100 mL
pH	6.5 - 9.0
Oxygen - Dissolved	Varies
2,4-D (herbicide)	0.004 μg/L

Determining water quality requires analysis of field samples for a number of chemical and biological constituents. The sampling period varies, depending on the nature of the monitoring program. Water quality monitoring of natural streams may depend on performing a broad range of tests on water samples obtained monthly, while large urban centres may conduct a limited number of tests on thousands of samples over a year. Automated instruments may monitor a limited number of physical properties, such as temperature, dissolved oxygen, electrical conductivity, and pH continuously. In addition, routine monitoring may be augmented by short-term surveys in a specific sub-basin. Many government agencies, at all levels, and private sector groups operate water-quality monitoring programs. Monitoring and reporting to government regulators are often requirements for industrial and natural resource developments.

Results of water-quality tests may be grouped in several categories, such as physical properties, major ions, bacteria, nutrients, metals and pesticides. Even then, getting a feel for the water quality of a stream at a specific location can be difficult for non-specialists. As a means of making water-quality reporting more understandable, the Canadian Council of Ministers of the Environment (CCME) has developed a standardized water quality index.[23] The index condenses many analytical results to a single number. The index compares the number of water-quality measurements for which guidelines were not met, the frequency with which guidelines were not met, and the amount by which guidelines were exceeded. The CCME has created national water quality guidelines, which provinces have added to or modified for their own use.

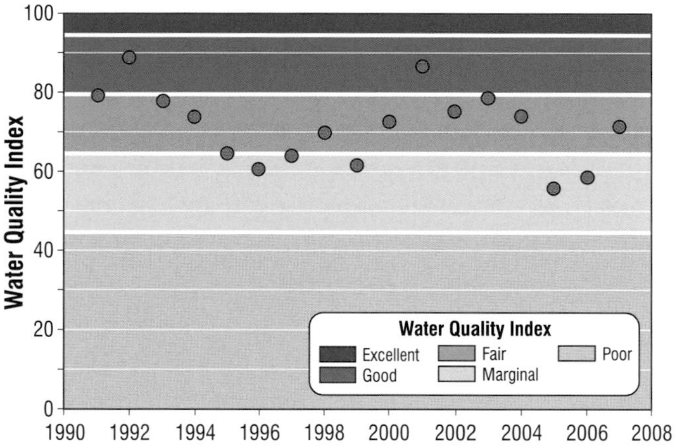

Figure 2.10. Water Quality Index for the North Saskatchewan River at the Interprovincial Boundary.

The index at a single location can be compared to previous indices at the same location. Figure 2.10 shows an example for the North Saskatchewan River at the interprovincial boundary. Changes in the index can be driven by both human and natural factors. The water quality index, for example, is often poorer in a flood year because of increased sediments in the water. It usually is not possible to compare indices from one location to another. Alberta produces an annual water quality index at five locations in the Saskatchewan River basin for pesticides, bacteria, nutrients and metals, as well as an overall index. Saskatchewan produces a general index for six locations. Environment Canada produces a general index at interprovincial sites for the Prairie Provinces Water Board and for sites in national parks. As these indices are based on differing parameter sets, it is not possible to compare results obtained by one agency to those obtained by another, or, in some cases, compare results obtained by the same agency on a different stream. A federal-provincial task group is examining the problem of inter-comparison of water quality indices.

Water quality is monitored at six interprovincial stream crossings within the Saskatchewan River basin by Environment Canada, on behalf of the Prairie Provinces Water Board. These include the North Saskatchewan, Battle, Red Deer and South Saskatchewan rivers near the Alberta-Saskatchewan boundary, and the Saskatchewan and Carrot rivers at the Saskatchewan-Manitoba boundary. Water-quality objectives are established at these locations and the Board routinely reports on whether these objectives are being met. The Board also performs periodic analyses of the data for trends. Environment Canada monitors the North Saskatchewan River at one location and the Bow River at two locations in Banff National Park.

Provincial agencies monitor water quality within a province, or direct others to carry out monitoring, and report results to the province. Alberta Environment's long-term river network monitors water quality at three sites on the North Saskatchewan River, two on the Battle River, three on the Red Deer River, seven on the Bow River, three on the Oldman River, and one site on the South Saskatchewan River. Saskatchewan monitors the North Saskatchewan River at four sites, the South Saskatchewan River at four sites, and the Saskatchewan River at one site. Manitoba monitors water quality at two locations on the Saskatchewan River.

The overall water quality indices produced by various agencies are presented in this report without modification. Readers are cautioned not to make comparisons among products from different agencies. One further difference in the indices is that Alberta presents its data on a fiscal year basis (April to March) rather than a calendar year, as for other provinces. A federal-provincial group is examining how best to present results obtained by multiple jurisdictions in large river basins.

BIODIVERSITY AND ECOSYSTEMS

Biodiversity refers to the variety of all living things and the ecosystems that support them. Biodiversity also includes genetic diversity within a single species and the interactions among species. Although the Saskatchewan River basin has been significantly altered by human activity, considerable landscape diversity and numerous plant communities provide habitat for many large and small mammals and birds. Riparian areas, wetlands, lakes, and streams support a wide array of terrestrial and aquatic species. Natural and cropped uplands adjacent to wetlands also provide habitat for some terrestrial species.

Principal threats to biodiversity include habitat fragmentation and loss of habitat. Habitat fragmentation may occur through construction of dams and weirs that block fish migration, or through linear features such as roads and seismic lines. Draining of wetlands and reduction in old growth forests through fire, disease or harvesting are two examples of habitat loss. Changes in the age structure of forests also affect biodiversity. Suppression of fire and insects leads to an older forest structure, while forest harvesting and wildfires lead to a younger. Harvesting may produce 60-year-old stands where some species require 100-year-old stands. Conversion of the plains to an agricultural landscape also represents a loss of habitat through loss of parkland forest and development of agricultural monocultures. The accompanying wetland loss reduces waterfowl populations.

The Saskatchewan River basin is an important watershed for continental waterfowl populations, providing critical habitat for nesting, staging, and migrating ducks, geese and swans. Canadian and American wildlife services survey approximately 86 percent of the basin each spring, producing an estimation of total ducks and breeding pairs (Table 2.6).[24] The long-term average population of ducks in the basin is approximately 8 million birds (all species combined), with about 3.6 million breeding pairs. This population represents approximately 25 percent of the ducks counted (breeding and total) in the traditional survey area of North America, 59 percent of the ducks counted in the Canadian 'Prairie Pothole Region' (agricultural Alberta, Saskatchewan and Manitoba), and 6 percent of the ducks counted in the Canadian Western Boreal Forest.

Table 2.6. Total Pairs and Total Ducks (long term average 1955-2005) in the Saskatchewan River Basin.

Sub-basin	Total Pairs	Total Ducks
North Saskatchewan River	740 674	1 657 937
Vermilion	151 725	329 603
Battle River	577 053	1 277 437
Sounding Creek	207 977	451 766
Eagle Creek	179 103	383 304
Red Deer River	549 284	1 200 788
Bow River	99 737	233 858
Oldman River	102 584	227 341
South Saskatchewan River	554 945	1 213 767
Saskatchewan River	446 973	1 066 315
Total in Basin	**3 610 055**	**8 045 116**

A federal-provincial-territorial process identifies species-at-risk and provides some legal protection for species identified. This process also calls for recovery plans for such species. The species-at-risk identified in the Saskatchewan River basin are shown in Table 2.7.

Riparian zones are important to sustaining both terrestrial and aquatic species. In many tributary sub-basins of the Saskatchewan River basin, riparian zones have been sampled and categorized as healthy, healthy-with-problems, or unhealthy. This report uses those indicators where available.

Table 2.7. Species at Risk in the Saskatchewan River Basin.

Species	Status	Location (ecodistrict)
Mammals		
Swift Fox	Endangered	Mixed Grassland
Woodland Caribou	Threatened	Mid-boreal Lowland
Birds		
Burrowing Owl	Endangered	Mixed Grassland
Perigrine Falcon	Threatened	Aspen Parkland
Sage Thrasher	Endangered	Mixed Grassland
Piping Plover	Endangered	Prairie Ecozone
Sprague's Pipit	Threatened	Prairie Ecozone
Loggerhead Shrike	Threatened	Prairie Ecozone
Plants		
Small-flowered Sand-verbena	Endangered	Mixed Grassland
Slender Mouse-ear-cress	Threatened	Mixed Grassland
Tiny Cryptanthe	Endangered	Mixed Grassland
Hairy Prairie-clover	Threatened	Moist Mixed Grassland
Lichen		
Flooded Jellyskin	Threatened	Mid-boreal Lowland
Fish		
Lake Sturgeon	Endangered	Prairie and Boreal Plain Ecozones
Eastslope Sculpin	Threatened	Northern Continental Divide
Molluscs		
Banff Springs Snail	Endangered	Northern Continental Divide

The aquatic food web consists of algae, plants, invertebrates, and vertebrates. Algae are single-celled organisms suspended in the stream or attached to rocks or plants as biofilm. They are important energy sources within food webs. The waters of the Saskatchewan River system tend to contain low concentrations of algae, but these concentrations increase greatly downstream of municipal wastewater treatment facilities because of the nutrient content of the effluent.[25] Although some prairie tributaries of the basin and the Saskatchewan Delta contain diverse populations of rooted plants, the mountain-fed mainstem rivers do not. Plant growth increases downstream from municipal wastewater treatment facilities.

Invertebrates are the insects and other animals without backbones that spend at least part of their life cycle in the water, or streambed, lakebed, or wetland substrates. They live on plants, dead organic matter or other invertebrates. These include many flies, worms, mollusks and other animals. Populations in the principal streams of the Saskatchewan River basin are relatively low, but diverse. This diversity is reduced in river reaches below major urban centres.[26]

Fish are the most evident vertebrates in a stream. The alpine and sub-alpine lakes and streams of the basin, especially those upstream of waterfalls, were almost devoid of fish until the lakes were stocked with rainbow trout, cutthroat trout or brook trout, beginning early in the 20th century. Some mountain lakes did contain longnose sucker, mountain whitefish or bull trout.[27] Some lakes, such as Waterton Lake, did contain lake trout, while adjacent streams contained cutthroat or bull trout. In general, indigenous fish have been displaced by stocked species. The lower warm-water reaches of the North and South Saskatchewan rivers contain species such as northern pike, walleye, goldeye, yellow perch and sturgeon. In recent years, fish populations have improved because of better water quality. Fish populations downstream of urban centres are sensitive to the nutrient content of the effluent and may decrease when nutrient concentrations are reduced. The greatest diversity of fish species is found in the Saskatchewan River Delta where 48 species have been identified.[28]

The soils over much of the basin create very nutrient rich aquatic habitats in mineral-based wetlands that are subsequently very rich in invertebrates - both diversity and populations. This is not the case for most peatlands.

One important need in sustaining biodiversity is protection and conservation of habitat. Establishing protected areas is one means of maintaining habitat.

PROTECTED AREAS

The establishment of protected areas is an important element of the Canadian Biodiversity Strategy, which promotes the conservation of biodiversity and the sustainable use of biological resources. In 1992, Canada's federal, provincial and territorial ministers of the environment, parks, wildlife and forestry signed *A Statement of Commitment to Complete Canada's Networks of Protected Areas*. These areas are representative of all natural regions. Identifying and conserving representative areas is particularly important, given that habitat loss and conversion and habitat fragmentation are frequently cited as having the greatest impact on Canadian biodiversity.

Protected areas are lands identified by governments as having natural and associated cultural value that are managed through legal or other effective means.[29] Examples of protected areas include national parks, wilderness areas, provincial parks, historic sites, recreation areas, and migratory bird sanctuaries. Management of protected areas is aimed at protecting and maintaining biological diversity. Biological diversity is essential for food, clean water, shelter, health, work, recreation and culture. Conserving natural ecosystems is fundamental to conserving biodiversity.

The Saskatchewan River basin contains six national parks. The basin includes four mountain parks: Canada's first national park, Banff – established in 1885, Waterton Lakes National Park, United States' Glacier National Park, and a small portion of Jasper National Park. The mountain parks are all designated UNESCO World Heritage Sites. Waterton Lakes National Park, together with Glacier National Park, was designated as an International Peace Park in 1932. Banff National Park also contains the only designated Canadian Heritage River in the basin – a 48.5 km reach of the North Saskatchewan River extending from the Columbia Ice Fields to the park boundary. Other national parks in the basin are Elk Island National Park in the aspen parkland near Edmonton, and Prince Albert National Park in the boreal plain near Prince Albert.

The basin contains six National Wildlife Areas, the largest by far being the 458 km^2 area on Canadian Forces Base Suffield. The basin also contains 11 Migratory Bird Sanctuaries.

Areas of ecological significance are also protected under provincial programs. In Alberta this is accomplished under a Special Places Program, in Saskatchewan under a Representative Areas Network, and, in Manitoba, under a Protected Areas Initiative. Approximately eight percent of the basin in Saskatchewan is protected under provincial legislation. The programs all aim to identify representative protected natural areas within previously defined ecological regions. These areas can serve as benchmarks for monitoring environmental change and provide other opportunities for scientific research. There are many smaller protected areas maintained on private lands through land purchases by organizations such as Ducks Unlimited Canada and the Nature Conservancy Canada, or through conservation easements.

One precursor to designating protected areas is identification of important habitat. Detailed information on migratory bird habitat in the basin is available. Breeding, moulting, and staging areas are identified for ducks and geese, as well as breeding and staging areas for birds living in colonies, such as gulls. Breeding habit for the six endangered bird species identified above and many non-game species are also identified. The Saskatchewan River Delta and an area in the Sounding/Eyehill Creek sub-basin on the Alberta-Saskatchewan boundary, known as the Sibbald Plain, are deemed nationally important overall.[30] Other areas are considered nationally important to a certain class of migratory bird. Bird Life International has identified the Saskatchewan River Delta as internationally important. There are many other Important Bird Areas, particularly in the prairie ecozone.

ENDNOTES

[1] Ecological Stratification Working Group 1996. *A National Ecological Framework for Canada*. Canadian Soil Information System (CanSIS), Agriculture and Agri-Food Canada, Ottawa, ON.

[2] Rosenburg *et al.* 2005. Rosenburg, D.M., P.A. Chambers, J.M. Culp, W.G. Franzin, P.A. Nelson, A.G. Salki, M.P. Stainton, R.A. Bodly, and R.W. Newbury 2005. "Nelson and Churchill River Basins". Chapter 19 in *Rivers of North America*, edited by A. C. Benke and C. E. Cushing. Elsevier Academic Press.

[3] Maathuis, H. and L.H. Thorleifson 2000. *Potential Impact of Climate Change on Prairie Groundwater Supplies: Review of Current Knowledge*. SRC Publication No. 11304-2E00. Saskatchewan Research Council, Saskatoon, SK.

[4] National Wetlands Working Group 1988. *Wetlands of Canada*. Ecological Land Classification Series No. 24. Environment Canada, Ottawa, ON.

[5] Warner, B.G. and C.D.A. Rubec (editors) 1997. *The Canadian Wetland Classification System, Second Edition*. National Wetlands Working Group. Wetlands Research Centre, University of Waterloo. Waterloo, ON.

[6] Ecological Stratification Working Group 1996. *supra.*

[7] Rosenburg, D.M., P.A. Chambers, J.M. Culp, W.G. Franzin, P.A. Nelson, A.G. Salki, M.P. Stainton, R.A. Bodly, and R.W. Newbury 2005. *supra.*

[8] Maathuis, H. and L.H. Thorliefson 2000. *Potential Impact of Climate Change on Prairie Groundwater Supplies: Review of Current Knowledge*. Saskatchewan Research Council Publication No. 11304-2E00. Saskatoon, SK.

[9] McMillan, A.D. and E. Yellowhorn 2004. *First Peoples in Canada*. Douglas & McIntyre, Vancouver and Toronto.

[10] Davies, K.G. 1969. "Henry Kelsey". *Dictionary of Canadian Biography*. Volume II. University of Toronto Press and Les Presses de l'université Laval.

[11] Wilson, C. 1952. "La Vérendrye Reaches the Saskatchewan." *Canadian Historical Review*, 33(1): 39-50.

[12] Wilson, C. 1954. "Across the Prairies Two Centuries Ago". *The Canadian Historical Association*. Eds. P.G. Cornell, Rev. Pouliot, S.J., and J.S. Moir. Report of the Annual Meeting held in Winnipeg, June 2-5, 1954, with Historical Papers.

[13] Spry, I.M. 2000. "John Palliser". *Dictionary of Canadian Biography*. Vol. XI. University of Toronto Press and Les Presses de l'université Laval.

[14] Wilson, G. 2007. *Frontier Farewell: The 1870s and the End of the Old West*. Canadian Plains Research Centre, University of Regina. Regina, SK.

[15] Lucas, A.R. 1990. *Security of Title in Canadian Water Rights*. Canadian Institute of Resources Law, University of Calgary, Calgary, AB.

[16] Watrecon Consulting 2005. "People to Water or Water to People? How Should Alberta Allocate Water in the Future?" Report prepared for the Alberta Institute of Agrologists. In *Proceedings, Canadian Water Resources Association Annual Conference*, June 2005. Banff, AB.

[17] AMEC 2007. *Current and Future Water Use in the North Saskatchewan River Basin (Alberta)*. Report for the North Saskatchewan Watershed Alliance. Report EE27028. AMEC Earth & Environmental, Edmonton, AB.

[18] Prairie Provinces Water Board (PPWB), 1982. *Water Demand Study*. Prairie Provinces Water Board. Regina.

[19] AMEC 2007. *supra.*

[20] Clipperton, G.K., C.W. Koning, A.G.H. Locke, J.M. Mahoney, and B. Quazi 2003. *Instream Flow Needs Determinations for the South Saskatchewan River Basin, Alberta, Canada*. Alberta Environment, Edmonton, AB.

[21] Alberta Environment 2007b. *Information Synthesis and Initial Assessment of the Status and Health of Aquatic Ecosystems in Alberta*. Technical Report 278/279-01. Alberta Environment, Edmonton, AB.

[22] Laing, R.D. 2002. *Report of the Commission of Inquiry into Matters Relating to the Safety of the Public Drinking Water in the City of North Battleford, Saskatchewan*. Province of Saskatchewan, Regina, SK.

[23] Canadian Council of Ministers of the Environment 2001. *CCME Water Quality Index 1.0*. Technical Report and Users Manual. Ottawa, ON.

[24] Slattery, S. 2008. Unpublished data from Ducks Unlimited Canada.

[25] Rosenburg *et al.* 2005. *supra.*

[26] Rosenburg *et al.* 2005. *supra.*

[27] Donald, D.B. 1987. "Assessment of the Outcome of Eight Decades of Trout Stocking in the Mountain National Parks, Canada." *North American Journal of Fisheries Management*. 7:545-553.

[28] Rosenburg *et al.* 2005. *supra.*

[29] Environment Canada 2006. *Canadian Protected Areas Status Report, 2000-2005*. Environment Canada. Ottawa, ON.

[30] Poston, B., D. Ealey, P. Taylor, and G.B. McKeating 1990. *Priority Migratory Bird Habitats of Canada's Prairie Provinces*. Environment Canada, Edmonton, AB.

CHAPTER THREE
INSTITUTIONAL ARRANGEMENTS

Dinosaur Provincial Park, Alberta.

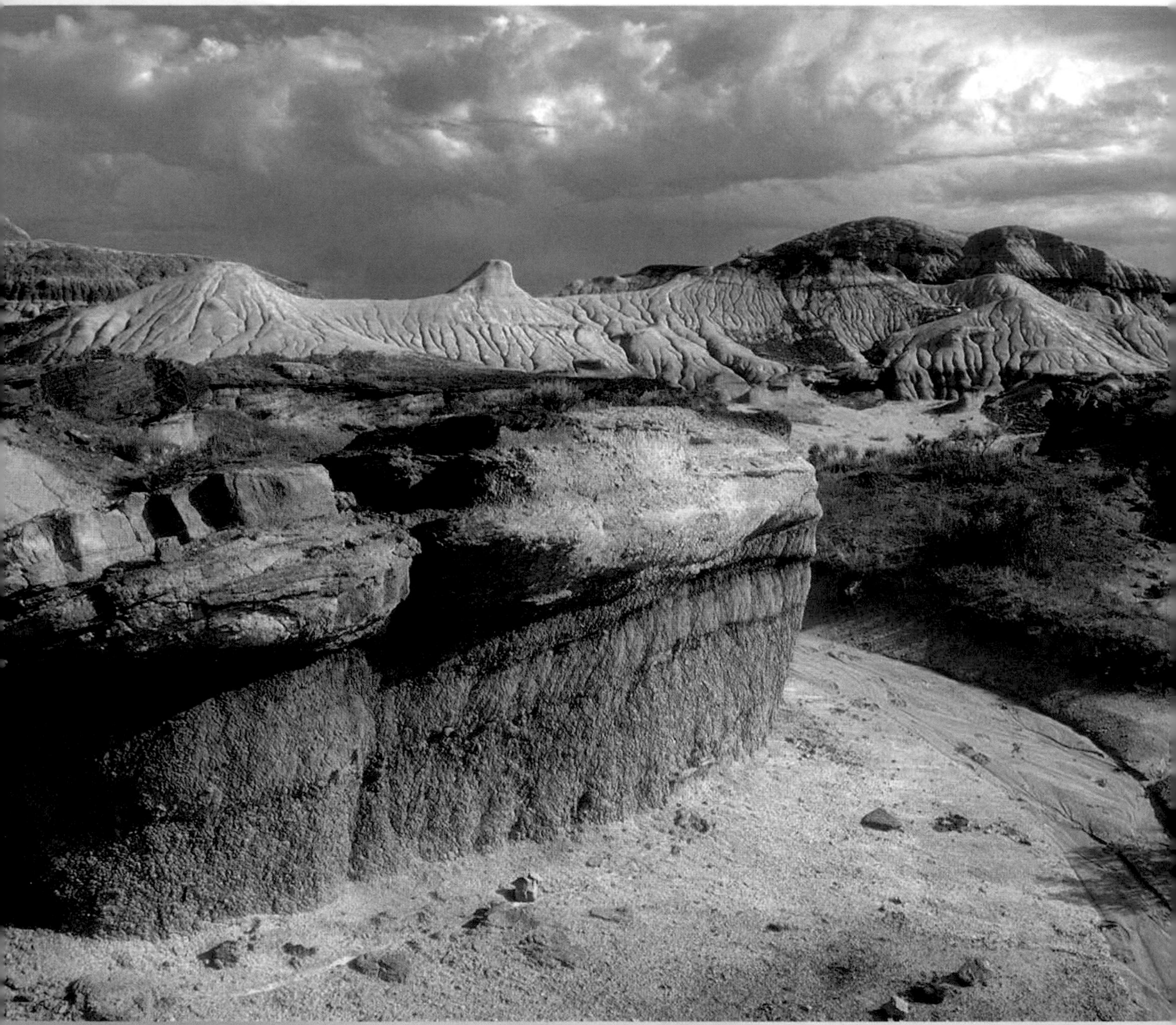

CHAPTER THREE
INSTITUTIONAL ARRANGEMENTS

The Constitution Act *of 1930 and its scheduled agreements between Canada and each of the western provinces transferred administration and control over or responsibility for land and resources, including water, to the provinces. Each province prepared its own related legislation, reiterating the provisions of the agreement. The stated motivation of the transfer at the time was to ensure the western provinces became equal partners in confederation and had the same arrangements with the federal government, related to lands and resources, as did the provinces east of Manitoba. These agreements, called the Natural Resources Transfer Agreements, state that they are subject to existing rights at the time of transfer. This includes treaty and Aboriginal rights in western provinces.*

Little was said in the agreements about water. Each province's agreement noted that water power developments within the provinces no longer had to be 'to the general advantage of Canada.' Responsibility for fisheries management was explicitly given to the provinces.

As water use expanded and resource management became more of an issue, more detailed arrangements have emerged so that the following responsibilities now seem to be accepted among respective governments.

Provincial governments perform the primary roles of water management on provincial lands including:

- Control and regulation of water control infrastructure
- Flood forecasting
- Regulation of drinking water and management of water quality
- Protection of source water
- Licensing of water uses
- Regulation of fisheries.

The federal government has responsibility for:

- Trans-boundary water issues
- Protection of fish habitat and prevention of pollution harmful to fish
- Regulation of toxic substances
- Regulation of navigation and shipping
- Shared international waters
- Federal property
- First Nations and lands and waters reserved for them, including provision of safe drinking water and waste water services on reserves.

INTERNATIONAL PERSPECTIVES

In the early part of the last century, a number of water disputes, including one related to irrigation water rights to the St. Mary and Milk rivers in Alberta and Montana, led to the signing of the *Boundary Waters Treaty* and creation of the International Joint Commission (IJC) in 1909 to implement the Treaty. The Treaty provides upstream jurisdictions exclusive control over their waters but provides the same legal remedies for injured parties irrespective of country. It should be noted that the Treaty defines 'boundary waters' as the waters of lakes and rivers that actually make up the international boundary – some 3900 km of waterways.

The Treaty deals with the sharing of the waters of the transboundary St. Mary and Milk rivers and their tributaries. The St. Mary River is a headwaters tributary of the Saskatchewan River system. The IJC issued an Order in 1921, adjudicating the respective claims of Canada and the United States pertaining to sharing the waters of the St. Mary and Milk rivers. This Order continues in place today.[1]

Tributaries of the St. Mary River such as Lee and Rolph creeks are also subject to the IJC Order. Other transboundary streams in the same general area, the Waterton and Belly rivers, are also headwater tributaries of the Saskatchewan River system. These rivers are not specifically identified in the Treaty and are not subject to the 1921 Order. Water use from these rivers in the United States is minor, although the waters are very important to Canadian irrigators.

INTER-GOVERNMENTAL PERSPECTIVES

In the early days of European settlement of the Saskatchewan River basin, water was allocated according to priorities and procedures contained in the *North-west Irrigation Act* of 1894, a federal act administered by the Department of the Interior. Discussions pertaining to sharing of inter-provincial waters took place as early as the 1920s and, with transfer of natural resources administration, including water, to the governments of the Prairie Provinces in 1930, a Western Water Board was created, but never functioned. A new proposal in 1937 also failed, but in 1945 negotiations among the federal government and the governments of the three Prairie Provinces led to establishment of a Prairie Provinces Water Advisory Board and, subsequently, the Prairie Provinces Water Board in 1948. The new board was charged with making recommendations pertaining to the best use of inter-provincial waters and with recommending the allocation of water among provinces for streams flowing from one province to the other. In 1969, governments signed the *Master Agreement on Apportionment* and reconstituted the Prairie Provinces Water Board to administer the agreement. The Board is chaired by Environment Canada and is made up of members from Agriculture and Agri-Food Canada and water administrators from the governments of the three Prairie Provinces.

The *Master Agreement on Apportionment* sets out the rights and duties of the three Prairie Provinces concerning apportionment of eastward-flowing, inter-provincial streams. Often described as a Saskatchewan River basin agreement, the Master Agreement applies to all streams that flow eastward across either of the Alberta-Saskatchewan or Saskatchewan-Manitoba boundaries, or both. The Master Agreement also applies to trans-boundary lakes and to groundwater.[2]

The essence of the Master Agreement is that the Province of Alberta is entitled to make a net depletion of one-half of the natural flow of the waters arising in that province, allowing the remainder to flow into Saskatchewan. Further, Saskatchewan is entitled to make a net depletion of one-half of the water flowing in from Alberta and of waters arising in Saskatchewan and must allow the remainder to flow into Manitoba. These entitlements are subject to certain exceptions.

The Master Agreement has five schedules. Among other things, these schedules pertain to division of waters between Alberta and Saskatchewan and Saskatchewan and Manitoba, respectively, and to water-quality objectives for specified trans-boundary river reaches. The water-quality objectives are applied to the North Saskatchewan, Red Deer, and South Saskatchewan rivers at the Alberta-Saskatchewan boundary, and the Saskatchewan River at the Saskatchewan-Manitoba boundary.

The Master Agreement defines natural flow as the quantity of water that would occur in any watercourse had the flow not been affected by human interference or intervention, excluding any water that is part of the natural flow, but is not available for use because of the provisions of any international treaty. From the early days of the Master Agreement, the difficulties of calculating a true natural flow were evident. The Board agreed in 1976 that 'effects on runoff of changing land-use patterns are not considered in the computation of natural flow (changes in land use include land clearing for agriculture, drainage, forestry, industrial and urban development and other land uses). Changes in natural flow due to groundwater inflow or recharge are not considered in the computations.'

Calculating natural flows for apportionment involves identification and measurement or computation of depletions due to storage, diversion, evaporation and consumptive use, and routing these depletions to the point of apportionment, where they are applied to the recorded flows at that point to produce natural flows.

Some additional apportionment concepts must be considered. The first relates to the apportionment period. The PPWB apportions streamflow on an annual basis. That is, the agreement is met if the annual natural flow is not depleted by more than 50 percent. The Master Agreement, however, also speaks of 'equitable apportionment.' This implies consideration of the volume and timing of the water released to the downstream party. In the case of the South Saskatchewan River, two specific constraints relate to equitable apportionment.

- Alberta is entitled to a 2 589 300 dam^3 minimum net annual depletion as long as the depletion does not reduce the flow at the boundary to less than 42.5 m^3/s.
- Alberta must maintain a minimum daily discharge at the boundary of 42.5 m^3/s or one-half the natural flow, whichever is less.

The result is that flows are apportioned annually based on the calendar year. Meeting the conditions of equitable apportionment, however, requires periodic audits. For the South Saskatchewan River, there are quarterly audit periods, and, when flows are low, monthly or shorter audit periods are employed. As streamflow conditions become more exigent, the monitoring grows more intensive.

THE FEDERAL ROLE IN WATER MANAGEMENT

The federal government transferred responsibility for resources, including water, via the Natural Resource Transfer Agreements by the *Constitution Act* of 1930. This means the current federal role in water management is focussed through specific federal heads of power that relate to water and other resources and their protection. These include:

- Federal lands and Indian reserves
- Navigation and shipping
- Seacoast and inland fisheries
- Agriculture
- Inter-provincial and international trade and commerce
- Regulation of facilities which are inter- or extra-provincial (such as pipelines)
- General laws for the Peace, Order and Good Government of Canada (emergency, doctrine of national concern

The federal agencies most directly involved in water matters in the Saskatchewan River basin are Agriculture and Agri-Food Canada, Environment Canada, and Fisheries and Oceans Canada. Agriculture is a shared responsibility under the *Constitution Act*. Because of the intrinsic link between agriculture and water, especially in the semi-arid prairie provinces, Agriculture and Agri-Food Canada has significant involvement in sustainable land management, rural water supplies, and improving and protecting water quality. Environment Canada responsibilities include research, monitoring of quality and quantity, facilitation of governance through the IJC and PPWB, and regulatory and enforcement activities. Fisheries and Oceans Canada has responsibilities for research, fish habitat, and regulatory and enforcement activities. These responsibilities are more specifically reflected in the following legislation:

The Fisheries Act – requires specific approvals if activities are going to damage fish habitat or result in substances deleterious to fish getting into the water.

The Navigable Waters Act – requires specific approvals for activities that affect the navigability of a body of water.

The Boundary Waters Treaty Act – identifies processes for resolving water disputes across the international boundary.

The Indian Act – Indian and Northern Affairs Canada provides funding for water services and infrastructure such as construction, upgrading, operation and maintenance of water treatment facilities on First Nations reserves. The department also provides financial support for the training and certification of treatment plant operators.

The Constitution Act – was used to transfer responsibility for resource management to the provinces, and also requires a formal consultation process with First Nations, Inuit and Métis peoples if there is a possibility of a treaty or Aboriginal right (e.g. access to resources) being infringed by a government decision.

The Health Act – Health Canada provides environmental health services to First Nations communities through its Environmental Health Program. The department monitors and provides advice on drinking water quality to First Nations communities.

The Canadian Environmental Protection Act – Environment Canada develops standards, guidelines and protocols for wastewater treatment on federal and First Nations lands and identifies and prescribes handling of toxic materials.

The Species at Risk Act – includes provisions for habitat protection as well as recovery planning for aquatic or terrestrial species of special concern, threatened or endangered.

The Canadian Environmental Assessment Act – requires federal departments to conduct environmental assessments for prescribed projects and activities before providing regulatory approval or financial support for the undertaking.

The Prairie Farm Rehabilitation Act – commits Agriculture and Agri-Food Canada to 'secure the rehabilitation of the drought and soil drifting areas in the Provinces of Manitoba, Saskatchewan and Alberta, and to develop and promote within those areas, systems of farm practice, tree culture, water supply, land utilization and land settlement that will afford greater economic security....'

The Federal Water Policy – promulgated in 1987, identifies the federal government as having two main goals related to water: to protect and enhance the quality of the water resource and to promote wise and efficient management and use of water. The policy contains five strategies and specific policy statements in 25 subject areas.

In addition, in 1991 Environment Canada published *The Federal Policy on Wetland Conservation*. For nearly three decades, Canada has been a signatory of the international Ramsar Convention. This convention calls for establishment of wetlands policies in each signatory nation to improve institutional and organizational arrangements, to address legislative needs, to increase knowledge and awareness of wetland values, to identify program priorities, and to develop action plans for specific sites. The federal policy is aimed at maintaining wetland values, having no net loss of wetlands on federal lands and waters, and securement of wetlands of significance to Canadians, among other objectives. The policy applies to federal lands and to any project that receives federal money for its execution.

THE ROLE OF FIRST NATIONS AND OTHER AGENCIES IN FIRST NATIONS' WATER MANAGEMENT

The importance of water to First Nations may be characterized by different First Nations in different ways, but could include such perspectives as:

- water is life
- water is sacred
- water is a spirit for healing and cleansing
- water is important to the emotional, physical, spiritual and mental well-being of people.

Some traditional teachings emphasize the relationship between the way people treat water and how the land looks after people. Therefore it is believed that all human beings must accept responsibility for taking care of water.

First Nations advance strongly their rights to water through Section 35 of the *Constitution Act*. Government has a clear duty to consult First Nations when a treaty or aboriginal right may be affected. First Nations therefore assert their need to be involved in decisions that affect water resources, especially development decisions. Where a legal duty to consult is triggered by a possible negative impact on treaty or aboriginal right, First Nations' involvement in water use, protection, or planning would be as rights holders, as opposed to stakeholders.

Currently, the following agencies are typically involved in water management on First Nations reserves.

- Indian and Northern Affairs Canada (INAC) assists First Nations by funding the capital costs of plants and piped systems, and 80 percent of their operating and maintenance costs; by enforcing certain standards through funding agreements; and is expected to resume an earlier role of providing engineering advice and, approval.
- Public Works and Government Services assists with procurement and provides engineering advice and approvals.
- Health Canada ensures the delivery of drinking water monitoring programs, either directly or in an oversight role.
- Environment Canada is involved in source water protection through its powers to regulate wastewater discharge into federal waters or into water generally, where water quality has become a matter of national concern.
- Chief and Council generally govern management and running of systems, and have the power to enact resolutions to protect water.
- Technical service advisory groups may be responsible for training operators and preparing them for certification exams, as well as providing one-on-one help and advice on site.
- Regional councils (such as tribal councils), or separate environmental health organizations may be involved in water monitoring programs and in public health matters generally.
- Some responsibilities vary region to region. This could include the authority to issue boil-water advisories, for example.

Currently, there are serious problems concerning drinking water on First Nations reserves. For example, in 2008, there are at least 85 First Nations water systems at risk, and close to 100 boil water advisories in First Nations communities. There are no federal laws or regulations that govern the provision of drinking water in First Nations communities.[3]

Programming and relative roles and responsibilities are evolving. In 2003, INAC developed the First Nations Water Management Strategy. This followed review of water and wastewater issues on reserves and identification of 191 high risk communities, from the water and wastewater perspective. The federal government announced, in 2006, a Plan of Action for Drinking Water in First Nations Communities. In that plan of action, INAC committed to:

- Issuing a clear protocol on water standards
- Ensuring mandatory training and oversight of water systems by certified operators
- Addressing the drinking water concerns of all high risk systems beginning with the 21 highest risk communities
- Creating an expert panel to provide options for a regulatory regime for drinking water on reserve
- Committing to future reporting on progress on implementing the Plan of Action

INAC is currently consulting on water-related regulations.

MÉTIS PERSPECTIVES ON WATER MANAGEMENT

The Métis National Council defines a Métis as 'a person who self-identifies as Métis, is of historic Métis national ancestry, is distinct from other

Aboriginal Peoples and is accepted by the Métis Nation.' As recognized by Section 35 of the *Constitution Act (1982)*, the Métis are one of three distinct Aboriginal Peoples of Canada. There is a Métis governing body in each of the three Prairie Provinces – the Manitoba Métis Federation, Métis Nation – Saskatchewan, and Métis Nation of Alberta. Each of these governing bodies has an elected president who, in turn, sits on the Board of Directors of the Métis National Council.[4]

The Métis subscribe to a strong stewardship ethic. They are inclined to look on development favourably so long as development can take place in a sustainable manner and will respect the three pillars of sustainable development – economics, conservation and socio-cultural.

Métis governments take the view that Section 35 of the *Constitution Act* affirms their right to access to water resources. Therefore, they also consider they should be at the table for water resources planning, such as Integrated Watershed Management Planning (IWMP) processes. Broadly speaking, formal involvement in IWMP processes in the Prairies may be at an even lesser level than that of First Nations at present. In Manitoba, at least, individuals of Métis background may be invited to the table. However, they are not at the table representing Métis governance in any formal way.

The primary concerns of Métis people with respect to water revolve around water quality and the fishery resource, as the two relate to human health, economic sustainability and a traditional way of life. There are several Métis communities within the Saskatchewan River basin in all three provinces, and most residents of these communities are tied very closely to the land and water base.

The Métis are engaged in water resource management in different ways than First Nations. An example is the Manitoba Métis Federation pilot project, the fish hatchery at St. Laurent, now in its third year of operation. The hope is the hatchery will be able to place fingerlings into the three larges lakes in Manitoba, including Lake Winnipeg itself.

Most Métis participants in watershed planning processes in the basin are probably engaged as citizens, not as representatives of Métis governments. There are different possibilities in Alberta, where there are formal Métis settlements, some located within the North Saskatchewan basin.

WATERSHED PLANNING AND MANAGEMENT IN THE PROVINCES

The three provinces of the Saskatchewan River basin have watershed planning and management processes in place that emphasize local engagement and participation in decision-making, and local participation in implementation of any plans. From an assessment and planning perspective, Alberta's process is the most mature, followed by Saskatchewan's and then Manitoba's, which has been most recently rolled out. On the implementation front, Manitoba has decades of experience with their Conservation Districts (CDs) model, although the context for the various water management projects in the Manitoba Conservation Districts has been relatively narrow. The following discussion illustrates the framework under which integrated watershed resource management takes place in the Prairie Provinces.

Alberta

Watershed management and planning in Alberta is largely focussed through Alberta Environment. This department has responsibility for approvals for integrated watershed management planning, municipal water systems, related operator certification, compliance and inspection of operations that could pose a threat to water, water level and flow forecasting, monitoring and reporting on surface and ground water, and policy development and implementation on all aspects of watershed management.

Water for Life Strategy

All water management activities are conducted under Alberta's Water for Life Strategy. Alberta established the Water for Life Strategy for sustainability in November 2003, based on three key goals:

- Safe, secure drinking water supply
- Healthy aquatic ecosystems
- Reliable, quality water supplies for a sustainable economy

The Strategy lays out short, medium and long-term actions to achieve these. As a fully accepted policy throughout the provincial government, the goals and actions are reflected in appropriate business plans throughout provincial agencies.

The Alberta Water Council conducts an annual review of the implementation of Water for Life. The Water for Life Strategy is currently going through a renewal process, following its first three-year implementation period.

The Alberta Water Council is a broad umbrella council with oversight responsibilities for water policy application. The Council has representation from six of the departments with major water responsibilities. The Water Council is supported by the Cross-Ministry Steering Committee that has a broader representation, as it integrates Water for Life initiatives in the Alberta government.

Legislation

The Water Act – aimed at conservation and management of water. The Act mandates establishment of a framework for water management planning, which must include a strategy for protection of the aquatic environment and allow for formation of water management planning areas. The Act regulates water rights and the setting of the priority of uses. The South Saskatchewan Basin Allocation Regulation under this Act regulates water allocation within the South Saskatchewan basin.

The Environmental Protection and Enhancement Act – intended to support and promote the protection, enhancement and wise use of the environment. It regulates release of substances into water, including collection and treatment of stormwater and wastewater and the treatment of potable water.

The Drainage Districts Act – intended to govern operations of formal drainage districts.

The Irrigation Districts Act – provides for formation, dissolution and governance of Alberta's 13 irrigation districts so that management and delivery of water occur in an efficient manner and provide for the needs of users.

Government of Alberta Codes – guide establishment and operation of various water and wastewater treatment systems.

The Municipal Government Act – allows for municipalities to plan for development and use of land, through land use zoning.

The Public Lands Act – assigns ownership of the bed and shores of all naturally occurring water bodies to the province. Use or disturbance of the bed or shore requires authorization under this legislation.

The Alberta Fisheries Act – guides overall management and protection of the fisheries resource.

The North Red Deer Water Authorization Act – allows a diversion of treated water from the Red Deer River for use by some Battle River watershed communities and ultimate release as wastewater into the Battle River.

Watershed planning has been going on in Alberta for many years, although it has certainly evolved substantially in the recent past.[5] From early beginnings, when such planning did not include land use, to a relatively new integrated approach, some parts of Alberta have considerable experience in watershed planning. It is not too much of a stretch to characterize the current approach as somewhat of an experiment in shared governance for water management. The following organizations or entities are involved in water management in the emerging approach to watershed planning and management in the province:

- **The Alberta Water Council** – which is keeper of the regional water management process and is creating a revised framework for watershed management planning. A related workbook was developed in the fall of 2007. It provides advice to Watershed Planning and Advisory Councils (WPACs) and is a catalyst for watershed planning. The Water Council includes six provincial and one federal representative. Other members are from municipal governments, First Nations, ENGOs, and industry.
- **The Watershed Planning and Advisory Councils (WPACs)** – which prepare state of the basin assessments and watershed management plans. They are made up of members who have power and authority to make decisions in watersheds and who have decided, of their own volition, to work together within a watershed.
- **The Alberta Stewardship Network and Watershed Stewardship Groups** – administers smaller grants to Watershed Stewardship Groups. Watershed Stewardship Groups are composed of various interests who wish to undertake water-related projects or activities.

Watershed management planning is guided by Alberta's principles for integrated resource management. These are:

- **Comprehensive and Integrated** – considering the full range of environmental, social, health and economic interests.
- **Proactive and Predictable** – anticipating future resource management issues and providing a predictable context for users of Alberta's resources.
- **Responsive and Flexible** – application of adaptive management.
- **Consultative** – those affected by decisions will be consulted prior to taking action.
- **Fairness** – decision-making processes will be fair and the public is to be given access to relevant information.
- **Knowledge-based** – decisions are to be based on understanding potential consequences of choices.
- **Timely and Results Oriented** – decision processes are to strive for efficient use of financial and time resources, and decisions should support provincial goals and objectives.
- **Accountable** – decision-makers are accountable for their actions.
- **Clear and Understandable** – products and processes will be straightforward. Roles and responsibilities will be well-defined.

The watershed planning process is very respectful of the time and effort invested by the various participants in the process. WPACs are the forum in which planning choices are debated. The resulting plans are not subject to a Water Council approval process. The power resides in the legislature, but the governance model ensures the debate that occurs in the WPACs is not second-guessed.

The Alberta WPACs have formed a WPAC forum, the agenda for which is evolving. It is being used for sharing lessons learned and allowing new WPACs to benefit from the experiences of the more mature WPACs. Increasingly, the WPAC Forum agenda is being set by the WPACs. The forum is supported financially by the province.

Sub-basins within the Saskatchewan River basin already actively engaged in integrated watershed management in Alberta include:

- The North Saskatchewan River
- The Battle River
- The Bow River
- The Red Deer River
- The Oldman River
- The South Saskatchewan River

The only geographic gaps in WPAC process in the Saskatchewan basin in Alberta relates to the

Sounding/Eyehill Creek sub-basin, a watershed that is part the North Saskatchewan River sub-basin. The planning process is at different stages in different sub-basins, and some are just getting off the ground.

The process portrayed in Figure 3.1 can be further elaborated by the following points:

- The WPAC is composed of members with authority locally to make decisions related to water management.
- The draft terms of reference are not merely the rules that will govern the WPACs and the activities of its various committees. They must also address the principles or philosophies that will guide the work and the consultation processes which will be used. They must also provide detail on the work proposed.
- The WPAC, assisted by representatives of a number of provincial agencies with responsibilities for resource management, collects data and information and then prepares a state of the basin report.
- Beginning with the state of the basin report and its own analyses, the WPAC then develops the Integrated Watershed Management Plan.
- It is then up to the WPAC to implement the plan and to monitor activities and the extent to which those activities are effective. Depending on observed results, the plan must then be updated or amended as appropriate.
- The provincial government provides partnership funding for initiatives that the WPACs put forward. The provincial government also provides some funding to the Alberta Stewardship Network for its granting responsibilities.

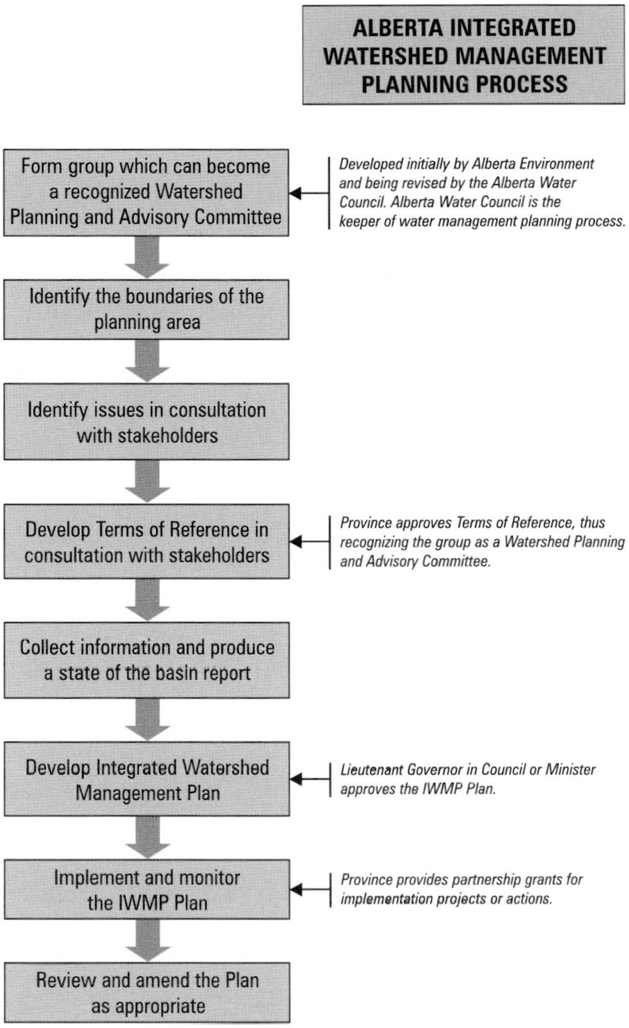

Figure 3.1.

Saskatchewan

Watershed planning and management activities are undertaken by a number of agencies in Saskatchewan. The primary agencies include:

The Saskatchewan Watershed Authority (SWA) – responsible for management of both groundwater and surface water in the province, including approving and licensing water-use projects, as well as reviewing project proposals that may impact source waters. The Authority also manages the watershed planning process for the province and plays a significant role in water quantity monitoring.

The Saskatchewan Watershed Authority is advised by the Saskatchewan Watershed Authority Advisory Committee. This body is appointed for three-year terms and represents a broad spectrum of the public. Its mandate is to identify and evaluate a wide range of water issues, challenges and opportunities, and to provide the SWA Board and Executive with perspectives and advice.

SaskWater – is the Crown water utility service provider, whose business includes potable and non-potable water supply, wastewater treatment and management, and provision of certified operation and maintenance services to customer-owned facilities.

Saskatchewan Ministry of Environment – has responsibility for regulating release of pollutants into water, and thus for regulating water quality as well as drinking water. The ministry carries out water-quality monitoring in the province. It also has responsibility for administration and application of the *Environmental Assessment Act* in Saskatchewan.

Saskatchewan Ministry of Municipal Affairs – has responsibility for developing and participating in the federal-provincial infrastructure agreements.

The Long-term Safe Drinking Water Strategy

In 2002, Saskatchewan released the Long-term Safe Drinking Water Strategy. This strategy identified a vision of 'a sustainable, reliable, safe and clean supply of drinking water that is valued by the citizens of Saskatchewan.' It also identified principles related to human health, preventing risks, openness and clear communication, realistic pricing, and accurate and timely information. It also recognized the need for all levels of government and citizens to work together. The same year, Saskatchewan prepared *Protection of our Water: A Watershed and Aquifer Planning Model for Saskatchewan*.[6] This document has provided the framework for watershed management planning in the province. While most directly linked to the Long-term Safe Drinking Water Strategy, this planning model also follows the principles identified in the Water Management Framework. This framework includes a vision for 'safe and reliable water supplies within healthy and diverse aquatic ecosystems.' The framework also identifies six principles – principles that remain important and are reflected in the Safe Drinking Water Strategy:

Stewardship – protecting the quality and quantity of water resources for the benefit of present and future generations.

Partnership – a commitment to work cooperatively with citizens, businesses, other governments of all natures to develop and implement water management decisions.

Integrated Management – recognition that effective water management requires full awareness within government of the inter-relationship of various government programs and interaction among the responsible agencies.

Value of Water – recognition that water has social/cultural, economic and environmental importance and should be valued as such.

Sustainable Development – project and programs that are bound by the principles of sustainable water use will be supported.

Best Practice – effective use of existing and emerging technologies and best management practices will help achieve the vision.

The Water Management Framework is currently in the early stages of being renewed and updated.

Legislation

The following legislation is key to watershed planning and management in Saskatchewan. However, this list could be augmented with several other pieces of legislation where the link to water is less direct.

The Saskatchewan Watershed Authority Act – establishes the Watershed Authority and outlines its mandate to manage, control and protect water resources, watersheds and related lands by regulating water development and water use. This Act also includes the ability to regulate groundwater exploration, use and abandonment of wells, other water rights, construction and operation of drainage works, and proper use and development of shorelines in designated Reservoir Development Areas.

The Water Power Act – provides for regulation of water power developments.

The Conservation and Development Act – enables rural landowners to establish a conservation and development area to facilitate development of works to conserve and develop agricultural land and water resources.

The Watershed Associations Act – enables two or more agencies to establish a watershed association to facilitate planning and development of works to conserve and develop land and water resources on a watershed basis.

The Environmental Management and Protection Act – prohibits or regulates discharges of pollutants, enables collection and analysis of water quality data, regulates provision of safe water for human consumption, permits construction of water works or wastewater works and regulates their operation, and regulates shoreline alterations.

The Fisheries Act – regulates commercial and sport fishing in Saskatchewan.

The Environmental Assessment Act – regulates application of an environmental assessment process to developments within the province.

The Water Appeal Board Act – continues the Water Appeal Board. The Water Appeal Board hears appeals raised under the Saskatchewan Watershed Authority Act with respect to drainage works.

The Public Health Act – regulates private water supplies and sewage works.

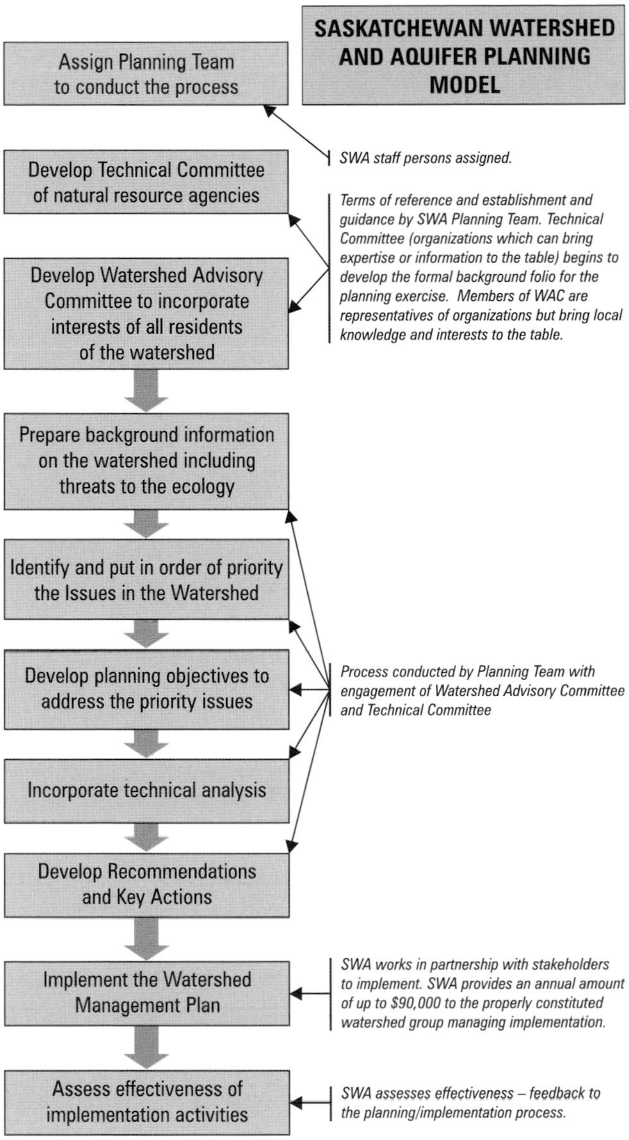

Figure 3.2.

Figure 3.2 displays the watershed planning model. Of course, there may be some departures in practice. The following points add some detail:

- The planning team is composed of two watershed planners from the Saskatchewan Watershed Authority. The Planning Team has overall responsibility for guiding and facilitating the planning process from its initiation to its conclusion.
- The Technical Committee is made up of representatives of resource agencies from the provincial and federal governments, as well as organizations such as Ducks Unlimited that have considerable data and analysis to offer the planning process.
- The Planning Team and the Technical Committee focus on developing critical background material for the planning exercise.

- After some of the background has been assembled, the Watershed Advisory Committee (WAC) is formed of representatives of locally present and engaged organizations, including municipal governments, First Nations and NGOs.
- The WAC meets several times to learn about and add knowledge to the background information, to identify issues in the watershed, to set objectives to address the issues, and to make recommendations and set action plans that collectively form the water source or aquifer protection plan.
- WACs rely heavily on the efforts of volunteers, although some representatives may be on salary while engaging in IWMP activities. Because of distances of travel in some Saskatchewan watersheds, it often makes sense for the planning work to go on in sub-basins where the travel distances and time are shorter. To bring this information up to a full watershed level, sub-basin WACs must come together through a representative process that sees them amalgamate their issues, their objectives, and their recommended actions.
- Once the plan is in place, various members of the WACs involved will form a formal legal entity that will take on the roles of implementer and watershed manager. SWA will then assist this group in two ways – an unfettered annual implementation grant of up to $90,000 and support, on a partnership basis, for specific projects within the watershed.

The following sub-basins within the Saskatchewan River basin are already engaged in watershed management planning in Saskatchewan:

- The following three sub-basins have completed their work and have been combined into single South Saskatchewan basin for which the plan has been completed.
    - The South Saskatchewan River West sub-basin
    - The South Saskatchewan River Lake Diefenbaker sub-basin
    - The South Saskatchewan River North sub-basin
- The following four sub-basins have completed their work and been combined into a single North Saskatchewan basin for which the plan has been completed.
    - The North Saskatchewan River Battle River sub-basin
    - The North Saskatchewan River West sub-basin
    - The North Saskatchewan River Central sub-basin
    - The North Saskatchewan River East sub-basin

The planning process has begun for Swift Current Creek and the Carrot River. Source water protection plans will be the eventual outputs of those planning processes now in their early stages.

Manitoba

Watershed planning and management within the province of Manitoba is largely focussed within the Department of Water Stewardship. This department has responsibility for all forms of water licensing for both surface and ground water no matter the nature of the use proposed, for flood forecasting and protection for much of the province, for water quality, drinking water, and for fisheries management. The Manitoba Water Services Board assists Manitobans living outside Winnipeg in developing safe and sustainable water and sewerage facilities.

In April 2003, Manitoba published *The Manitoba Water Strategy*.[7] This strategy identifies the need for action in the following areas: water quality, conservation, use and allocation, water supply, flooding and drainage. The implementation framework for the strategy has three elements:

- Development of an integrated water planning and management system
- Review and consolidation of water legislation
- Development of mechanisms for financing water management and planning.

The *Water Protection Act* establishes the Manitoba Water Council to monitor development and implementation of watershed plans, advise the Minister of Water Stewardship on water issues, coordinate various and diverse water-related advisory boards, and assist in sustainability reporting for water.

Legislation

Manitoba's new *Water Protection Act* is the cornerstone of Manitoba water-related legislation, and is fundamental to implementation of the Manitoba Water Strategy as it focusses on:

- Comprehensive watershed planning
- Source water protection
- Endorsement of the scientific approach including development of objectives, standards and guidelines
- Protection of riparian areas and wetlands
- Use of financial incentives to protect and enhance water, aquatic ecosystems or drinking water sources
- Establishment and responsibilities of the Water Council
- Establishment of the Water Stewardship Fund to support research, implementation of watershed management plans, and water conservation programs.

Other relevant Manitoba legislation includes:

The Conservation Districts Act – provides for establishment of conservation districts to support conservation, control and prudent use of resources, while respecting the rights of landowners.

The Conservation Agreements Act – permits land owners and conservation agencies to enter into agreements for protection and enhancement of natural ecosystems, wildlife or fisheries habitat and plant or animal species.

The Drinking Water Safety Act – establishes, by regulation, drinking water quality standards and regulates the provision of drinking water in the province.

The Fisheries Act – governs commercial fishing in the province.

The Ground Water and Water Well Act – allows for regulation of use of ground water and protection of ground water. It also governs activities and qualifications of well-drillers.

The Manitoba Habitat Heritage Act – establishes the Manitoba Habitat Heritage Corporation, with the objectives to conserve, restore and enhance wildlife and fish habitat and wildlife and fish populations.

The Planning Act – requires that planning take place in rural Manitoba and recognizes that plans should consider any integrated watershed plans.

The Public Health Act – enables the government to protect water sources, restrict activities in designated sanitary areas, regulate supplies of drinking water, regulate development and operation of sewage treatment facilities.

The Water Power Act – allows the province to regulate use of water for purposes of generation of electricity.

The Water Resources Administration Act – continues the administrative structure to manage several pieces of water-related legislation that permits designation of flood areas, of reservoir areas and of diking systems.

The Water Resources Conservation Act – broadly prohibits the taking, storage conveying or selling of water from a basin or a sub-basin and notes that water is not a manufactured or produced product.

The Water Rights Act – requires licensing of the extraction of water for agricultural, industrial or domestic purposes.

The Manitoba Water Services Board Act – continues the Manitoba Water Services Board which has the following objectives: obtaining, development, transmission, distribution and control of water supplies for the people of the province and the collection, treatment and disposal of sewage. The focus is on areas outside the city of Winnipeg.

The Water Supply Commissions Act – allows for establishment of water commission areas and water commissions that would have the purpose of supplying all residents of the area with water to meet their needs.

Manitoba has defined Integrated Watershed Management Planning (IWMP) as planning to ensure that water and related resources are managed to provide for the environmental, social, and economic well-being of the entire watershed. The Manitoba IWMP process involves, generically, the steps laid out in Figure 3.3. The following notes augment information on that diagram.

- The Water Planning Authority (WPA) is established to guide the planning process.
- Compilation of a state of the watershed report and source water assessment is done with technical assistance from various provincial and federal agencies. The source water assessment is to be a part of the state of the watershed report.
- In conducting public consultation during preparation of the draft plan, the WPA has responsibility to engage representatives of all watershed residents in the process.
- The draft plan for source water protection and watershed management should address the issues and propose mitigation and protection measures where necessary or desirable. It should reflect a balance of local and provincial priorities.

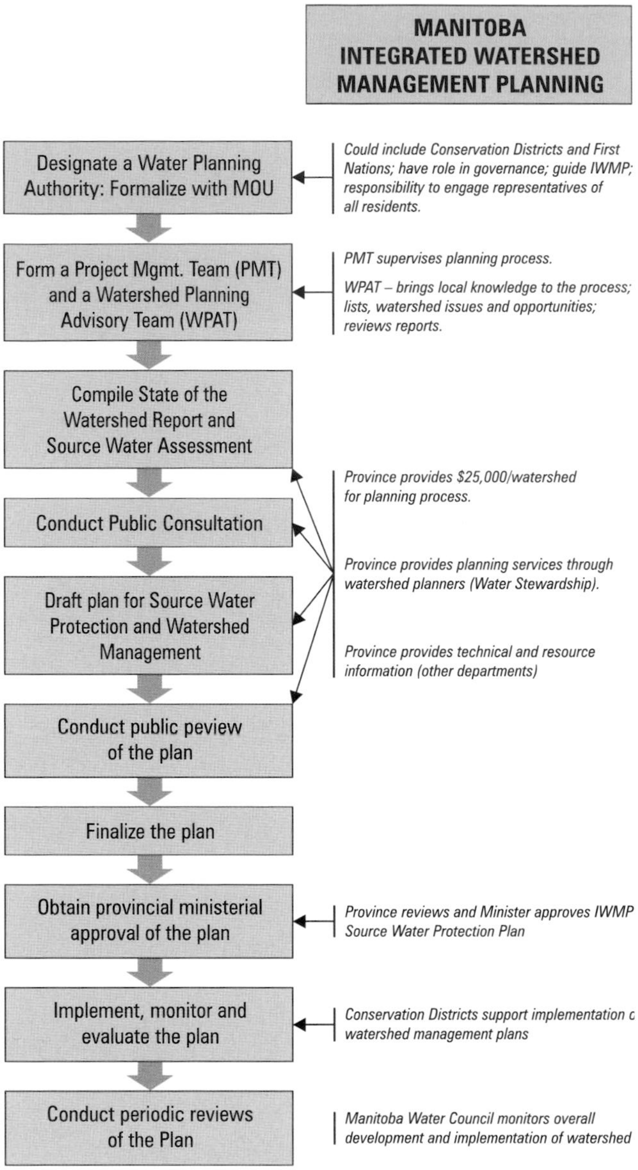

Figure 3.3.

The IWMP goals for the province are to have 75 percent of the plans started in the first five years and to have 90 percent completed in 10 years. The province provides $25,000 for each watershed to assist in the planning process.

It is the intent that Manitoba's Conservation Districts (CDs), a part of the water administration setting for many years in Manitoba, and a vehicle for implementing watershed protection measures, will be front and centre in production of state of the basin reports and formation and implementation of integrated watershed management plans. This and other changes related to what conservation districts do, and how they finance it, are all part of a consultation currently in progress.

There is no formal integrated watershed management planning activity in the Saskatchewan River basin currently underway in Manitoba; however, the Kelsey Conservation District has been established. This Conservation District includes a major portion of the Saskatchewan River basin in Manitoba.

SUPPORT FOR INTEGRATED WATERSHED MANAGEMENT PLANNING

Wetland Policies on the Prairies

Wetlands information is critical to preparation of any state of the basin report, and the wetlands policy context is an important underpinning for watershed planning and watershed plan implementation.

Alberta and Saskatchewan are both concluding wetlands policy development processes, while Manitoba is initiating theirs. In Saskatchewan and Alberta, current wetlands policy development is aimed at updating and replacing previous policies. On the other hand, in Manitoba, the policy development process represents a first comprehensive effort towards wetlands policy. Given that Manitoba's process is just beginning, it is unlikely a new wetland policy would be in place there in less than two years.

The new Alberta wetlands policy applies to all areas of the province. Previously, there were two policies - one for the south, or the white zone of the province, and one for the north, or forested green zone. The new policy applies to the whole province and to all classes of wetlands. In September of 2008, the Alberta Water Council recommended the new policy to the Alberta government, along with recommendations for a policy implementation plan. The policy itself identifies a number of guiding principles that reflect the high value of wetlands. It elaborates an overall goal to 'maintain wetland area in Alberta such that ecological, social and economic benefits that wetlands provide are maintained' and 'Albertans have healthy watersheds that provide safe and secure drinking water supplies for a sustainable economy.' The policy lays out a wetland mitigation decision framework. The recommendations for a policy implementation plan includes action plans for each of five strategic directions. The Alberta government is reviewing the recommendations and is currently crafting a new wetlands policy that could reasonably be expected to be ready for release in the spring of 2009.

The new Saskatchewan wetlands policy replaces a policy released in 1993. The new policy is intended to elaborate on the 1993 version and be more specific in terms of linking the policy to on-the-ground actions. The new policy is awaiting release, probably later in 2009.

The Integration of Land Use Planning and IWMP

The effectiveness of integrated watershed management planning will be heavily influenced by the degree to which it can be integrated with land-use planning in the watershed. This integration occurs to varying degrees within the Saskatchewan River basin.

In Alberta, work has been underway for some time on a new land-use framework. Development of that framework has been both an extensive and intensive effort, with a large breadth of engagement and significant effort required of those most engaged in its committee and sub-committee work. The draft land-use framework was recently released

The land-use framework contemplates and lays out a detailed schedule for development of six regional plans. The six regions are largely congruent with major watersheds but also have to fit with municipal boundaries. The regional planning effort must encompass use and management of land, air, water and biodiversity. Integrated watershed management plans will have to be in compliance with these six new landscape-level plans. If the IWMP process is already well-advanced, the appropriate WPACs will be asked to contribute to development of the regional plan. For these existing watershed management plans to be compliant, some adjustments may be required, once the provincial Cabinet has approved the regional plan. On the other hand, if the IWMP process is in its early stages when the development of the regional plan begins, the relevant WPACs may choose to await the outcome of the regional land-use planning process before doing the detailed IWMP process. This will be one way of ensuring congruity. The schedule for preparation of the six regional land-use plans has them all completed by 2012.

In Saskatchewan, there is no formal land-use planning undertaken in the southern part of the province, where IWMP processes are currently underway, with the exception of some special area plans, such as that for the Great Sand Hills. Land-use zoning is done by rural and urban municipalities. All municipalities within a watershed are invited into the integrated watershed management planning process. It is hoped that municipal representatives will take back to their respective administrations the implications of the integrated watershed management plans for their own municipality, and work towards congruence.

In Manitoba, the two Acts most focussed on this question reference each other. *The Planning Act* indicates that in preparing a development plan or amending a development plan by-law, consideration must be given to any watershed plan approved under *The Water Protection Act*. Similarly, *The Water Protection Act* requires that the preparation of any watershed management plan consider any development plans (as defined by *The Planning Act*). In practice what this means is that local planning staff of the provincial Community Planning Services Branch participate in development of recommendations of the integrated watershed management plan, at the invitation of the Water Planning Authority. This is a new process and it is straining resources for the planning people, but the will to make it work appears to be strong.

Riparian Management

Riparian health is an important consideration in state of the basin reporting and in development and implementation of a watershed management plan. There are a number of tools and supports available to watershed managers in all three provinces.

In Alberta, the Cows and Fish Program is strong and vibrant, and is based on creating partnerships with producers and communities, in which local communities identify riparian land-use issues and develop ways to deal with them. The Cows and Fish Program focusses heavily on process, which consists of five main parts:

- Awareness, in which presentations, workshops and field days are used to help people understand the functions and value of healthy riparian zones, as well as how riparian areas can be sustained or improved.
- Team building, in which local interests are encouraged to come together to learn about and address riparian health issues. This approach recognizes and reinforces that many must come together to tackle riparian issues.
- Tool building, in which experience and research is used to develop locally appropriate solutions to resolving riparian issues.
- Community-based action, in which community engagement ensures local people own both the process and the outcomes of riparian assessment and management. This leaves a legacy of effectiveness and longevity.
- Monitoring, in which local communities can know regularly the state of riparian health and the effectiveness of their actions to improve riparian health. In addition they can contribute to ongoing improvements in the Cows and Fish program delivery.

Cows and Fish Program activities do not include assistance for funding land and water management initiatives. However, the staff will guide landowners towards funding sources. Approximately 4000 people are exposed to the extension and education activities of the program in Alberta, annually. Evaluations done after the fact indicate the program is making a difference in the way approximately 60 percent of participants are managing their riparian areas.

In Saskatchewan, a vibrant program of education, extension and technical assistance on riparian management thrives. It occurs through a collaboration of provincial and federal agencies, including the

Saskatchewan Watershed Authority, the Saskatchewan Ministry of Agriculture and PFRA. Saskatchewan researched their approach to the program at about the same time as Alberta did, and the two provinces adopted many of the same principles around the same time, the early 1990s. At the same time, Saskatchewan has borrowed a number of elements of the Alberta Cows and Fish Program, although the focus in Saskatchewan is also on individual producers, not only groups of producers. A strong principle of the Saskatchewan programming in this area is that incentives are far more effective than is an attempt at enforcement of requirements.

Riparian management in Saskatchewan currently occurs hand-in-hand with delivery of the Farm Stewardship Program. In addition to providing good background information and strong technical support to individual producers as they develop their environmental farm plans, Saskatchewan has emphasized, through the budgeting process, a sub-set of the standard list of BMPs of particular use in managing riparian areas, two of the chief ones being riparian management and winter-site management. By reserving a certain amount of the funding available for BMPs solely for the sub-set, the uptake of certain BMPs is, reportedly, higher in Saskatchewan than in the other Prairie Provinces.

As part of the Farm Stewardship Program, there are 10 agro-environmental group plans; that is, environmental farm plans for groups of producers, those groups being defined largely on a watershed basis. Here, again, water resource-related BMPs are emphasized.

Saskatchewan is also working very closely with the First Nations Agriculture Committee, a non-government organization successfully implementing BMPs on First Nations' agricultural lands.

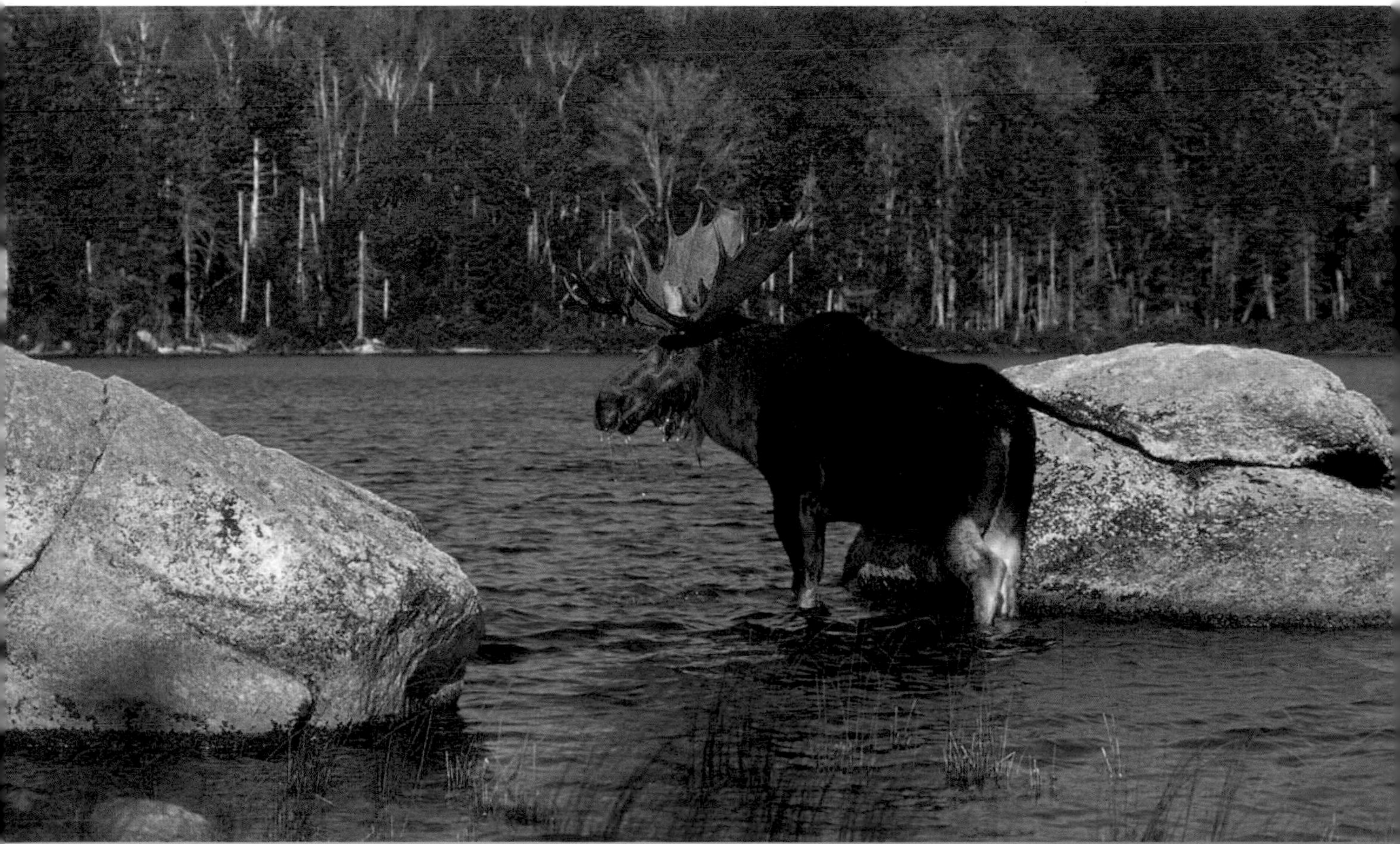

Saskatchewan's expectation is that current momentum can be continued into the replacement for the Agriculture Policy Framework, Growing Forward.

In Manitoba, also, the riparian health program, known as Managing the Water's Edge (MWE), is adapted from the Cows and Fish Program. However, one major difference is that there is no real emphasis on community engagement, as the focus is more clearly on the individual producer in Manitoba.

Several government agencies came together under the umbrella of the Riparian Health Council to develop the MWE program. In addition to government agencies, conservation districts are also involved at a more local level. The program currently consists of workshops (which the organizing agencies collectively deliver) that help to inform producers and other land owners of the value of riparian areas, and of the application of the rapid riparian assessment technique. Guidance and advice on how to protect and improve riparian areas are also available. However, while some funding for related beneficial management practices (BMPs) has been available through the local conservation districts, for the most part it has been occurring most recently through the environmental farm planning process and related BMPs. However, the process is now in hiatus as Growing Forward, the anticipated replacement for the Agricultural Policy Framework, is negotiated.

The MWE process in Manitoba is not currently heavily subscribed, due, in part at least, to the present state of the livestock industry. However, an initiative with one of the western Manitoba school divisions is underway. This acquaints Grade 11 or 12 school students with riparian issues and with protection and improvement strategies. The initiative is in its second year. The first year yielded very positive results in terms of student interest, student learning, and progression of the students to higher learning opportunities.

SOME LESSONS LEARNED IN WATERSHED PLANNING AND MANAGEMENT IN THE SASKATCHEWAN BASIN

Common Lessons

The following lessons have emerged in more than one province:

- Local watershed planning bodies have found it immensely helpful to be able to base decisions or choices they have to make, as much as possible on good science, rather than on assumptions. Assumptions are often a bad foundation for planning.
- Local driving of the IWMP process is of critical importance.
- Locally based watershed planning and management activities require a strong commitment of resources that fit the responsibilities assigned or assumed. In many cases, the current assignment of resources is seen as not being sufficient.
- Having the right people and all the critical interests at the table is essential. In respect of the former, good leadership and championing of the IWMP philosophy is quite important.
  In terms of the latter, there will be inadequate buy-in to the plan and to implementation if the critical interests are not appropriately engaged throughout.
- There has been limited success in engaging First Nations in the IWMP process. Appropriate protocols are needed for engaging First Nations. The protocol should address, for example:
  - Reasons for and scope of engagement
  - Principles of process
  - A non-impact on rights statement
  - How partners will communicate
  - Decision-making scope
  - Government-to-government relationships

- It is further noted that in dealing with First Nations, one should not take a one-size-fits-all approach. Each community may well be different. Further, this requires relationship-building and one should allow considerable time for this to develop with each community.
- Strong and relevant technical advice is essential to the IWMP process.

Jurisdiction-specific Lessons

Alberta has found that:

- Establishment of ground rules for operation of the WPACs, prior to any conflict arising, has been quite important. These ground rules often stress openness, honesty, integrity, and absence of hidden agendas.
- Use of open forums to exchange information within and amongst WPACs has been useful, where applied, in dispelling suspicion and improving understanding within WPACs and supporting mutual learning between WPACs.
- A more complete governance model development by the province prior to the implementation of the WPAC process would have been desirable. The uncertainty of roles and responsibilities is thought to have hindered progress in some areas.
- Some WPACs have had the good fortune to have extremely committed volunteers - people who participate in both the planning exercise and in completing on-the-ground activities.
- One WPAC identified a huge benefit from having one Board member who kept an ear to the ground, always bringing insights about what citizens wanted to see from the exercise.
- It has been helpful to ensure that local stewardship groups get appropriate profile and respect for their contributions.
- Use of a community approach increases the effectiveness of extension and education activities of the Cows and Fish program markedly.

Saskatchewan has found the following:

- Watershed planning projects for each of the North and South Saskatchewan rivers were so expansive geographically that, in retrospect, the division of these watersheds into smaller units might have assisted some of the logistics of planning, both for the stakeholders and the Saskatchewan Watershed Authority.
- There is uneven participation in the planning process over the long-term among the different stakeholders. While this may be attributed sometimes to satisfaction that their interests are being well served, in other circumstances, it may be because some stakeholders must participate on their own time and at their own expense.
- Due to the possibility that some major risks from point and non-point sources of pollution in the watershed may be missed in the current process, future planning will use a watershed risk assessment tool to evaluate issues raised by the Watershed Advisory Committees.
- It has been important to take time to conduct the process well – to do it right even if it seems slow.

Manitoba has found:

- Conservation districts have been effective as local implementers of provincial priorities. They have also proved to be adaptable to changes in government and policy. The CDs have been effective in education and outreach on topics such as riparian programming and, earlier, on initiatives like zero-till. They have also been effective in mobilizing community through local events, such as a water festival, which is having the effect of encouraging development of a water ethic in which everyone takes responsibility for water.

ENDNOTES

[1] Halliday, R.A. and G. Faveri (2007). "The St. Mary and Milk Rivers: the 1921 Order Revisited." *Canadian Water Resources Journal*, 32(1): 75-92.

[2] Kellow, R.L. 1989. "The Prairie Provinces Water Board: A Working Partnership for Prairie Water Management." *Proceedings, 7th Annual Red River Basin Land and Water Summit Conference*.

[3] Indian and Northern Affairs 2006. Report of the Expert Panel on Safe Drinking Water on First Nations, Volume 1. Indian and Northern Affairs, Ottawa, ON.

[4] Thompson, L.M. 2008. "Creating a Culturally Relevant Environmental Management System for a Métis Workplace." Masters Thesis, University of Manitoba.

[5] Alberta Environment 1999. *Framework for Water Management Planning*. Alberta Environment, Edmonton, AB.

[6] Saskatchewan Watershed Authority 2002. *Protecting our Water: A Watershed and Aquifer Model for Saskatchewan*. Saskatchewan Watershed Authority, Moose Jaw, SK.

[7] Manitoba Conservation 2003. *The Manitoba Water Strategy*. Water Branch Manitoba Conservation, Winnipeg, MB.

CHAPTER FOUR
THE WATER TOWERS

Figure 4.1. *The Water Towers of the Saskatchewan River Basin.*

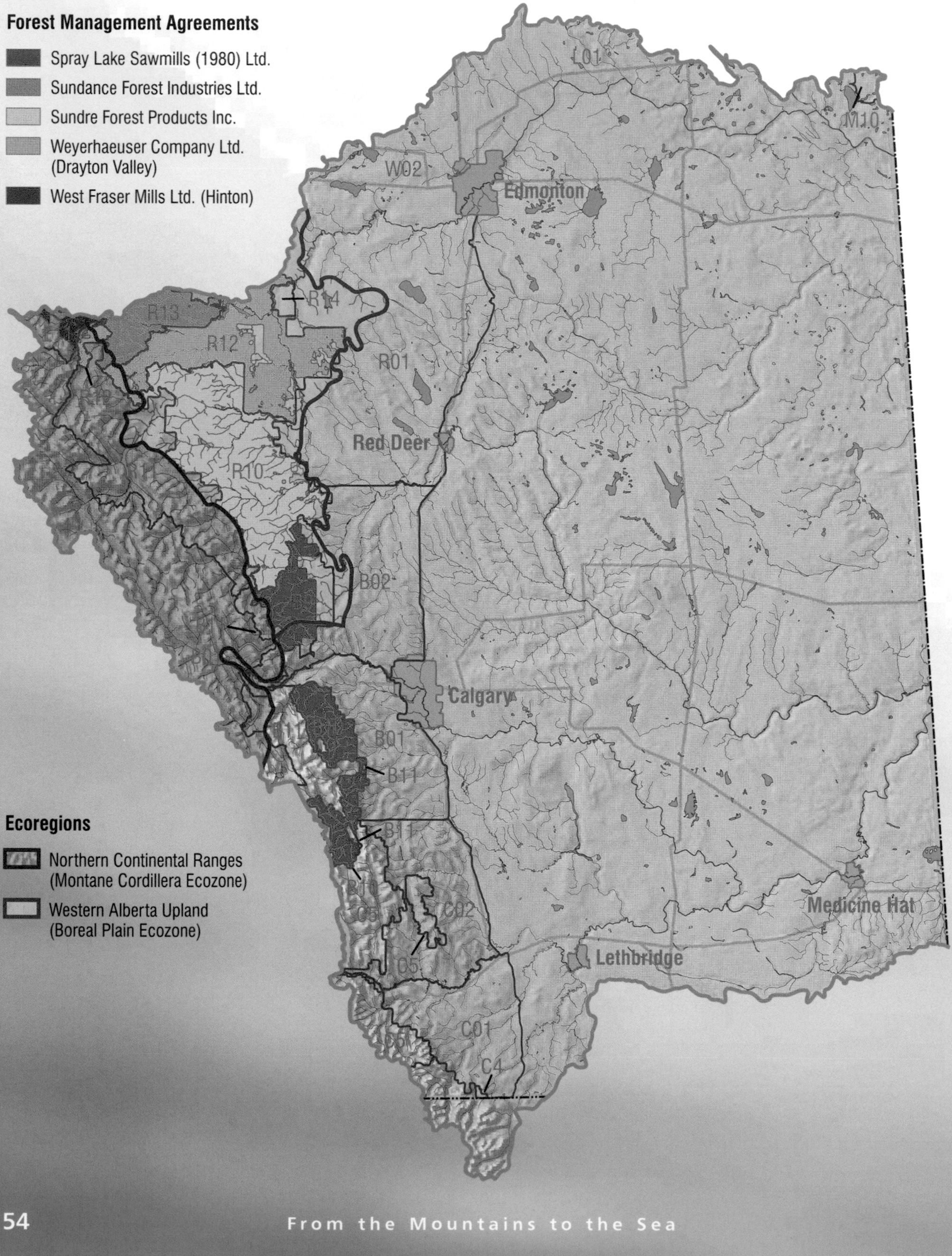

CHAPTER FOUR
THE WATER TOWERS

The mountainous headwaters of the Saskatchewan River basin can be described as the water towers of the basin: that is, they are the source of most of the water that flows across the plains. The term 'water towers' was coined about 10 years ago as a means of highlighting the importance of mountain environments to water resources.[1] In general, more than half the earth's runoff originates in mountains, while mountains cover less than a third of the planet's surface.[2] The world's food production is highly dependent on mountain runoff.

Water Towers Summary

Characteristics
- mountain peaks to forested foothills
- unique ecosystems

Hydrology
- high precipitation
- reliable flow
- some regulated streams

Water Quality
- excellent, naturally hard water
- potential for soil erosion

Biodiversity
- diverse and productive ecosystems
- headwaters protected

Key Issues
- terrestrial habitat fragmentation
- mountain pine beetle
- climate change
- long-range transport of air pollutants

Throughout the world, mountains are special places. While they are sacred places in many cultures and contain unique ecosystems worthy of protection, in others they are much sought-after recreation areas for urban dwellers. Mountains also contain mineral and forest resources that spur economic development. These conflicting attributes mean that mountain environments should be afforded a high level of protection.

The water towers of the Saskatchewan River basin shown in Figure 4.1 lie on the eastern slopes of the Rocky Mountains of Alberta and a small portion of Montana. The water towers include both the montane cordillera ecozone and the foothills forest of the boreal plain. The bare mountain peaks can exceed 3000 m in height while the forested river valleys are at elevations of 1000 to 1500 m. The mountains consist of upthrust and folded bedrock. There are steep slopes, enormous cliffs, and precipitous mountain faces. This rugged terrain varies in width from 10 km in the south to 100 km in the north. Unvegetated rock outcrops are

common along peaks and ridges. Alpine vegetation consists of lichens, grasses and low shrubs, with flowering plants on warmer sites. There is some soil development on the irregular, steeply sloping glacial deposits. The upper tree line is at about 2100 m at the northernmost part of the basin rising to about 2500 m near the international boundary. Below the tree line, there is still some exposed bedrock, but slopes are not as steep. Surface materials consist of glacier and stream deposits, and some wind-borne deposits. Spruce and pine forests are abundant.

The forested foothills adjacent to the mountains cover most of the Bow River headwaters and become wider to the north, taking in the headwaters of the Red Deer and North Saskatchewan rivers. Generally, the foothills consist of linear ridges, broad valleys and flat-topped hills that are 300 to 600 m higher than the surrounding areas. The foothills are underlain by deformed sandstone and shale.[3] They are covered with thin, gray, sandy-silty soils. Wetlands lie adjacent to the streams.

The foothills sedimentary geology contains considerable hydrocarbon resources. Nordegg and Cochrane are historic coal-mining communities. Oil and gas exploration is extensive.

The water towers contain several small communities and First Nations reserves. Human influences in this area tend to relate to forestry and to oil and gas exploration and development. National parks, provincial parks and wilderness areas provide many recreational opportunities. Recreationalists also use access roads and trails created by the forestry and oils and gas industries for back country access.

HYDROLOGY

The climate of the water towers is dominated by westerly flows of air masses from the Pacific Ocean. As these air masses move across the mountains of British Columbia, they lose moisture. Crossing the continental divide, they produce a considerable rain shadow on the eastern slopes of the Rocky Mountains. In general, annual precipitation is a function of altitude and distance from the continental divide. The eastern slopes are also affected by periodic easterly air flows. These systems can produce heavy spring snowfalls that enhance the winter snowpack. Annual precipitation at higher elevations is 800 to 1500 mm.[4] Annual precipitation in the foothills is 400 to 600 mm. At lower elevations, the winter snowpack can be depleted by periodic chinook winds. In general, the water towers are subject to the cold continental climate that dominates the entire basin. Montane regions, in particular, are subject to highly variable microclimates, depending on orientation to sunlight, slope, elevation, and wind.

Runoff originating in the water towers is determined by topography and climate, and is strongly influenced by the forest cover. Spring snowmelt, and rain during the snowmelt period, are dominant factors in determining annual runoff. At elevations higher than 1500 m – the elevation of Lake Louise – more than half the annual precipitation falls as snow. Winds redistribute and sublimate this mountain snowpack. Typically, in the absence of significant vegetation, the prevailing westerly winds create significant snowfields on eastward-facing slopes, and leave westward-facing slopes bare.

At lower elevations, the forest canopy intercepts the falling snow. This interception storage can range from 10 to 65 percent of the cumulative snowpack. A large proportion of the intercepted snow may sublimate during the course of the winter. This proportion may range from 12 to 45 percent of seasonal snowfall.[5] In the case of both interception and sublimation, the lower percentages are for mixed-wood forests, while the higher percentages are for homogeneous mature coniferous forests.

Solar irradiance, both direct and reflected from clouds and vegetation, drives snowmelt. As snow cover decreases, reflected energy from bare ground and brush becomes more important. South-facing slopes will melt more quickly than north-facing ones.

Once snowmelt begins, runoff from the water towers will depend on slope, vegetation and forest cover.[6] Although mountain landscapes are considered fairly impervious, infiltration into soils and rocky debris will affect the length of the flowpath, and, hence, the timing of runoff. Indeed, about half of the runoff from the water towers has existed as groundwater for at least part of its journey. The new water from the current year's snowmelt forces out old water stored in previous years.[7]

In the foothills, the age and composition of the forest cover will also influence the quantity and timing of runoff. Generally, older unbroken forests yield less runoff for a given annual snowfall than younger fragmented forests.

Figure 4.2 illustrates the typical mountain runoff using average daily flows for the Bow River at Banff, a period of almost 100 years. Spring runoff begins in very late in April, rises quickly to a peak in mid-June, then the flow recedes gradually through the remainder of the year. During low snowpack years such as 2001, the river rises even more quickly to a peak flow that may equal that of an average year, but the duration of the peak is brief.

In a typical year, runoff from the water towers of the Saskatchewan River basin accounts for almost 90 percent of the annual streamflow of the North and South Saskatchewan rivers. The figure is lower for the

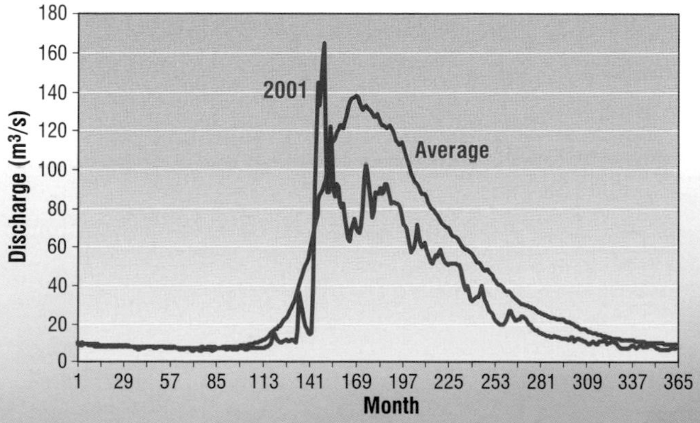

Figure 4.2. Streamflow for the Bow River at Banff.

Glaciers

The higher elevations of the Rocky Mountains contain many glaciers. Although these glaciers were studied for many years, the first glacier inventory was not produced until the mid-20th century. That inventory identified 1560 glaciers in the Saskatchewan River basin. Even at that time, there were very few glaciers in the Oldman River basin. There has been a dramatic loss of glacier ice since the mid-1800s – the approximate end of the Little Ice Age. Peyto Glacier, for example, has lost 70 percent of its volume over the 100-year period since it was first documented in 1896. From 1975 to 1998, glacier cover in the North Saskatchewan River basin decreased by 22 percent to 306 km^2. In the South Saskatchewan basin the equivalent loss is 36 percent to 88 km^2.

The contribution of glaciers to streamflow is made up of runoff from the annual precipitation that falls on the glacier, plus a contribution from glacier wastage. Glacier wastage, the amount of water coming out of storage from the glacier ice, is particularly evident since the mid-1970s, although it represents a relatively small portion of the total runoff. On an average annual basis, glaciers contribute 6.1 percent of the annual flow of the North Saskatchewan River headwaters, 3.7 percent of the Red Deer River and 2.8 percent of the Bow River. These percentage contributions are about twice as great during the summer melt period. In a low flow year such as 1970, glaciers contributed 13 percent of the annual streamflow at Banff, and, in August of that year, 56 percent of the streamflow. The effects of glacier runoff are ecologically significant and sustain human water uses in the headwaters but become much less significant downstream, in part because of the regulating effects of reservoirs. At Edmonton, glacier wastage contributes less than three percent of the annual flow of the North Saskatchewan River, while at Calgary the contribution to the annual flow of the Bow River is similar.

Red Deer River. Most of the sediment carried by these main rivers also originates in the water towers. The long-term sustainability of water uses in the entire Saskatchewan River basin is vulnerable, therefore, to anything that will affect water supplies originating in the water towers. Climate change and landscape change are important considerations. Temperature influences the timing of snowmelt and water supply. The water supply, in turn, affects the growth of high-altitude vegetation and tree growth at lower elevations. Indeed, vegetation will move upslope or downslope in response to temperature and precipitation changes. These climate effects are more significant than is the nature of the available soil cover.

FORESTS

The mixed sub-alpine forests of the water towers consist of limber pine, white spruce, and alpine fir. As well, closed stands of Douglas fir, intermixed with trembling aspen, and grassland ecosystems occur on the warmest, driest sites in the valley systems of the North Saskatchewan, Red Deer and Bow rivers. Further south, some hybrid spruce, western hemlock, and western red cedar occur at middle and lower elevations. At upper elevations, between 1600 and 2100 m, open stands of alpine fir are found. Regions that have experienced forest fires often have closed canopied forests of lodgepole pine.[8]

On the lower slopes of the Rocky Mountains, the mixed foothills forest consists of lodgepole pine, trembling aspen, and white spruce, with balsam poplar, paper birch, and balsam fir. Aspen and open stands of lodgepole pine occur on drier sites; black spruce and tamarack are associated with wetlands (bogs, fens and swamps). Conifers are more prevalent on cooler, higher elevations in the foothills, whereas aspen is more dominant in its lower plains section.

The montane-cordillera-ecozone portion of the water towers is partially protected by national parks, provincial parks and designated wilderness areas. Banff National Park had its origins in the discovery of hot springs by railway workers in 1883. The park is Canada's first such park and the world's third. The 6641 km^2 park includes the headwaters of much of the North Saskatchewan, Red Deer and the Bow rivers. A portion of the headwaters of the Brazeau River, a North Saskatchewan River tributary, lies in Jasper National Park. Adjacent to the two national parks, the White Goat, Siffleur and Ghost wilderness areas and Forest Management Unit (FMU) R11, known as the Bighorn Backcountry, provide high degrees of protection. The 5219 km^2 FMU contains many protected areas and generally has experienced little disturbance from forest harvesting or oil and gas exploration.[9]

Further south, Peter Lougheed Provincial Park and Kananaskis Country, adjoining Banff National Park, provide additional headwaters protection. Waterton Lakes National Park, a 505 km^2 park established in 1895, and Glacier National Park in Montana, established in 1910, include the headwaters of the Waterton, Belly and St. Mary rivers, which are Oldman River tributaries.

In recognition of the importance of forested lands, in 1948 Alberta established a 'green zone' within which land sales or settlements are forbidden. This zone includes the forested headwaters of the Saskatchewan River basin to the west of a roughly north-south line, extending from Waterton Lake National Park through Rocky Mountain House to the North Saskatchewan River. The zone also includes the forest lands north of the river from the Rockies to the Saskatchewan boundary. Lands that are deemed to have a better use than forestry can be withdrawn from the green zone.

Lands within the green zone are divided into FMUs, of which the Bighorn Backcountry is one. The FMUs tend to be relatively homogeneous. Harvesting rights are allocated in three different ways: timber permits, timber quotas, and Forest Management Agreements (FMAs). Timber permits involve small operators supplying local needs. Quota holders tend to be larger operators who are allocated a specific annual cut based on sustained yield principles. Holders of FMAs are granted a specific land area in which they may harvest timber over a 20-year renewable period. FMA holders must prepare a management plan for government approval. Holders are responsible for all aspects of forest management, including forest inventories, access road development, and reforestation. There are four FMAs in the foothills forest of the Saskatchewan River basin. These are listed in Table 4.1 and shown in Figure 4.1. The boundaries of these FMAs exactly follow the provincial FMUs. An FMA may also include some quota holders and oil and gas operations. There is no FMA covering the C5 FMU that extends from Kananaskis Country to Waterton Lakes National Park. Spray Lakes Sawmills holds a significant timber quota in this area.

The last 50 years have seen exponential growth in forest harvesting in Alberta. In the 1990s, the province established a new policy framework for management of its forests. The intent of this framework is to move from a sustained yield approach to an ecological management approach. That is, forest activities must be managed to conserve ecological integrity, biodiversity, long-term forest productivity, and the forest land-base. Holders of FMAs must incorporate these concepts into their detailed forest-management plans. These plans must embrace sustainable forest management, recognize other resource values and uses, explain how harvesting will be conducted, and identify performance measures. Public involvement in the preparation and review of the plans is required.

Timber harvesting clearcuts are made to emulate natural disturbance such as wildfires, insect outbreaks, and disease. That is, islands and peninsulas of undisturbed forest remain after the harvesting is complete. Reforestation must be initiated within two years of harvesting. The new stands are assessed twice to ensure adequate establishment and growth. Appropriate supplementary steps are taken, if necessary. Forest roads are usually reclaimed and planted to trees.

The quantity of timber harvested in the water towers by the forest industry is equalled by that harvested by the oil and gas industry. The land tenure process established by the FMAs for the forest industry involves large tracts of land, time periods of more than 20 years, and a requirement for ecosystem management. In contrast, the individual tenure arrangements for the oil and gas industry involve less than 100 km^2 of land and require that exploration be completed in less than five years. Oil and gas exploration involves establishing 2 to 4 m-wide cutlines through the forest at roughly 400 m intervals so that seismic surveys can be conducted. There are over one million kilometres of seismic lines in Alberta. These lines fragment the forest leading to an enormous growth in forest edges, compacted soils, and induced erosion. The lines seldom regenerate naturally.[10] There are no environmental conditions placed on exploration rights on public land. Exploration companies must report, however, on how they will meet provincial environmental regulations.

Table 4.1. Forest Management Agreements in the Water Towers.

FMA	FMU	Operator	Forest Management Plan	Basin
11	B9 & B10	Spray Lakes Sawmills	July 20, 2007	Red Deer, Bow, Oldman
12	R13	Sundance Forest Industries	March 18, 2008	North Saskatchewan (Brazeau)
13	R10	Sundre Forest Products		Red Deer, North Saskatchewan
14	R12	Weyerhaeuser (Drayton Valley)	November 10, 2006	North Saskatchewan

Drilling an exploration well requires construction of an access road, and developing a well field requires pipeline construction. While the effect of any one well may be small, the cumulative effects of a number of wells on the forests are significant. Long-term road and pipeline infrastructure must be developed to support oil and gas production. Forest production roads tend to be short-term.

Fire represents another disturbance of the forests of the water towers. First Nations burned forests as a means of maintaining open corridors and grasslands to attract bison. European settlement and the railroads led to further forest fires. The fires during the 1889-91 period were particularly extensive. Taking into account wildfires as well, the forests of the water towers burned, on average, every 50 to 300 years. The fire regime changed considerably in the last century. In Banff National Park, forest fires in the decade 1881-90 consumed one percent of the surface area of the park annually. This burn area gradually declined until it was negligible by 1940.[11] Fire suppression efforts to protect human development and other forest values led to significant reductions in fire frequency. Reduction in fire frequency increases the average age of forest stands, converts mixed-forest to conifer forest, and reduces the number of open areas such as meadows. At present, 60 percent of the eastern slopes pine forest is over 80 years old. This old growth forest is particularly susceptible to infestations of insects, such the mountain pine beetle.

In the 1990s, the national parks introduced measures to restore the role of fire in managing ecosystems. Prescribed burns aimed at emulating wildfires have tripled the fire frequency. Fire suppression has been reduced to instances where public safety or the security of infrastructure is a concern. These changes will restore deciduous forests and grasslands and improve the age structure of park forests.[12]

Alberta has a policy of suppressing forest fires before they exceed two hectares in size, and of containing all fires at four hectares or less. In general, about two percent of the fires accounts for about 98 percent of the area burned.[13] The province carries out prescribed burns to improve forest health. Human forest users are the dominant cause of forest fires in the water towers. In the foothills forest, lightning strikes are a significant factor as well.

Insect and disease outbreaks provide another stress on the forests. Currently the mountain pine beetle is a major concern. This beetle is a small flying insect that has a native range extending from Mexico to central British Columbia, with an eastern extent near the Alberta boundary. The beetles attack mature pine trees by boring through the bark to lay eggs and, in a mass attack by larvae, cutting off the flow of water and nutrients, causing the tree to starve. The ultimate consequence is stands of dead pine trees with reddish needles that turn grey within a year or so. The lodgepole pine is the primary host for the mountain pine beetle in Alberta. There are concerns that the infestation may spread to jack pine or even non-pine species such as spruce.

Severe winter temperatures tend to kill the beetle larvae, but several days of temperatures below -30°C are required. The mild winters of recent years combined with mature Alberta forests, are considered important factors in the current infestation. As winters continue to become warmer on the eastern slopes, the consequences for the forest cover are grave.

Although the beetle is not considered native to Alberta, outbreaks occurred in Banff in 1940 to 1943 and in the Waterton-Blairmore area in 1977 to 1985.[14] The second outbreak killed over one million cubic metres of lodgepole pine. (This represents the equivalent of some 4000 ha of forest cover.) In 1997, an infestation was discovered in Banff National Park. In 2002, the first pine beetles on Alberta provincial land were identified in Canmore. While the major outbreak is now generally north of Jasper National Park, infestations are occurring in the Saskatchewan River basin, from Canmore to the Crowsnest Pass area. Both the death of the trees due to the infestation and the preventive cutting in the FMAs to contain the infestation will change the habitat and the hydrology of involved areas. There is also evidence of beetle infestations in the Cypress hills.

Changes to forest stands brought about by timber harvesting, oil and gas exploration and development, fire, or insect infestations can have several water-related effects. The loss of forest canopy leads to more precipitation reaching the ground, thereby increasing moisture available for runoff. Decreased foliage on south-facing slopes increases melt rates, leading to earlier runoff. Reduced evapotranspiration because of decreased foliage leads to increased soil moisture, and thus greater runoff efficiency. Although there is some sublimation from winter snowpacks in harvested areas, sublimation loss from the former forest canopy is much greater. Reflected radiation in burns and clearcuts exposed to the sun leads to more rapid spring snowmelt. In the summer, the high temperatures in such areas reduce the viability of young plants and trees.

Harvesting equipment tends to compact the soil and decrease its capacity to absorb water. These effects can be mitigated by appropriate operating policies and procedures. Forest harvesting also requires construction of roads that create linear disturbances that may fragment wildlife habitat. These linear disturbances also interrupt or alter small-scale drainage patterns. Road construction may also lead to increased erosion and sediment loads in receiving waters. Some of these construction effects are mitigated by minimizing activity on steep slopes and leaving buffer strips adjacent to streams.

The overall effect of this transformation of the forest is to increase the average annual water yield of the Saskatchewan River basin. Relationships between

Herbert Lake, Alberta

forest cover and water yield, however, are very complex. While a general statement can be made for a very large basin, smaller-scale effects in any particular sub-basin may lead to either increases or decreases in water yield. Topographic effects such as solar exposure, slope, and elevation come into play, as do soil types, sub-surface geology, and the nature of the forest fragmentation. It is important to note that extreme precipitation events tend to overwhelm the hydrologic systems of a river basin. The effect of loss of forests on extreme hydrologic events is particularly difficult to determine.

WATER QUALITY

The waters rising in the water towers are naturally hard, with high levels of calcium and bicarbonate. This is a natural consequence of the nature of the basin's bedrock. The headwaters also tend to be low in nutrients. Based on low biological productivity, the headwaters lakes and streams can be considered oligotrophic.

Headwaters streams tend to be small and have limited capacity to assimilate human impacts. Water quality can be affected by commercial, industrial or recreational developments near the water's edge. The beneficial effects of the completion of the Banff sewage treatment facility in 1989 are evident in the water quality record. Construction of dams, such as for the hydroelectric stations in the Bow and North Saskatchewan basins, affect water quality by changing the streamflow and thermal regimes of those rivers. Water quality can also be degraded by natural phenomena. Winter ice cover may reduce dissolved oxygen levels; floods lead to higher sediment loads.

Environment Canada monitors the water quality of the Bow and North Saskatchewan River in Banff National Park, and Alberta Environment monitors water quality of the North Saskatchewan, Red Deer, Bow and Oldman rivers upstream of major population centres. Water-quality monitoring results can be compared to national and provincial water quality guidelines. Water quality indices based on this comparison show that the water quality is naturally excellent or good. Alberta Environment monitors a much larger number of parameters than Environment Canada, so the indices produced by the two organizations are not directly comparable.

BIODIVERSITY AND ECOSYSTEMS

The montane region of the water towers contain more than 50 species of mammals, including mountain goat, bighorn sheep, moose, elk and deer, as well as large predators such as cougar and grizzly bear. Outside of national park boundaries, big game hunting is common. There are more than 250 species of birds in the mountains. Some of these birds depend on old growth forest for habitat. In autumn, marsh and lake areas are heavily used by migrating ducks, swans and geese. Several bird and animal species in the water towers are considered to be in need of special attention or protection.

The water towers support a cold-water fishery that includes rainbow trout, brook trout, lake trout, bull trout, whitefish, and northern pike. Most of the mountain lakes were devoid of fish until stocking programs began in the early 1900s. Fish populations, where they existed, were dominated by mountain whitefish or longnose suckers. Stocked species included cutthroat trout, rainbow trout, and brook trout. The success of the stocking programs depended on both physical and biological factors. The native bull trout were harmed by introductions of brook trout, although angler pressure could also have been a factor. During the 1970s, Parks Canada curtailed stocking programs.[15, 16]

Fish in the high-altitude lakes of the water towers contain elevated concentrations of persistent organochlorine compounds associated with industrial contaminants and agricultural pesticides. Substances such as PCBs, DDT, toxaphene, and hexachlorobenzene are commonly found, and, with rare exceptions, no point sources of these contaminants are known.[17] Occasionally, concentrations approach levels that would trigger human health advisories. These compounds are the result of long-range transport in the atmosphere and subsequent snowfall in the high mountains.[18] In general, the higher the elevation, the greater the contaminant concentration. Glacier wastage may also contribute high concentrations of these contaminants to aquatic ecosystems. Sources of these contaminants includes Canada, the United States, Asia and probably Mexico.[19]

Streambeds in the water towers are composed of gravel, cobble and boulders. This, combined with low nutrient levels, leads to low, but highly-diverse, plant and animal communities. Upland riparian vegetation extends close to river banks. In general, riparian and aquatic communities are healthy and unaffected by human impacts. These communities are vulnerable, however, to forest harvesting and oil and gas activities in the foothills. Erosion control and maintenance of riparian buffer strips along watercourses is important.

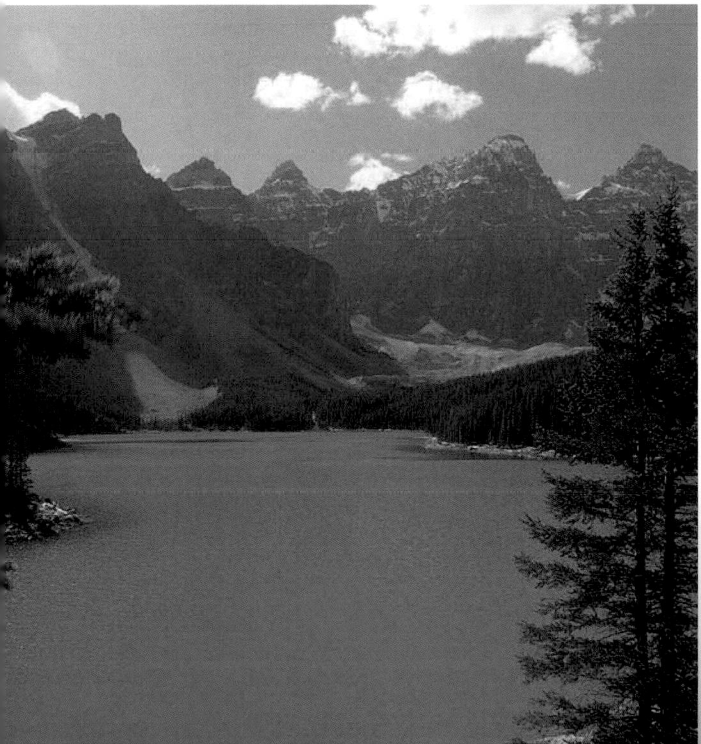
Moraine Lake, Alberta

References re Glaciers Box

Demuth, M.N., V. Pinard, A. Pietroniro, B.H. Luckman, C. Hopkinson, P. Domes, and L. Comeau 2008. "Recent and Past-Century Variations in the Glacier Resources of the Canadian Rocky Mountains – Nelson River System." *Terra Glacialis*, 11:248 27-52

Hopkinson, C and G.J. Young 1998. "The Effect of Glacier Wastage on the Flow of the Bow River at Banff, Alberta, 1951-1993." *Hydrological Processes* 13:10-11, 1745-1762.

ENDNOTES

[1] Messerli, B. 2006. "Mountains of the World – Water Towers for the 21st Century." *Proceedings, Rosenburg Forum*. Banff, AB.

[2] Viviroli, D., R. Weingartner and B. Messerli 2003. "Assessing the Hydrological Significance of the World's Mountains." *Mountain Research and Development*, 23:1 32-40.

[3] Alberta Online Encyclopedia 2008. http://www.albertasource.ca/aoe/ui/index.aspx

[4] Demuth, M.N., V. Pinard, A. Pietroniro, B.H. Luckman, C. Hopkinson, P. Domes, and L. Comeau 2008. "Recent and Past-Century Variations in the Glacier Resources of the Canadian Rocky Mountains – Nelson River System." *Terra Glacialis*, 11:248 27-52.

[5] Pomeroy, J.W., R.J. Granger, N.R. Hedstrom, D.M. Gray, J. Elliot, A. Pietroniro, and J.R. Janowicz 2004. "The Process Hydrology Approach to Improving Prediction of Ungauged Basins in Canada" In *Prediction in Ungauged Basins: Approaches for Canada's Cold Regions*, C. Spence, J.W. Pomeroy and A. Pietroniro, Editors. Environment Canada, Saskatatoon, SK.

[6] Ellis, C.R. and J.W. Pomeroy 2007. "Estimating Sub-Canopy shortwave Irradiance to Melting Snow on Forested Slopes." *Hydrological Processes*. 21: 2581-2593

[7] Liu, F., M.W. Williams and N. Caine 2004. "Source Waters and Flow Paths in An Alpine Catchment, Colorado Front Range, United States." *Water Resources Research*. 40:

[8] Ecological Stratification Working Group 1996. *A National Ecological Framework for Canada*. Canadian Soil Information System (CanCIS), Agriculture and Agrifood Canada. Ottawa, ON.

[9] Alberta Sustainable Development (no date). *R11 Forest Management Plan*. Alberta sustainable Development, Rocky Mountain House, AB.

[10] Schneider, R.R. 2002. *Alternatives Futures: Alberta's Boreal Forest at the Crossroads*. Alberta Centre for Boreal Studies. Edmonton AB.

[11] Fuenekes, U. and C.E. Van Wagner 1995. *A Century of Fire and Weather in Banff National Park*. Parks Canada, Banff, AB.

[12] Arno, S.F. and C.E. Fiedler 2005. *Mimicking Nature's Fire: Restoring Fire-Prone Forests in the West*. Island Press, Washington, DC.

[13] Tymstra, C.D. Wang and M.-P. Rogeau. *Alberta Wildfire Regime Analysis*. Wildfire Science and Technology Report PFFC-01-05. Forest Protection Division, Alberta Sustainable Development. Edmonton, AB.

[14] Ono, H. 2003. "The Mountain Pine Beetle: Scope of the Problem and Key Issues for Alberta. In Shore, T.L., J.E. Brooks and J.E. Stone, Eds, *Proceedings, Mountain Pine Beetle Symposium: Challenges and Solutions, October 30-31, 2003, Kelowna, British Columbia*. Information Report BC-X-399. Canadian Forest Service, Victoria, BC.

[15] Donald, D.B. 1987. "Assessment of the Outcome of eight Decades of Trout Stocking in the mountain National Parks, Canada." *North American Journal of Fisheries Management* 7:545-553

[16] Donald, D.B. and J.D. Stelfox 1997. "Effects of Fisheries Enhancement and Access on Adfluvial Bull Trout Poipulations in Mountain Lakes of Southern Alberta." In *Friends of the Bull Trout Conference Proceedings*. Mackay, W.C., M.K. Brown and M. Monita, eds.

[17] Donald, D.B., R. Bailey, R. Crosley, D. Muir, P. Shaw, and J. Sytgiannis 1993. *Polychlorinated biphenyls and Orgonochlorine Pesticides in the Aquatic Environment along the Continental Divide Region of Alberta and British Columbia*. Inland Waters Directorate, Environment Canada, Regina, SK

[18] Blais, J.M., D.W. Schindler, D.C.G. Muir, L.E. Kimpes, D.B. Donald, and B. Rosenburg 1998. "Accumulation of Persistent Organochlorine Compounds in Mountains of Western Canada." *Nature* 395: 685-688.

[19] Donald, D.B.J. Syrgiannis, R.W. Crosley, G. Holdsworth, D.C.G. Muir, B Rosenburg, A. Sole, and D.W. Schindler 1999. "Delayed Deposition of Organochlorine Pesticides at a Temperate Glacier." *Environmental Science & Technology* 23:11 1794-1798.

CHAPTER FIVE

THE NORTH SASKATCHEWAN RIVER SUB-BASIN

Figure 5.1. *The North Saskatchewan River Sub-basin.*

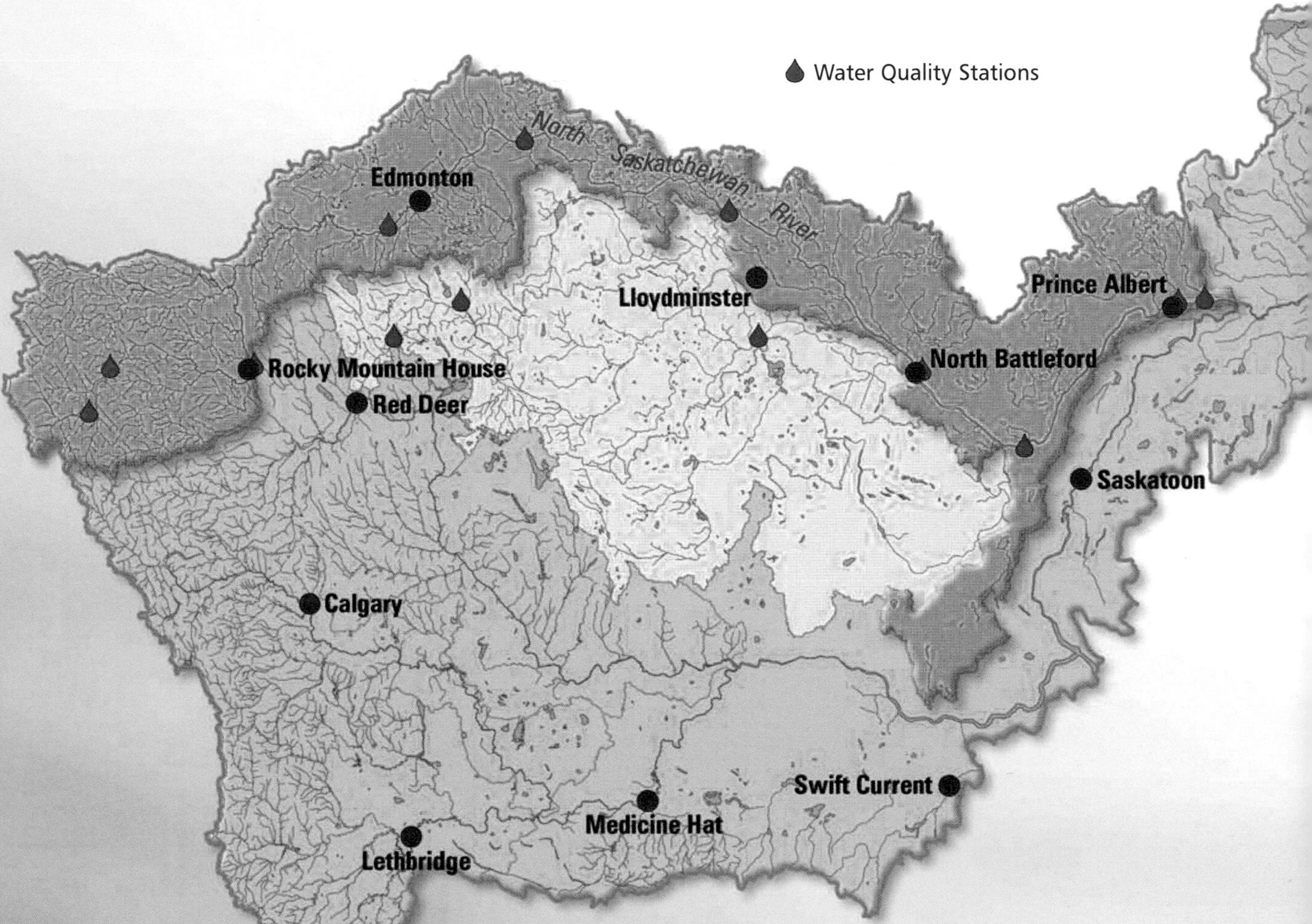

CHAPTER FIVE
THE NORTH SASKATCHEWAN RIVER SUB-BASIN

The North Saskatchewan River rises on the eastern slopes of the Rocky Mountains. Flowing from the montane cordillera ecozone, it crosses the foothills forest of the boreal plains, then follows the boreal plains-prairie ecotone for the remainder of its course through Alberta and well into Saskatchewan. After a loop through the prairie ecozone it emerges once again into the boreal plains ecozone, joining the South Saskatchewan River east of Prince Albert.

Sub-basin Summary

Characteristics
- high alpine to plains
- river length 1367 km
- gross drainage area 156 420 km^2
- effective drainage area 68 830 km^2

Hydrology
- reliable flow on headwaters tributaries and mainstem
- ephemeral flow on plains tributaries
- mainstem regulated

Water Quality
- excellent to good for headwaters tributaries and the mainstem to Edmonton
- fair to poor for plains tributaries and lakes and fair to good for the mainstem from Edmonton to The Forks

Biodiversity
- headwaters protected
- riparian zones generally healthy
- significant wetland loss

Key Issues
- land use - forestry and agriculture
- municipal and industrial effluents

The mountain headwaters of the basin lie at elevations over 2000 m above sea level. Mount Willingdon in the Clearwater River tributary headwaters, at 3373 m, is the highest point in the Saskatchewan River basin. The North Saskatchewan River itself drops rapidly from 1390 m at Saskatchewan Crossing to about 1000 m at its confluence with the Ram River. In this reach, it changes from a braided river to the channelized river seen at Rocky Mountain House. The river valley is typically 50 to 100 m deep. As it approaches the interprovincial boundary, upstream of its confluence with the Vermilion River, the North Saskatchewan River changes from a gravel bed stream to a sand bed stream.[1] The elevation of the river at the interprovincial boundary is about 500 m and it drops a further 100 m to its confluence with the South Saskatchewan River. The channel gradient, after decreasing gradually from the headwaters, increases slightly about 50 km upstream of Prince Albert.[2]

The alpine and sub-alpine ecosystems of the mountain headwaters are described in Chapter Four. The steeply-sloped mountain ranges have developed soils that support mixed forests of limber pine, white spruce and alpine fir. The major river valleys contain

Douglas fir mixed with trembling aspen and grassland ecosystems.[3] The headwaters of the North Saskatchewan River are in Banff National Park, although some smaller tributaries originate in Jasper National Park. The headwaters streams descend through the foothills – a region of ridges, rolling plateaus and broad valleys. Mixed forests of lodgepole pine, trembling aspen and white spruce dominate the region. Balsam poplar, paper birch, and balsam fir are also common. Black spruce dominates lower elevations wet sites. Conifers are found at the cooler high elevations, while aspen are found in the lower plains. Leaving the foothills, the North Saskatchewan flows though a region consisting of boreal transition forest to the north and aspen parkland to the south of the mainstem. The hummocky to rolling plain is dominated by deciduous forest and farmland. Agricultural lands upstream of Edmonton tend to be rangelands, while the lower basin consists of cropland. There are also many wetlands of all classes. In the boreal plain ecozone, the wetlands tend to be peatlands, while in the prairie ecozone the wetlands are mineral-based. The major plains tributaries of the North Saskatchewan River that enter the river from the south are discussed in Chapter Six.

The North Saskatchewan River basin contains 4 national parks, 10 Alberta provincial parks, 3 Saskatchewan provincial parks, and 35 First Nations reserves. It also has two Alberta wilderness areas and three Alberta ecological reserves. There are numerous crown wildlife areas and private conservation lands

Steamboats on the North Saskatchewan

By the early 1870s Fort Garry (present day Winnipeg) had become the Hudson's Bay Company's dominant centre for shipment of trade goods. The company initiated steamboat service on Lake Winnipeg in 1872 to transport goods between Fort Garry and the mouth of the Saskatchewan River at Grand Rapids. On August 1, 1874 the *S.S. Northcote* – named for a former governor of the Hudson's Bay Company – entered service and travelled upstream to Fort Carleton. Water levels were low and the boat was unable to travel to the head of navigation at Fort Edmonton. The following year the *Northcote* made one run to Fort Edmonton and a second run to Fort Carleton. When river flows permitted, steamboats could transport as much cargo from Winnipeg to Edmonton in a month as 150 to 200 ox carts in an entire summer.

The steamboats on the North Saskatchewan River had to contend with two significant navigational problems. Between The Forks and Prince Albert, La Colle Falls presented a series of rapids that during high flows were difficult to ascend, especially when barges were being towed. From Prince Albert to the confluence with the Vermilion River, the North Saskatchewan River channel was broad, included many islands and had shifting sand bars. It was difficult to navigate in low flows.

The *Northcote* was joined by the *S.S. Lily* in 1877. Following this very profitable year during which the boat made six upstream journeys, the *Northcote* was modified so that it could transport up to 50 passengers. Steamboat activity on the North Saskatchewan River was significant by the early 1880s. The *Northcote* and *Lily* were already steaming the Saskatchewan when in 1882 they were joined by the *Marquis*, the *Manitoba* and the *North West*. The relative speed and reliability of the steamboat service was a boon to settlements along the North Saskatchewan River. The arrival of a steamboat in any community was an event for both the passengers and the community.

By 1888, a combination of changed channel conditions, wrecks, and misadventure had reduced service on the river to one boat, the *North West*. On August 17, 1899, the boat broke loose from its moorings at Edmonton during a flood, struck the submerged piers of the Low Level Bridge, which was then under construction, and sank. This was the end of commercial steamboat traffic on the North Saskatchewan River.[4]

in this sub-basin. The population of the North Saskatchewan River sub-basin was 1.25 million in 2006. The dominant population centre of the sub-basin is the Edmonton metropolitan area, whose population of over one million accounts for more than 80 percent of the sub-basin's population.

HYDROLOGY

The North Saskatchewan River originates at the Saskatchewan Glacier in Banff National Park. It flows generally easterly to Rocky Mountain House. It then loops north through Edmonton and flows generally easterly until it crosses into Saskatchewan, flowing southeasterly through the Battlefords before turning north to Prince Albert and joining the South Saskatchewan River at The Forks. The river is 1367 km long and has a drainage area of 131 000 km^2. The effective drainage area is 68 839 km^2.[5] Headwaters tributaries include the Cline, Brazeau, Ram, and Clearwater rivers and, as explained in Chapter Four, other mountain and foothills streams account for up to 90 percent of the water that flows in the North Saskatchewan River. The North Saskatchewan River channel is relatively straight. From Rocky Mountain House to near Edmonton, and downstream of the interprovincial boundary the channel contains many vegetated islands and unvegetated bars. The plains tributaries that join the river from the south, notably the Vermilion and Battle rivers, contribute relatively little flow; they will be discussed in Chapter Six. The Goose Lake sub-basin rises in Saskatchewan and terminates in Goose Lake adjacent to Eagle Creek. This relatively large sub-basin contributes no flow to the North Saskatchewan River.

The flow of the North Saskatchewan River is regulated by Bighorn Dam, constructed on the mainstem near the mouth of the Bighorn River in 1972, and Brazeau Dam, constructed on the Brazeau River near its confluence with the North Saskatchewan River in 1961. These dams are operated for hydroelectric power generation. As electricity demand is highest in the winter, the effect of the dams is to increase winter flows while decreasing summer flows. The effects of

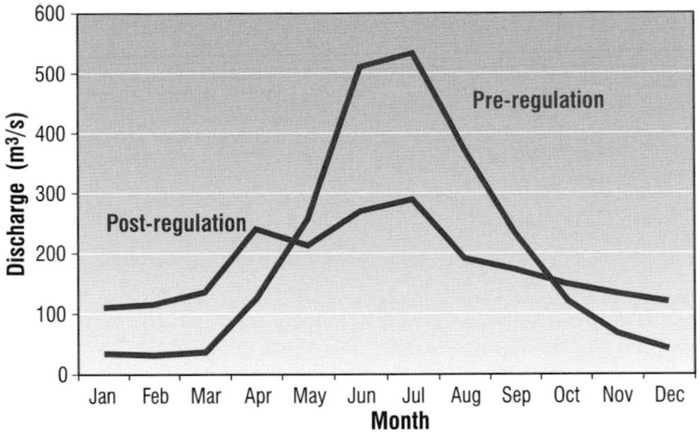

Figure 5.2. Effects of River Regulation on Median Monthly Discharge at Edmonton.

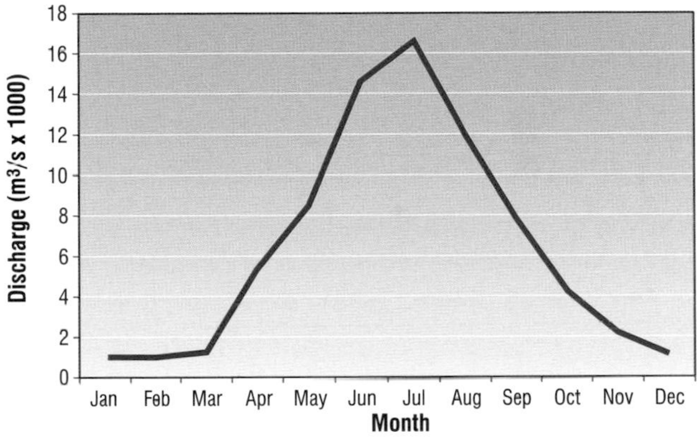

Figure 5.3. Naturalized Median Monthly Discharge at the Interprovincial Boundary.

river regulation are made clear in Figure 5.2. Increased winter flows facilitate operation of downstream water intakes and assist waste assimilation. Decreased summer flows mean the flushing flows that sustain some plant, invertebrate and fish species occur less frequently than before regulation.

The annual precipitation in the headwaters valleys of the sub-basin is about 600-800 mm, with about half of that falling as snow. Precipitation at higher elevations is even greater. The annual precipitation decreases with elevation to as little as 373 mm at North Battleford but increases slightly to over 400 mm near The Forks. Annual precipitation in the southern plains portion of the sub-basin near the interprovincial boundary can be as little as 320 mm. Once the sub-basin enters the plains, about three-quarters of the annual precipitation falls as rain.

The Water Survey of Canada, the Saskatchewan Watershed Authority and Alberta Environment operate 21 water level and 78 discharge gauging stations in the North Saskatchewan River sub-basin. The work is carried out under federal provincial cost-sharing agreements.

Annual runoff in the headwaters tributaries can be as great as 900 mm, while runoff in plains tributaries is as little as 10 mm.[6] Figure 5.3 shows the annual naturalized hydrograph for the North Saskatchewan River at the interprovincial boundary. Although there is an increase in runoff in April, due in part to runoff from the plains, most of the runoff in the sub-basin is driven by the melting of the mountain snowpack and the precipitation that falls during this melt period. Usually, peak runoff does not occur until July. Although there are no long-term trends in annual runoff for the North Saskatchewan River itself, there are indications of increased runoff in March and April and decreased runoff later in the year – a consequence of earlier spring snowmelt.[7]

Even without the benefits of flow regulation, the mountain runoff of the North Saskatchewan River is much more reliable than the flow of tributaries originating on the plains. The natural flow range is small in comparison to the median flow. The flow of the North Saskatchewan River is more reliable than that of the South Saskatchewan River.

There are few natural lakes on the main streams of this sub-basin. Abraham Lake was created by Bighorn Dam and Brazeau Reservoir was created by Brazeau Dam. Some plains streams originate at lake outlets and the sub-basin contains myriad small lakes and numerous wetlands. The lakes include both pothole lakes in the hummocky landscape and chain lakes along stream valleys. These features frequently provide opportunities for water-based recreation. Among the most significant are Lake Wabamun and Lac Ste. Anne near Edmonton, Pigeon Lake in the Battle River basin headwaters, and Emma and Christopher lakes adjacent to Prince Albert National Park. The basin also contains terminal lakes such as Manitou and Redberry lakes.

WATER USE

The licensed water allocation from the North Saskatchewan River, including the plains tributaries discussed in the following chapter, is 2 196 481 dam^3 from surface water and 60 716 dam^3 from groundwater. The surface water allocation is about one-third of the median naturalized flow of 6 794 000 dam^3 at the interprovincial boundary. Overall water consumption is only 317 977 dam^3 from surface water and 39 676 dam^3 from groundwater. Figure 5.4 shows the breakdown of licensed allocation and annual water consumption from surface water for the entire basin.[8, 9]

The largest water consumers in the sub-basin are industrial and petrochemical facilities, many of which are near Edmonton. Major industrial users also include thermal power stations, chemical plants and fertilizer plants. Thermal power stations withdraw large quantities of water but most of the water is returned to a lake or river. Other industrial water users include manufacturing and mining. The Highvale Coal Mine near Wabamun Lake is the largest such mine in Canada.[10] The pulp and paper mill near Prince Albert, Saskatchewan was a significant industrial water user prior to its closure in 2006. Gas and petrochemical plants consume relatively high quantities of water, as does water injection for enhanced gas and oil recovery. Water injection in Saskatchewan is almost entirely from groundwater.

The next largest water consumer is the 'other' sector. Much of this use consists of environmental services. This includes lake stabilization for habitat enhancement, primarily for waterfowl. Several of the projects are Ducks Unlimited Canada projects. Projects may also improve habitat for fish and wildlife. Almost all of the water withdrawn to support this use is consumed through evaporation and does not return to the stream. About one-quarter of this water consumption consists of diversions in Saskatchewan to stabilize Jackfish and Emma lakes. These lakes are extensively used for water-based recreation.

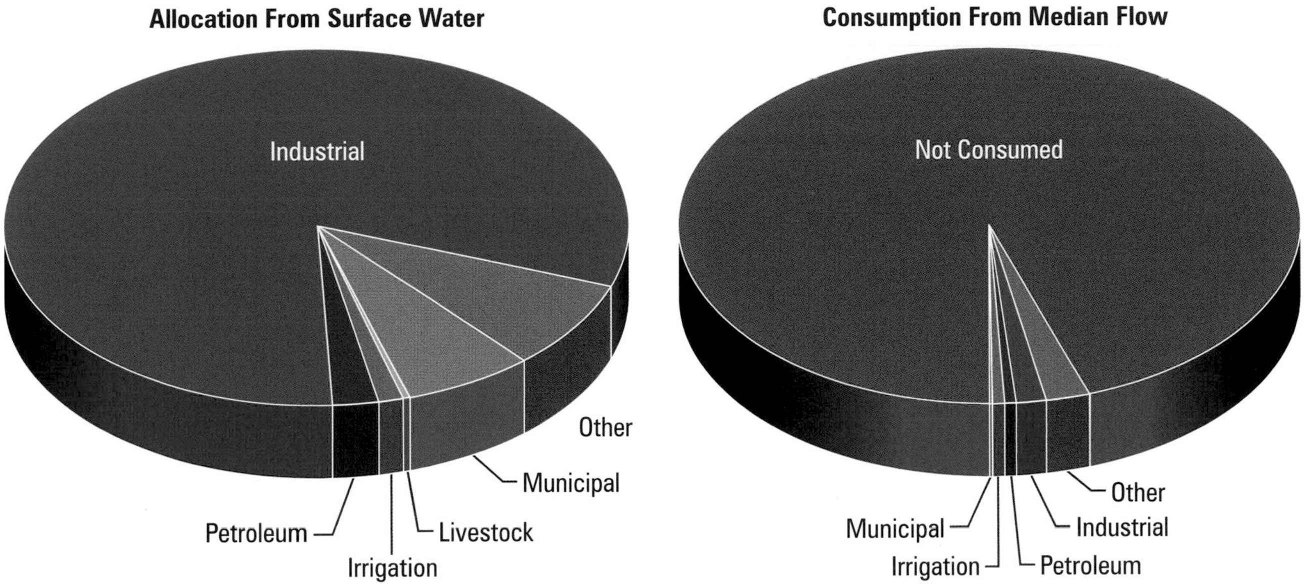

Figure 5.4. Licensed Surface Water Allocation and Consumption.

Other less significant water consumers in the sub-basin include irrigated agriculture, livestock, and municipal use. Private irrigators use water primarily for forage production. Water use is small in comparison to that of district irrigators in the South Saskatchewan sub-basin. Similarly, water for livestock does not represent a major water use. Municipal water consumption is also small, as much of the water withdrawn, including groundwater, is returned to surface water.

The flows in the North Saskatchewan River and its eastward flowing tributaries, such as the Battle River at the interprovincial boundary, are subject to the PPWB *Master Agreement on Apportionment*. Under the agreement, for its own use Alberta is entitled to 50 percent of the naturalized annual flow of the North Saskatchewan River and each of the tributaries crossing the interprovincial boundary. Consumptive water uses in the basin in the Alberta portion of the sub-basin are small in comparison to the natural flow. This relatively low water use, combined with the reliable flow of the North Saskatchewan, means that administering apportionment of the river is quite straightforward. Water uses on the transboundary tributaries are also relatively small in comparison to the median flow. The highly variable flows of these streams, however, mean that apportionment concerns can be raised during low flow years.

WATER QUALITY

Water quality of the streams and lakes of the North Saskatchewan River sub-basin is influenced by the landscape through which the streams flow, as well as by human factors. As the North Saskatchewan River and its headwater tributaries originate in the Rocky Mountains and most of the water flowing in the river constitutes mountain runoff, the quality of the mainstem and upper sub-basin tributaries is good to excellent. The water tends to be naturally hard and nutrient poor. During high flows, the water contains elevated levels of particulate phosphorus. This phosphorus tends not to be biologically available and has little effect on eutrophication or on river biota. On the other hand, the tributaries and small lakes of the plains tend to have water that is naturally highly mineralized and nutrient rich. The natural quality of the sub-basin's waters is influenced by municipal and industrial effluents, and by runoff from urban and agricultural lands.[11]

Water quality is monitored at several locations on the mainstem of the North Saskatchewan River, its important tributaries, and some lakes, particularly those used for water-based recreation. Table 5.1 and Figure 5.1 display key locations at which water quality is routinely monitored. Environment Canada monitors water quality in Banff National Park on behalf of Parks Canada and at the interprovincial boundary on behalf of the Prairie Provinces Water Board, while Alberta Environment and the Saskatchewan Environment monitor water quality at other locations within their respective provinces. The provincial agencies also conduct periodic water quality assessments on other provincial streams and lakes. In Alberta, these assessments have been conducted on the Brazeau, Clearwater, Sturgeon and Vermilion rivers.

There is a natural increase in nutrient levels as mountain-fed rivers move downstream. This is the cumulative effect of sediment processes such as erosion and scouring. The mountain headwaters of the North Saskatchewan River are oligotrophic, as is the river reach upstream of Edmonton. The river is mesotrophic downstream of Edmonton to The Forks. The plains tributaries of the North Saskatchewan River tend to be eutrophic. Alberta monitors 37 small lakes and two reservoirs in the sub-basin. The lakes are in areas that are predominantly agricultural rangeland. The lakes tend to be hypereutrophic or eutrophic based on one or more criteria. Larger lakes such as Wabamun Lake and Pigeon Lake in the Battle River sub-basin are eutrophic, while Lac Ste. Anne is hypereutrophic. The wetlands in the sub-basin tend to be rich in total phosphorous but relatively low in algal mass. Most have elevated salinity levels.[12] The nutrient levels of the waters of the plains tributaries can be attributed to both natural levels and human additions from municipal effluents and agricultural use.

Monitored data are used to calculate a water quality index for several locations on the mainstem of the North Saskatchewan River and its important

Table 5.1. Long Term Water Quality Monitoring Locations.

Stream	Location	Agency	Remarks
North Saskatchewan River	Whirlpool Point	Environment Canada	Banff National Park
North Saskatchewan River	Abraham Lake	Environment Canada	Downstream of dam
North Saskatchewan River	Rocky Mountain House	Alberta Environment	
North Saskatchewan River	Devon	Alberta Environment	Upstream of Edmonton
North Saskatchewan River	Pakan Bridge	Alberta Environment	Downstream of Edmonton
North Saskatchewan River	Hwy. 17 (Lea Park)	Environment Canada	PPWB site at interprovincial boundary
North Saskatchewan River	North Battleford	Saskatchewan Environment	
North Saskatchewan River	Borden Bridge	Saskatchewan Environment	
North Saskatchewan River	Prince Albert	Saskatchewan Environment	Upstream of Prince Albert
North Saskatchewan River	Cecil Ferry	Saskatchewan Environment	Downstream of Prince Albert
North Saskatchewan River	Codette Reservoir	Saskatchewan Environment	
Battle River	Ponoka	Alberta Environment	Upstream of Ponoka
Battle River	Driedmeat Lake	Alberta Environment	Upstream end of Driedmeat Lake
Battle River	Unwin	PPWB	At interprovincial boundary

tributaries. In general, the water quality in the mainstem is rated as good to excellent from the headwaters to Edmonton, then fair to good from Edmonton to the interprovincial boundary. Figure 5.5 shows the index for the North Saskatchewan River upstream and downstream of Edmonton. Mountain tributaries are also rated as good to excellent, while plains tributaries may be rated as fair or even poor because of high nutrient content.

Water quality throughout the North Saskatchewan River sub-basin is affected by non-point sources varying from atmospheric deposition to agricultural runoff. Much of the sub-basin from the vicinity of Edmonton downstream is also affected by point source pollutants such as municipal and industrial discharges. Wabamun Lake receives effluent from a wastewater treatment plant and cooling water and ash lagoon discharges from the Wabamun generating station.

Municipal discharges from the Edmonton metropolitan area have a significant impact on the quality of the North Saskatchewan River. These discharges include 238 storm water outfalls, 19 combined sewer outflows, 2 water treatment plants, and 2 wastewater treatment plants. In addition there are some 26 petrochemical plants in the vicinity of Fort Saskatchewan.[13] The degraded water quality downstream of Edmonton is the result of many point and non-point sources of pollution. In general, nutrients and bacteria are the primary concern. Rainstorms, in particular, tend to raise concentrations through both natural processes and urban runoff. The City of Edmonton is planning to reduce the impacts of combined sewers by providing additional primary level treatment to combined sewer overflows. Figure 5.5 shows the effect of improvements in 1998 to municipal wastewater treatment on downstream water quality. The recent decrease in the index relates to increased bacteria levels. The cause is under investigation.

Saskatchewan has examined trends in seven water quality parameters at several locations from the interprovincial boundary to The Forks for the period 1986 to 2002. The results showed a long-term, generally decreasing trend in total phosphorous, chloride, sodium, and ammonia. There tends to be no trend in nitrate/nitrite, total dissolved solids and pH.[14] The overall water quality of the North Saskatchewan River in Saskatchewan is rated as fair.[15] Figure 5.6 shows the water quality index at the interprovincial boundary. The index values are based on different water quality analyses than those for Alberta sites and therefore are not directly comparable to those in Figure 5.5.

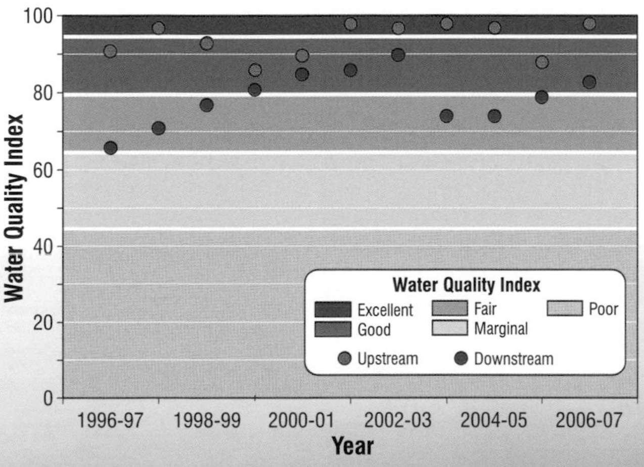

Figure 5.5. Water Quality Index Upstream and Downstream of Edmonton.

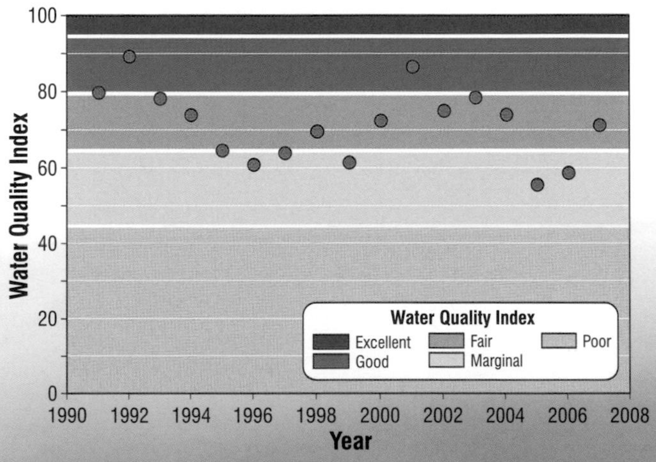

Figure 5.6. Water Quality Index for the North Saskatchewan River at the Interprovincial Boundary.

In the Saskatchewan portion of the sub-basin, North Battleford, Battleford and Prince Albert operate secondary sewage treatment facilities that discharge continuously to the North Saskatchewan River. Lloydminster obtains its drinking water from an Alberta facility but municipal effluents are treated by a lagoon system in Saskatchewan that discharges continuously. About 60 percent of the effluent is diverted for irrigation; the remainder is discharged to the river. There are some 60 other lagoon systems in the Saskatchewan portion of the sub-basin. Some discharge continuously, while others discharge in the spring or in spring and fall. The receiving bodies could be the North Saskatchewan River, smaller streams, lakes or groundwater.[16] Saskatchewan calculates a water quality index based on monitoring data upstream and downstream of Prince Albert. There is considerable scatter in the values, with downstream indices usually being lower than the upstream indices.

BIODIVERSITY AND ECOSYSTEMS

The headwaters of the North Saskatchewan River sub-basin and major headwaters tributaries including the Brazeau, Ram and Clearwater rivers lie in a relatively undisturbed landscape. As indicated earlier, two major dams modify the flows of the river itself. The headwaters areas of the sub-basin are unmodified by human activity as the area is protected by Banff and Jasper national parks. Much of the remainder of the upper sub-basin lies within the Rocky Mountain Forest Reserve where some protection is provided by wilderness areas, ecological reserves and provincial parks. Unprotected areas within the reserve are subject to forest management agreements. About one percent of the area is cut each year. Other industrial activity includes oil and gas exploration and development. Less than two percent of the upper sub-basin is disrupted by linear features, primarily cutlines, rights of way and roads. There are few wetlands in the upper sub-basin. The lower Clearwater sub-basin near Rocky Mountain House contains significant agricultural forage land.

Table 5.2. Fish species of the North Saskatchewan Sub-basin[17, 18]

Species Type	Common Name
Coldwater Species ** Introduced Species*[19]	Arctic Grayling* Brook Trout* Brown Trout* Bull Trout Cutthroat Trout* Golden Trout Lake Trout Mountain Whitefish Rainbow Trout*
Coolwater Species	Burbot Goldeye Lake Sturgeon Lake Whitefish Mooneye Northern Pike Sauger Walleye Yellow Perch Walleye Yellow Perch
Non-game Species	Brook Stickleback Emerald Shiner Fathead Minnow Flathead Chub Finescale Dace Iowa Darter Lake Chub Longnose Dace Longnose Sucker Mountain Sucker Northern Redbelly Dace Shorthead Redhorse Pearl Dace Quillback River Shiner Silver Redhorse Spoonhead Sculpin Spottail Shiner Trout-Perch White Sucker

The grassy slopes and forests of the sub-alpine portion of the upper sub-basin provide habitat for many mammals, large and small. The forests support migratory songbirds and non-migratory birds such as owls and woodpeckers. Several species are threatened by habitat fragmentation and the loss of old-growth forest. The ecological resources of the upper sub-basin provide extensive outdoor recreation and ecotourism opportunities. Terrestrial animals and birds are often dependent on the riparian zone of streams and wetlands for their sustenance. The streams of the upper sub-basin provide a significant coldwater fishery (Table 5.2).

In general, the riparian areas of major streams in the North Saskatchewan River sub-basin are largely undeveloped. This encourages abundant plant and animal species and promotes biodiversity. Extensive studies of the North Saskatchewan River upstream of Edmonton find that the riparian and aquatic communities at that location are generally healthy.[20] The City of Edmonton is developing its riparian areas and ravines as open spaces that conserve the natural environment and provide recreational opportunities.

The mid-basin landscape from the confluence with the Brazeau River to the interprovincial boundary is much more open than the headwaters. Overall, only about 13 percent of the mid-basin is tree-covered and most of that lies in provincial forest north of the North Saskatchewan River. Agricultural forage cover is about 16 percent, much of that upstream of Edmonton, while agricultural cropland and grasslands each represent about 31 percent of the land cover. Cattle densities are moderate. About three percent of the mid-basin is affected by linear features.[21] Most of these features consist of roads, but there are oil and gas-related features as well.

Elk Island National Park near Edmonton is entirely within the sub-basin. The park lies in the Cooking Lake Moraine and contains grassland, woodland and wetland habitat. Nearby Beaverhill Lake is a designated wetland of international importance. Provincial parks in the mid-basin provide some ecological protection as well. The North Saskatchewan River transitions from a coldwater to coolwater fishery in the reach from the confluence with the Brazeau River to Edmonton. One effect of the altered thermal regime produced by the Brazeau Dam was to move that transition zone closer to Edmonton. Coolwater fish species (Table 5.2) become more abundant and dominant downstream of the city.

The effect of the Edmonton metropolitan area on aquatic ecosystems in the North Saskatchewan River has been monitored for many years. In general, the health of aquatic ecosystems is good upstream of metropolitan Edmonton. Ecosystems degrade through the city then recover further downstream. Benthic invertebrate communities increase as the river moves through the Edmonton region – an effect of increased nutrients from municipal and industrial effluents. The community structure also changes to more pollution-tolerant species. The extent of these effects changes seasonally, depending on streamflow. Aquatic biomass as measured by chlorophyll *a* tends to be low upstream of Edmonton and increases through the city. Benthic, algal and invertebrate communities tend to recover from nutrient enrichment by the interprovincial boundary. The aquatic condition of the lakes and semi-permanent wetlands in the mid-basin tends to be consistent with their trophic state.[22]

About 40 percent of the lower sub-basin in Saskatchewan is cultivated, 17 percent is native grassland, and an additional 3 percent is in forage or pasture. Some 23 percent of the landscape is treed. An arc of provincial forest lies to the west and north of Prince Albert. Waterbodies and wetlands account for the remaining six percent of the surface area. Despite significant alterations to the sub-basin by human activity, there are good populations of large mammals such as moose, elk and deer. Populations of the threatened woodland caribou also exist. The Sturgeon and Spruce river tributaries originate in Prince Albert National Park. Provincial parks also provide some ecological protection and recreational opportunities.[23]

Few systematic surveys have been conducted in this portion of the sub-basin to assess riparian and aquatic ecosystem health.

ENDNOTES

[1] Golder Associates 2007. *North Saskatchewan River Instream Flow Needs Scoping Study.* Report for North Saskatchewan Watershed Alliance. Edmonton, AB.

[2] Ashmore, P.E. 1987. *Sediment Station Analysis: North Saskatchewan River at Prince Albert.* IWD-WNR (S)-WRB-SS-87-1. Environment Canada, Ottawa, ON.

[3] Ecological Stratification Working Group 1996. *A National Ecological Framework for Canada.* Canadian Soil Information System (CanCIS), Agriculture and Agrifood Canada. Ottawa, ON.

[4] Bruce Peel, Steamboats on the Saskatchewan, 1972.

[5] Prairie Farm Rehabilitation Administration 2008. Personal communication.

[6] Golder Associates 2007. *supra.*

[7] Bruce, J.P., H. Martin, P. Colucci, G. McBean, J. McDougall, D. Shrubsole, J. Whalley, R. Halliday, M. Alden, L. Mortsch and B. Mills 2003. *Climate Change Impacts on Boundary and Transboundary Water Management.* A Climate Change Action Fund Project. Project A458/402, Natural Resources Canada, Ottawa.

[8] Alberta Environment 2007. *Current and Future Water Use in Alberta.* Prepared by AMEC Earth & Environmental. Alberta Environment. Edmonton, AB.

[9] Anderson, D. 2008. Personal Communication.

[10] North Saskatchewan Watershed Alliance 2005. *State of the North Saskatchewan Watershed – 2005.* North Saskatchewan Watershed Alliance. Edmonton, AB.

[11] Alberta Environment 2007b. *Information Synthesis and Initial Assessment of the Status and Health of Aquatic Ecosystems in Alberta: Surface Water Quality, Sediment Quality and Non-Fish Biota.* North/South Consultants, Calgary, AB.

[12] Alberta Environment 2007b. *supra.*

[13] Alberta Environment 2007b. *supra.*

[14] Saskatchewan Watershed Authority 2007. *Preliminary Background Report: North Saskatchewan River Watershed.* Saskatchewan Watershed Authority, Moose Jaw, SK.

[15] Saskatchewan Watershed Authority 2007. *State of the Watershed Report.* Saskatchewan Watershed Authority. Regina, SK.

[16] Saskatchewan Watershed Authority 2007. *supra.*

[17] Golder 2007. *supra.*

[18] Merkowsky, J.J. 1997. *Biological Survey of the Saskatchewan River.* Fisheries Technical Report 87-4. Saskatchewan Parks, Recreation and Culture. Regina, SK

[19] North Saskatchewan Watershed Alliance 2005. *supra.*

[20] Alberta Environment 2007b. *supra.*

[21] North Saskatchewan Watershed Alliance 2005. *supra.*

[22] Alberta Environment 2007b. *supra.*

[23] Saskatchewan Watershed Authority 2007. *supra.*

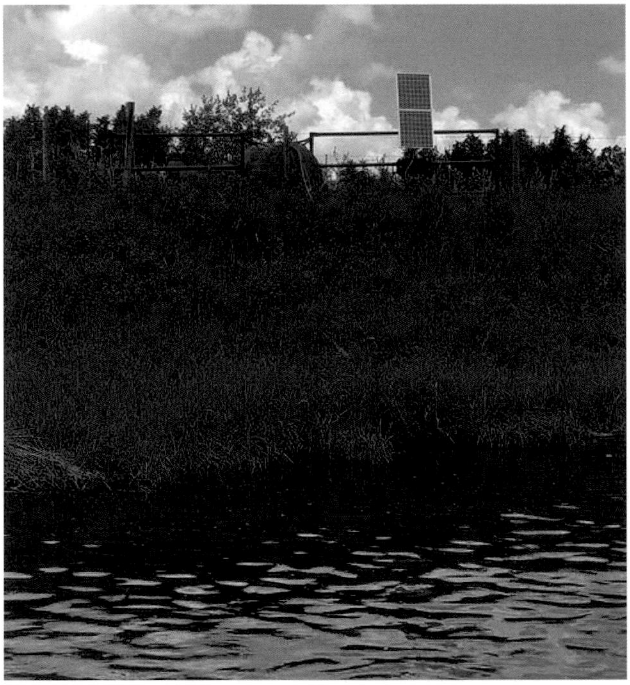

CHAPTER SIX

THE SOUTHERN TRIBUTARY SUB-BASINS OF THE NORTH SASKATCHEWAN RIVER

Figure 6.1. *Southern Tributaries of the North Saskatchewan River*

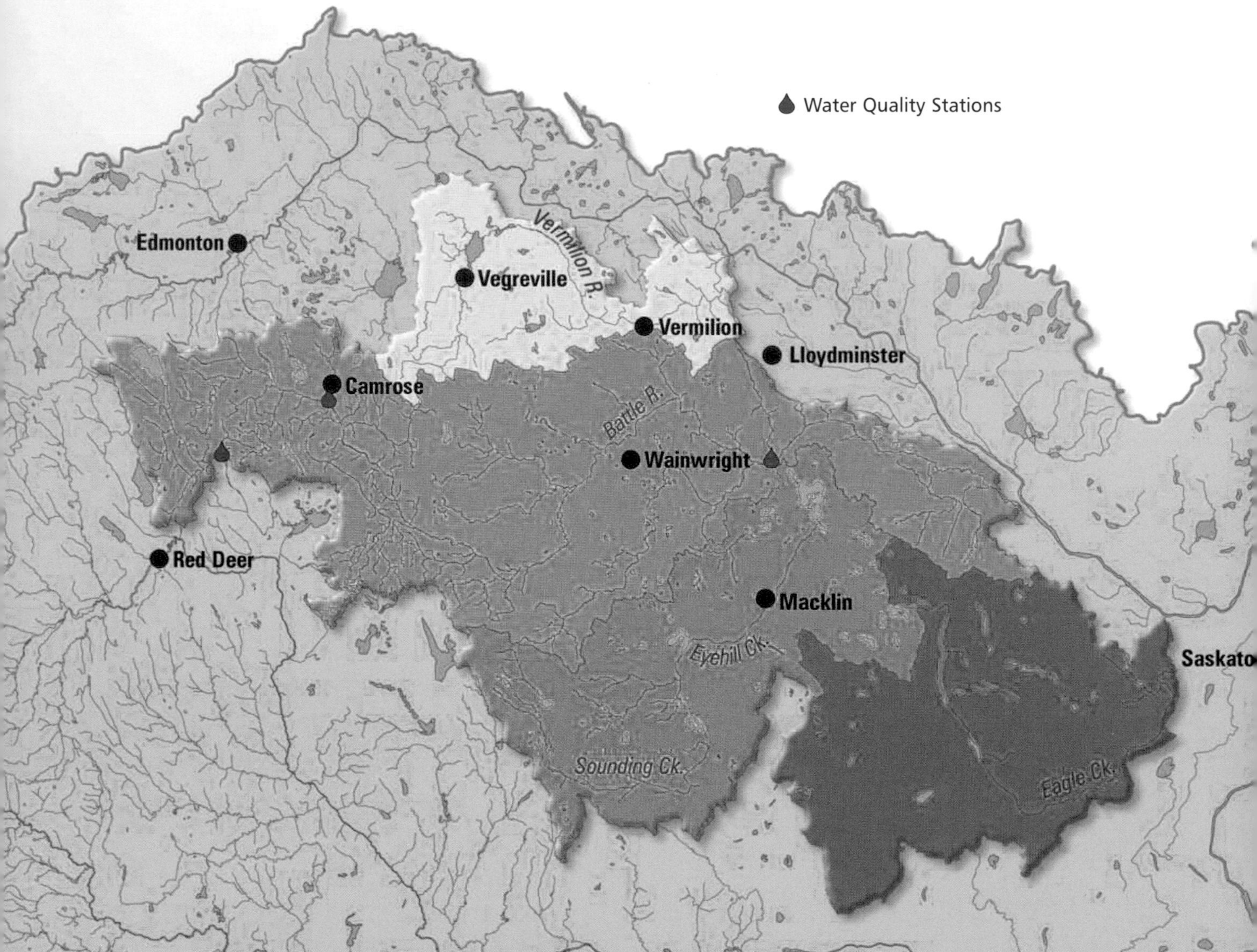

CHAPTER SIX

THE SOUTHERN TRIBUTARY SUB-BASINS OF THE NORTH SASKATCHEWAN RIVER

The southern tributaries of the North Saskatchewan River lie in the prairie ecozone and include the Vermilion River, Battle River, Sounding/Eyehill Creek, and Eagle Creek. They are shown in Figure 6.1. For the most part, the Vermilion and Battle river sub-basins and the Sounding Creek sub-basin lie in the aspen parkland ecoregion, while the Eagle Creek sub-basin is largely in the moist mixed grassland ecoregion.

Sub-basin Summary

Characteristics
- open plains
- extensively cultivated
- gross drainage area 85 213 km^2
- effective drainage area 19 120 km^2

Hydrology
- low gradient, slow moving streams
- ephemeral flows
- regulated

Water Quality
- fair overall
- impaired by nutrients, pesticides

Biodiversity
- riparian zones unhealthy
- significant wetland loss

Key Issues
- water allocation and use
- land use
- municipal and industrial effluents

These plains regions are underlain by sandstone, mudstone and shale, with occasional bentonite or coal beds. The sub-basins are covered by a thick layer of undulating to kettled glacial till typical of the prairie pothole landscape. There are also areas of level lacustrine deposits and hummocky to ridged deposits laid down by glacial meltwater. In the Sounding Creek sub-basin the land is level to very gently rolling.[1]

The dominant tree is the trembling aspen. Balsam poplars ring the small lakes, ponds, and sloughs that provide major habitat for waterfowl. In aspen groves, the deciduous understorey contains berries such as Saskatoon and chokecherry.[2] As well as providing major breeding habitat for waterfowl, the sub-basins contain habitat for white-tailed deer, coyote, snowshoe hare, cottontail, red fox, northern pocket gopher, Franklin's ground squirrel, and bird species like sharp-tailed grouse and black-billed magpie.

Owing to the climate and fertile black soils, the sub-basins contain productive agricultural lands. For this reason, much of the original aspen parkland has given way to agricultural development. The sub-basins produce a wide diversity of crops, including spring wheat and other cereals, oilseeds, forage, and several specialty crops. In the south, dark brown soils are dominant, but significant areas of salty soils are also found, giving rise to alkaline sloughs and ponds.

Cow-calf operations dominate beef production in the sub-basins. As well as agricultural production, the economy of the sub-basins depends on oil and gas exploration and development and coal mining. The population of the Battle River sub-basin is over 125 000, with most residents located in Alberta. The population of the Vermilion River sub-basin was 25 200 in 2005.

A History of Ducks Unlimited Canada

With a drought gripping the Prairies in the dusty and dirty days of the Great Depression, wetlands dried up and waterfowl numbers dwindled. In 1938, a group of conservation-minded sportsmen set out to raise funds from private sources for habitat restoration and creation projects in Canada, where more than 70 percent of North America's waterfowl originate. They called their effort Ducks Unlimited. The first project in the Saskatchewan River Basin, at Waterhen Marsh, was completed in 1938.

Ducks Unlimited Canada's (DUC) mission and program has since broadened but remains true to its roots, focussing on wetlands and waterfowl, while also conserving the ecological integrity of the larger watershed. Today, DUC is a science-based, non-profit and charitable organization with a mission to conserve, restore and manage wetlands and associated habitats for North American waterfowl, other wildlife and people. DUC collaborates with sister-organizations DU Inc (USA) and DUMAC (Mexico) to ensure a continental approach in conserving the waterfowl resource through habitat conservation. This program is accomplished with the financial support and volunteer efforts from thousands of supporters.

DUC believes that collaborating with a variety of partners including governments, academic institutions, individuals, industries, and other conservation groups is critical to achieving its mission. One important pillar of DUC's program is the North American Waterfowl Management Plan (NAWMP).

Established in 1986, NAWMP is a partnership of government, non-governmental organizations, private companies and many individuals, all working together towards achieving better wetland habitat to sustain continental waterfowl populations at the average level of the 1970s.

The prairies and boreal forest of western Canada are considered the waterfowl factory of North America and, consequently, these regions are the primary target of NAWMP programs. The Saskatchewan River Basin straddles both these ecozones and is home to an estimated eight million waterfowl each spring. DUC has 6153 projects in this basin conserving an estimated 17 000 km^2 of habitat. These initiatives include:

- Developing conservation easements with landowners to protect parts or all of their property in perpetuity;
- Promoting winter wheat as an economically viable crop that is "duck friendly;"
- Working with ranchers to design grazing systems that conserve habitat;
- Developing and operating water control structures to maintain the ecological integrity of the Saskatchewan River Delta; and
- Working with all partners including government and industries to develop corporate and public policies that sustain wetland habitats for the ecological goods and services they provide to society.

HYDROLOGY

The plains streams discussed in this chapter share an open, rolling landscape that produces relatively little streamflow. Large portions of these sub-basins do not contribute streamflow to the main stream under normal circumstances. Some of this non-contributing area never contributes flow to the North Saskatchewan River, even in very wet years.

The Vermilion River rises near Viking in east-central Alberta, loops north through Vegreville then flows east before joining the North Saskatchewan River near the interprovincial boundary. The river is 464 km long. The drainage area of the sub-basin is 7867 km^2 and the effective drainage area is 2364 km^2. The flow of the river is regulated by structures at Watts/Bens lakes, a stop log structure at Morcambe, and a dam at Vermilion. The latter two structures are operated by Alberta to provide a riparian flow, except in the winter. The structures are also operated during summer rains because of concerns about land drainage and agricultural flooding in the sub-basin.

The Battle River basin is situated in east-central Alberta and west-central Saskatchewan. The river itself is 1035 km in length; about 800 km lies in Alberta. The Battle River headwaters originate at Battle and Pigeon lakes in central Alberta. From Battle Lake the river flows in a southeast direction meandering 100 km within a low, well-defined valley. At Ponoka, the river flows east for 48 km into a low, flat area near Samson Lake. Passing through Samson Lake, the river continues north through 64 km of gradually steepening valley as it approaches its confluence with Pipestone Creek. Downstream of Pipestone Creek, the river flows through a larger, more rugged valley carved out by the outflow from glacial Lake Edmonton, which once covered most of Alberta. The Battle's large river valley and *chain lakes*, such as Coal Lake and Driedmeat Lake, are evidence of the glacial spillway carved over 10 000 years ago. The Battle River continues to flow through this larger valley in an easterly direction until it joins the North Saskatchewan River at Battleford. The drainage area of the sub-basin is 45 654 km^2, a little over half being in Alberta. The effective drainage area is only 12 498 km^2.

Water supply for the Battle River is regulated by reservoirs. Water levels on Pigeon Lake are partially controlled by a stop-log weir at the outlet of the lake. Coal Lake, a tributary lake and municipal water supply for Wetaskiwin, is regulated by an earth-fill dam. The dam, which stores 38 000 dam^3, is occasionally operated to supplement downstream flows on the Battle River. On the Battle River, riparian flow downstream of Driedmeat Lake, the municipal water supply for Camrose, is regulated by a stop-log weir containing a fishway two metres wide. The impoundment stores 14 200 dam^3 and an increase to 24 000 dam^3 is under consideration. The ATCO Power dam on the Battle River near Forestburg is used to store cooling water for a 670 MW coal-fired electricity generating station. Forestburg reservoir, which stores 9000 dam^3, is also used to maintain a year-round base flow on the Battle River. Water levels of Ribstone Lake near Wainwright are regulated by a stop-log weir for recreation and waterfowl habitat. Ducks Unlimited Canada operates 27 smaller structures in the Ribstone area to create wetlands and back-flood hay meadows for agriculture and habitat improvement. There are no water storage structures on the Battle River in Saskatchewan. Total available storage in the sub-basin is about 30 percent of the naturalized flow at the interprovincial boundary.

Like the Battle River sub-basin, the Sounding/Eyehill Creek sub-basin extends from east-central Alberta into west-central Saskatchewan. The 340-km creek starts some 20 km north of Hanna and meanders about 60 km southeast towards Youngstown, passing through Antelope Lake, before turning east and then north, passing through Grassy Island Lake on its way to Sounding Lake. Sounding Lake, which has been dry since 1971, is essentially a terminal lake that can overflow to Eyehill Creek. Overflow has occurred in only one year. From Sounding Lake the creek then flows northeast for a further 80 km, where it joins Manitou Lake. This lake has a prehistoric spillway to the Battle River but since European settlement there has been no overflow. The drainage area of Manitou Lake is 15 541 km^2 and the effective drainage area is only 2126 km^2. A dam near the town of Macklin, Saskatchewan allows water to be diverted into Macklin Lake during high flows. A control structure on the lake impounds water for stockwatering and maintains water levels. The total storage is 4800 dam^3.

The Eagle Creek sub-sub-basin lies in west-central Saskatchewan. The 453-km creek starts near Unity and flows south through Eagle, Tramping and Opuntia lakes then turns east, then north, in a long arc, joining the North Saskatchewan River south of Radisson. The gross drainage area is 16 241 km^2 and the effective drainage area is only 2132 km^2. Flows upstream of Tramping and Opuntia lakes are usually contained by those lakes. Opuntia Lake, which stores 19 000 dam^3, is regulated by a low dam and weir.

The average annual precipitation in the Vermilion River sub-basin is about 400 mm. The average annual precipitation in the Battle River sub-basin ranges from 480 mm in the headwaters to 373 mm at North Battleford. Average annual precipitation is as little as 320 mm in the Sounding/Eyehill and Eagle Creek sub-basins. Since average annual potential evaporation is 800 mm or greater, the sub-basins have a significant water deficit. Surface water runoff typically is less than ten percent of the annual precipitation, while only a few percentage points of the precipitation recharges groundwater. Most of the annual precipitation returns to the atmosphere through evaporation from water bodies or from the soil surface, or through transpiration from growing plants. Typically, this situation leads to annual runoff from the surface area of the sub-basins being equivalent to 10 mm or less.

The hydrograph of streams originating on the plains shows most of the annual flow occurring with spring snowmelt runoff in April and May, with very little winter flow. Intense rainfall events may lead to occasional short-duration summer flows, while flows later in the year are sustained by groundwater inflows.[3] In general, streamflow in these prairie sub-basins is small compared to the surface area of the sub-basin. The flow varies considerably from year to year. Available water supplies are much less reliable than those originating in mountain streams.

Figure 6.2 shows the hydrograph of median monthly flows for the Vermilion River.

The median naturalized monthly flows of the Battle River are shown in Figure 6.3. Annual flows in Sounding/Eyehill and Eagle creeks are even less reliable. While the streams exhibit the same general flow pattern as the Battle River, months with little or no flow are common.

The Water Survey of Canada, Saskatchewan Watershed Authority, and Alberta Environment operate 28 gauging stations in these sub-basins. Distribution of stations is shown in Table 6.1.

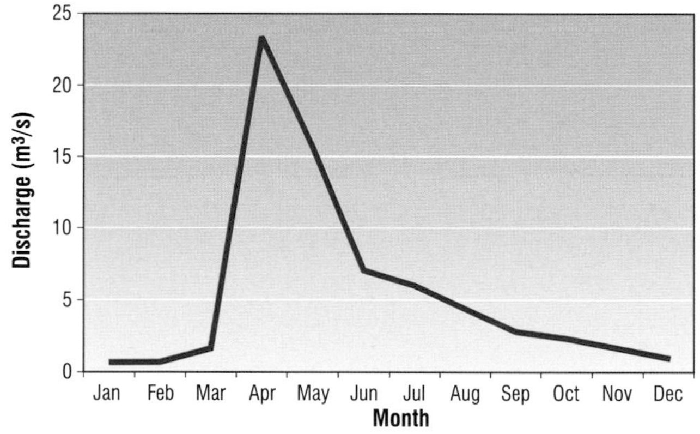

Figure 6.2. Median Monthly Discharge for Vermilion River near Marwayne.

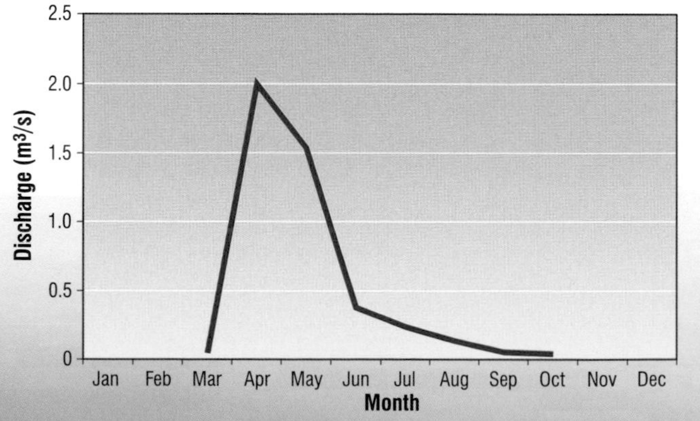

Figure 6.3. Median Monthly Naturalized Discharge for Battle River.

Table 6.1. Gauging Stations in the Southern Tributaries Sub-basins.

Sub-basin	Discharge	Water Level
Vermilion	5	2
Battle	9	3
Sounding/Eyehill	5	1
Eagle	2	1

WATER USE

Water use in these sub-basins represents a significant proportion of available supplies. The licensed overall allocation from surface water is 818 524 dam^3 and from ground water is 35 414 dam^3. Almost 90 percent of that allocation is for cooling water for a thermal power station in the Battle River sub-basin. Water used for cooling is withdrawn from a reservoir and returned so consumption is small. Figure 6.4 shows the distribution of licences and consumption from surface water. More than half the surface water consumption in the sub-basin is in the 'other' sector, largely environmental services such as lake stabilization for wildlife and habitat enhancement and for flood control. The next largest surface water uses are for irrigation and stockwatering. Petroleum-related activities account for almost one-half of the groundwater consumption in the sub-basin. Stockwatering and municipal use are the next largest consumers. The distribution of licences and water consumption varies considerably from sub-basin to sub-basin.

Vermilion River Sub-basin

The licensed water allocation from the Vermilion River sub-basin is 5383 dam^3 from surface water and almost 90 percent of that is consumed. Groundwater allocation is significant, compared to surface water. The allocation is 5009 dam^3 with about 60 percent of that being consumed. Figure 6.5 shows the licensed allocation from surface water and groundwater.

About two-thirds of surface water consumption in the sub-basin is for maintaining wetland habitat and for lake stabilization – included in the 'other' sector. Almost all of the water diverted for this purpose is consumed. Stockwatering accounts for almost all the remaining consumption from surface water and is the principal consumer of groundwater, accounting for about 80 percent of consumption. Almost all of the remaining consumption from groundwater is for

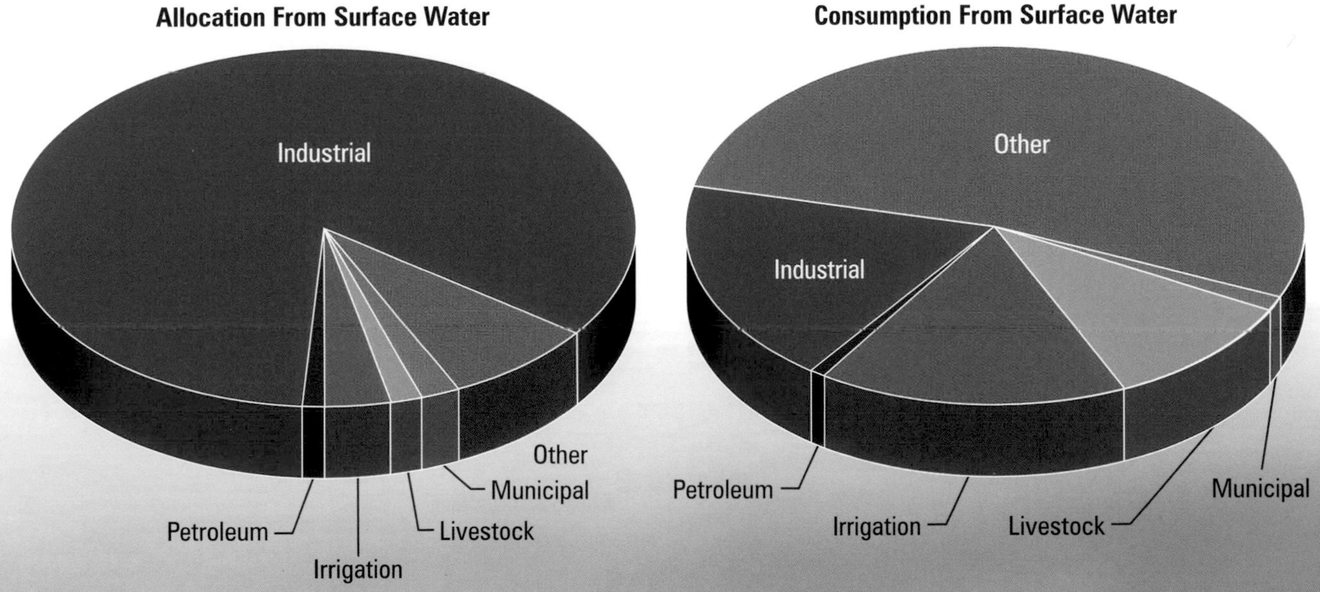

Figure 6.4. Overall Licensed Allocation and Consumption from Surface Water.

domestic use. Much of the water used for that purpose, while lost to the groundwater system, returns to surface water.[4]

Battle River Sub-basin

The licensed water allocation from the Battle River sub-basin includes 770 632 dam³ from surface water and 18 996 dam³ from groundwater.[5] The surface water quantity appears extremely large taking into account the long-term median flow of the Battle River, but 691 737 dam³ of that allocation is cooling water from Forestburg Reservoir for ATCO Power. Water consumption for this project is only two percent of the withdrawal. Figure 6.6 shows licensed surface water allocations and average annual consumption.

Surface water consumption in the Battle River sub-basin is about one-third of the median natural flow. About 90 percent of this consumption is in Alberta.

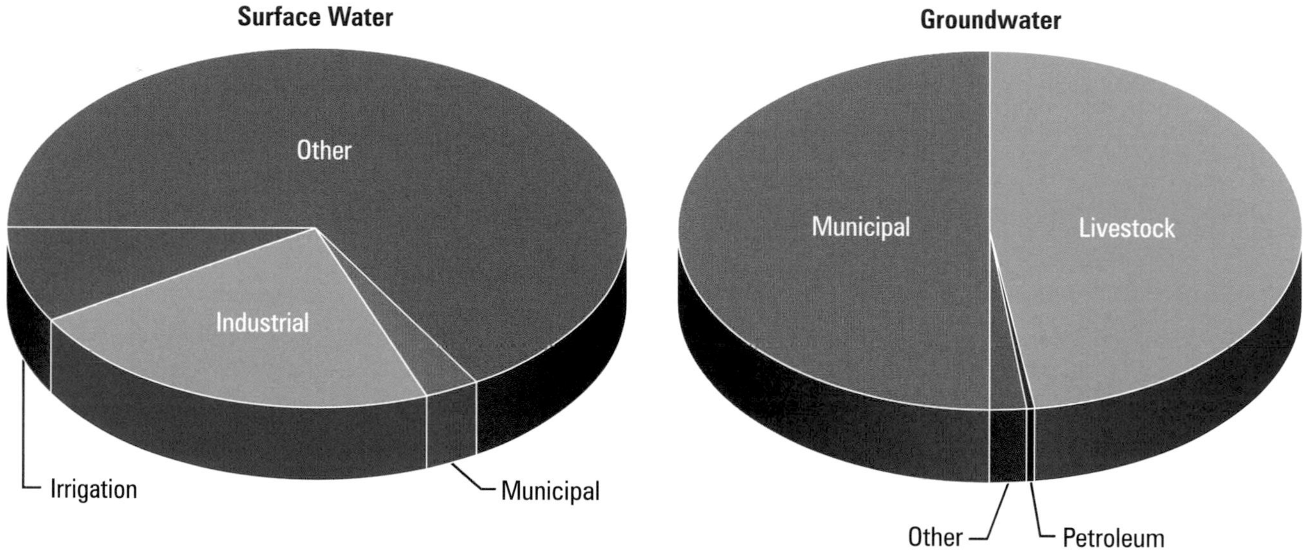

Figure 6.5. Licensed Water Allocation in the Vermilion River Sub-basin.

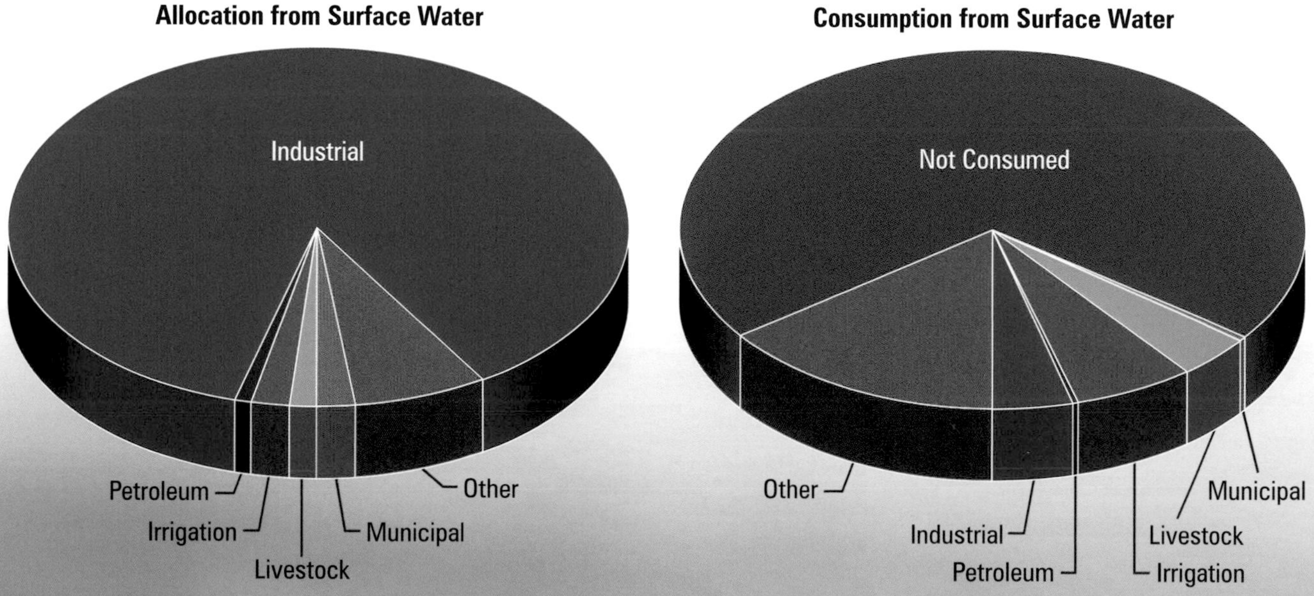

Figure 6.6. Licensed Water Allocation and Consumption from Surface Water for the Battle River Sub-basin.

The largest water consumption in the sub-basin is, by far, for environmental purposes, shown as 'other' in Figure 6.6. Uses of the water include lake stabilization, primarily for waterfowl, and fish, wildlife, and habitat enhancement. Many of the projects are Ducks Unlimited Canada projects. Almost all of the water withdrawn to support this use is consumed and does not return to the river, accounting for more than one-half of the water consumption in this sub-basin. The next largest water consumer in the basin is irrigated agriculture, followed by industrial consumption and stockwatering. Livestock operators tend to fill dugouts and small storage reservoirs in the spring, when river flows are high. Most of the water retained is consumed by livestock directly, by evaporation, and by other losses. Most of the irrigation water used in the sub-basin is by private irrigators producing forage for livestock. Almost all the water diverted is consumed or lost.

Industrial users in the sub-basin consume surface water for fertilizer plants, manufacturing and mining. The most significant use is cooling water for the ATCO thermal electric generating station but, as indicated earlier, very little of this water is consumed.

Domestic water consumption from surface water is inconsequential for the Battle River. There are two reasons for this. First, the towns of Stettler and Millet obtain their water from the Red Deer River and the North Saskatchewan River respectively, but effluent flows from these towns enter the Battle River. Secondly, five communities and many rural municipal users draw their water from groundwater. Much of the water withdrawn returns to the Battle River as effluent, making a positive contribution to surface water. Water use by the petroleum sector, primarily for well injection, is also very small.

Groundwater consumption in the sub-basin is about one-quarter of surface water consumption. More than one-half of this consumption is for stockwatering. Irrigated agriculture and petroleum-related industries constitute most of the remaining consumption.

The flow in the Battle River at the interprovincial boundary is subject to the PPWB *Master Agreement on Apportionment*. Although Alberta's water consumption has increased by some 88 percent from 1979 to 2004, there is no time from 1980 to present when the province retained more than its share of the river. In 2002, a drought year, Alberta passed 51 percent of the naturalized flow to Saskatchewan – close to the required minimum. Projections for increased water use in Alberta show modest increases, well within the terms of the existing licenses. Under this scenario, Alberta will be able to meet the requirements of the Master Agreement when streamflow conditions are normal; however, a series of very dry years with low runoff could present a challenge.

Sounding/Eyehill Creek Sub-basin

The licensed water allocation in the Sounding/Eyehill Creek sub-basin is 29 404 dam^3 from surface water and 6885 dam3 from groundwater. About 90 percent of each of the allocations is consumed. About 70 percent of surface water use is for environmental purposes, shown as 'other' in Figure 6.7. Uses of the water include lake stabilization, primarily for waterfowl, and fish, wildlife, and habitat enhancement.

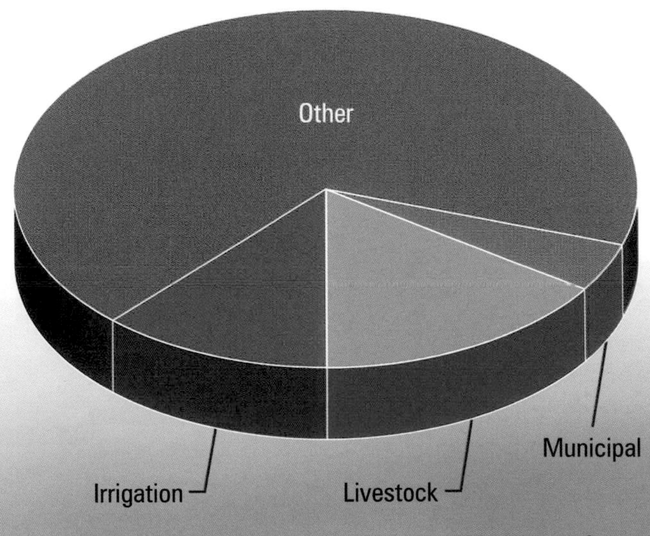

Figure 6.7. Licensed Allocation from Surface Water for Sounding/Eyehill Sub-basin.

Stockwatering and irrigated agriculture make up most of the remaining surface water consumption. Since Sounding Lake rarely overflows, the entire Sounding Creek watershed, where most of the surface water consumption occurs, lies in non-contributing drainage.

The petroleum industry accounts for 60 percent of the groundwater consumption in this sub-basin. The remaining consumption is by stockwatering and municipal use. As stated earlier in this chapter, groundwater consumption for domestic purposes results in discharges to surface water.

The flow in the Sounding/Eyehill Creek at the interprovincial boundary is subject to the PPWB *Master Agreement on Apportionment*. A study many years ago indicated that water consumption in the Eyehill sub-basin constituted no more than 18 percent of the median naturalized annual flow, but identified a potential problem with water apportionment in extremely low flow years.[6] Recent examinations of water use by Alberta do not indicate significant increases in water use over the years.

There are local concerns regarding the effect of water use on levels of Manitou Lake. The lake has dropped about five metres in the last twenty-five years (Figure 6.8), most likely attributable to changes in precipitation and land use. The problem is influenced by the effects of Sounding Lake. In extremely wet years, Sounding Lake may overflow and spill excess water downstream. In normal and dry years, Sounding Lake will intercept all runoff from the upper sub-basin, thereby reducing the surface area contributing to flow in the lower sub-basin.[7]

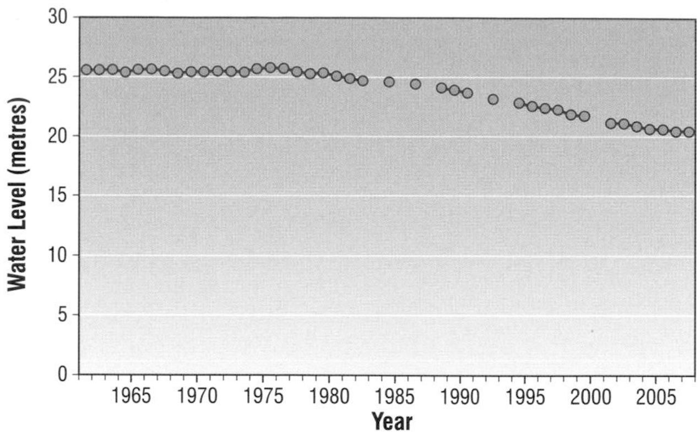

Figure 6.8. Water Levels on Manitou Lake.

Eagle Creek Sub-basin

The licensed water allocation for the Eagle Creek sub-basin is 16 358 dam^3 from surface water and 10 296 dam^3 from groundwater. About 60 percent of each of the licensed allocations is used. Figure 6.9 shows the distribution of allocations.

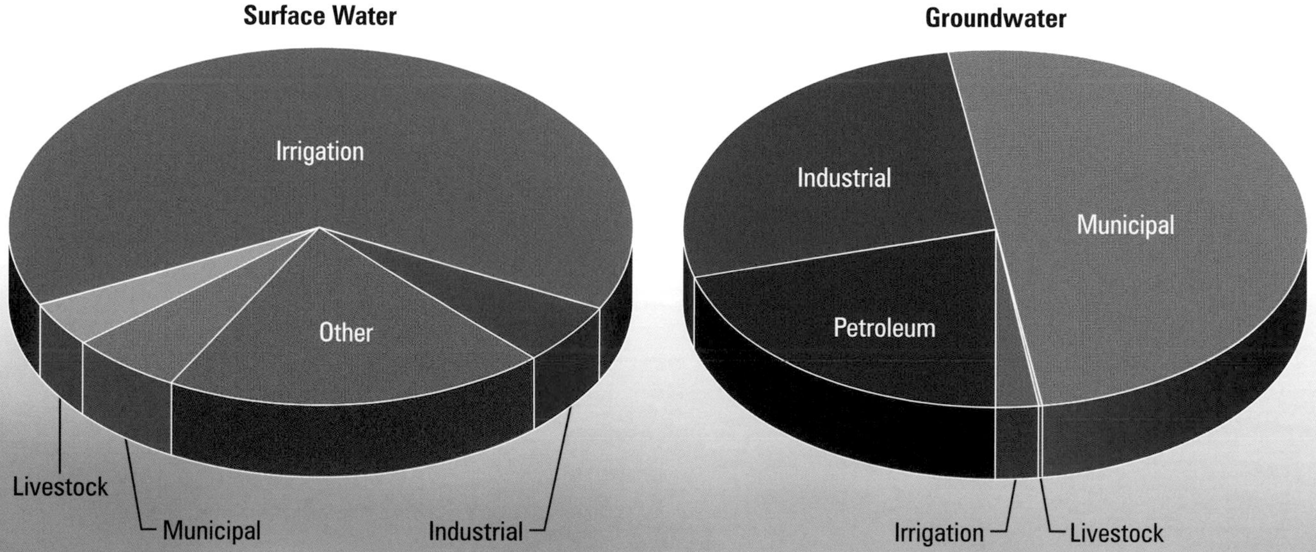

Figure 6.9. Licensed Surface Water and Groundwater Allocations for the Eagle Creek Sub-basin.

About 60 percent of surface water consumption in the Eagle Creek sub-basin is for irrigated agriculture. The next largest consumer of water is the 'other' sector, primarily water management and habitat enhancement. Industrial, stockwatering and domestic uses make up the rest of the consumption. Groundwater consumption relates primarily to industrial uses, including consumption by the petroleum industry.

More than 40 percent of the median annual flow of Eagle Creek has been licensed.[8] It is likely that water use must be curtailed during years when surface water supplies are low.

WATER QUALITY

Water quality is influenced by the landscape and geology through which the stream flows, by the seasonal and highly variable flows in these sub-basins, and by human factors. Prairie streams, like the ones discussed in this chapter, are naturally high in nutrients because of nutrients in the soil. These low-gradient streams drain predominantly agricultural landscapes and meander slowly from their source to the North Saskatchewan River or, in the case of Sounding/Eyehill Creek, to Manitou Lake. Small lakes and sloughs impede their flow. Even in the spring it takes about a month for Battle River water to travel from the source to the mouth; during low flows this travel time is much greater.[9] Point sources of pollutants include municipal effluents and industrial sources. Municipalities in the sub-basins operate sewage lagoons that are emptied in the spring or fall, or both. Although this effluent is reasonably good quality, the quantity released is significant in comparison to the flow of the river, particularly for fall releases. Releases from industrial sources tend to be continuous, but much smaller. Water quality is also influenced by the reductions in flow caused by the significant water use in these sub-basins. Water quality monitoring and assessments in the southern tributaries sub-basins relate mainly to the Battle River.

Water quality of the Battle River is influenced by runoff from agricultural lands, coal-mining operations, and urban areas. These sources are particularly important during spring runoff. Forestburg Reservoir has an unusual influence on water quality. The reservoir is heated due to operations of the ATCO generating station, and the warmer water released from the reservoir can raise the temperature of the river for some 200 km downstream. The open water downstream of the reservoir in the winter helps oxygenate the water. The reservoir also provides a year-round baseflow. A further influence on water quality is the groundwater inflow that contributes to baseflow.

Alberta has long-term monitoring network stations on the Battle River in the headwaters upstream of Ponoka and at the upstream end of Driedmeat Lake. Water quality is considered fair to good in the headwaters and fair at Driedmeat Lake. The river is either mesotrophic or eutrophic because of high nutrient levels. The reach between Ponoka and Driedmeat Lake, in particular, is affected by municipal point sources. Dissolved oxygen levels are depleted during the winter. Pesticide levels can be elevated.[10] Alberta has recently begun to calculate a water quality index for the Battle River at the two monitoring locations.

The Prairie Provinces Water Board has monitored water quality of the Battle River near the Alberta-Saskatchewan boundary for many years. Parameters frequently exceeding established water-quality guidelines include sodium, total dissolved solids, total phosphorous, fecal coliforms, dissolved oxygen and pH. Phosphorous from municipal effluents accounts for 60 percent of the phosphorous measured at the interprovincial boundary.[11] Trend analysis of data from 1986 to 2002 indicates no trend for total phosphorous, nitrate/nitrite, fecal coliforms, and dissolved oxygen. There appeared to be an increasing trend in total dissolved solids, sulphate, chloride and pH.[12] The water quality of the Battle River is considered poor to fair.

Alberta and Saskatchewan routinely monitor water quality at other locations on the Battle River and Alberta has conducted periodic assessments of water quality on Sounding/Eyehill Creek. The PPWB does not monitor Eyehill Creek at the boundary.

Saskatchewan calculates a water quality index for Eyehill Creek near Macklin. The water quality is considered fair.[13] There are insufficient data to calculate a water quality index for Eagle Creek. Low flows in Eagle Creek combined with municipal effluents lead to impaired water quality.

BIODIVERSITY AND ECOSYSTEMS

The Vermilion and Battle rivers, Sounding/Eyehill Creek and Eagle Creek sub-basins have been completely transformed by agricultural production. Loss of the original prairie grassland represents a major shift in biodiversity. Less than two percent of the land is now treed and water bodies cover four to five percent of the sub-basins. Additional wetlands are few and ephemeral. About three percent of the sub-basins is affected by linear features such as roads, rail lines, pipelines and transmission line rights-of-way, and by other features such as industrial facilities.[14] These linear features, usually roads, tend to fragment terrestrial habitat and, depending on the nature of stream crossings, may fragment aquatic habit. Urban areas take up a further two percent of the sub-basins. There are ten First Nations Reserves in the Battle Creek sub-basin and four in the Eagle Creek sub-basin.

Protected areas in the Vermilion sub-basin include Vermilion Provincial Park and Minburn Provincial Grazing Reserve. Protected areas in the Battle Creek sub-basin include Pigeon Lake and Ma-Me-O

Provincial Parks on Pigeon Lake, and Big Knife Provincial Park, also in the upper sub-basin. Other notable land areas in this sub-basin include the Wainwright Dunes Ecological Reserve, Canadian Forces Base Wainwright, and the Ribstone Creek Heritage Rangeland. Gooseberry Lake Provincial Park, Alberta is the only provincially protected area in the Sounding Creek sub-basin. Other smaller privately held land holdings are also protected.

The Sibbald Plain that straddles the interprovincial boundary in the Sounding/Eyehill Creek sub-basin and extends into the Eagle Creek sub-basin is nationally important habitat for migratory birds. This classification is based primarily on its importance for waterfowl staging. Most of the rest of the southern tributaries sub-basins is considered regionally or locally important.[15]

Vermilion River Sub-basin

About half of the Vermilion sub-basin consists of cropland, with almost all of the remaining land cover being grassland. Livestock density is generally moderate although it is high in the north-central part of the sub-basin. The riparian health assessment of the river indicates 16 percent of the sites examined are healthy, 30 percent healthy with problems, and 54 percent unhealthy.[16] No assessments have been made of aquatic plants, benthic invertebrates or fish resources of the Vermilion River.

Battle River Sub-basin

Overall, about 40 percent of the Battle River sub-basin is devoted to cropland and a similar percentage to grassland. Forage crops are grown in a little over ten percent of the sub-basin. These average values vary considerably throughout the sub-basin, however. The headwaters of the Battle River, including tributaries, consist of almost 40 percent forage and 30 percent cropland. This part of the sub-basin also has high livestock density. The remainder of the Alberta portion of the sub-basin tends to have moderate livestock densities, with densities increasing again in Saskatchewan. Riparian health has been assessed in the upper sub-basin where it is generally good or healthy with problems. Although riparian health has not been assessed on downstream tributaries, it tends to degrade moving downstream. By the interprovincial boundary, about 30 percent of sites are deemed to be unhealthy. There are no assessments of aquatic plants or benthic invertebrates for the Battle River. White sucker and northern pike occur in the sub-basin although fish movements are impeded by low flows and structures such as dams and weirs. Lake whitefish, burbot and yellow perch are found in Battle and Pigeon lakes in the headwaters and walleye have been reintroduced in Pigeon Lake.[17]

Sounding/Eyehill Creek Sub-basin

The almost treeless Sounding River sub-basin is predominantly grassland, reflecting the semi-arid climate of the region. About 30 percent of the sub-basin is cropland. Livestock densities are moderate. Riparian health and aquatic resources of this sub-basin have not yet been assessed.[18]

Eagle Creek Sub-basin

Most of the Eagle Creek sub-basin is cultivated and wetland loss is high. Little data exist pertaining to aquatic ecosystems of the creek, and it is possible that riparian and aquatic ecosystems are not healthy.

ENDNOTES

[1] Ecological Stratification Working Group 1996. *A National Ecological Framework for Canada.* Canadian Soil Information System (CanCIS), Agriculture and Agrifood Canada. Ottawa, ON.

[2] McGillivray, W.B. 2007. *The Aspen Parkland: A Biological Perspective.* Accessed on-line http://www.albertasource.ca/aspenland/eng/society/article_aspen_parkland.html

[3] Saskatchewan Watershed Authority 2007a. *Preliminary Background Report: North Saskatchewan River Watershed.* Saskatchewan Watershed Authority, Moose Jaw, SK.

[4] North Saskatchewan Watershed Alliance. *Current and Future Water Use in the North Saskatchewan River Basin.* Report EE27028. AMEC Earth & Environmental. Edmonton, AB.

[5] Alberta Environment 2007. *Current and Future Water Use in Alberta.* Prepared by AMEC Earth & Environmental. Alberta Environment. Edmonton, AB.

[6] Prairie Provinces Water Board 1984. *Eyehill Creek Natural Flow.* PPWB No. 68. Prairie Provinces Water Board. Regina, SK.

[7] van der Kamp, G., D. Kier and M. Evans (2008). "Long-term Water Level Changes in Closed-basin Lakes of the Canadian Prairies." *Canadian Water Resources Journal* 33:1 23-38.

[8] Saskatchewan Watershed Authority 2007. *State of the Watershed Report.* Saskatchewan Watershed Authority, Regina, SK.

[9] Anderson, A.-M. 1999. *Water Quality of the Battle River – Overview.* Water Sciences Branch, Alberta Environment. Edmonton, AB.

[10] Alberta Environment 2007b. *Summary Report on the Initial Assessment of Ecological Health of Aquatic Ecosystems in Alberta: Water Quality, Sediment Quality and Non-Fish Biota.* North/South Consultants, Calgary, AB.

[11] Anderson, A.-M. 1999. *supra.*

[12] Saskatchewan Watershed Authority 2007a. *supra.*

[13] Saskatchewan Watershed Authority 2007b. *State of the Watershed Report.* Saskatchewan Watershed Authority. Regina, SK.

[14] North Saskatchewan Watershed Alliance 2005. *supra.*

[15] Poston, B., D.M. Ealey, P.S. Taylor, G.B. McKeating 1990. *Priority Bird Habitats of Canada's Prairie Provinces.* Environment Canada, Edmonton, AB.

[16] North Saskatchewan Watershed Alliance 2005. *supra.*

[17] North Saskatchewan Watershed Alliance 2005. *supra.*

[18] North Saskatchewan Watershed Alliance 2005. *supra.*

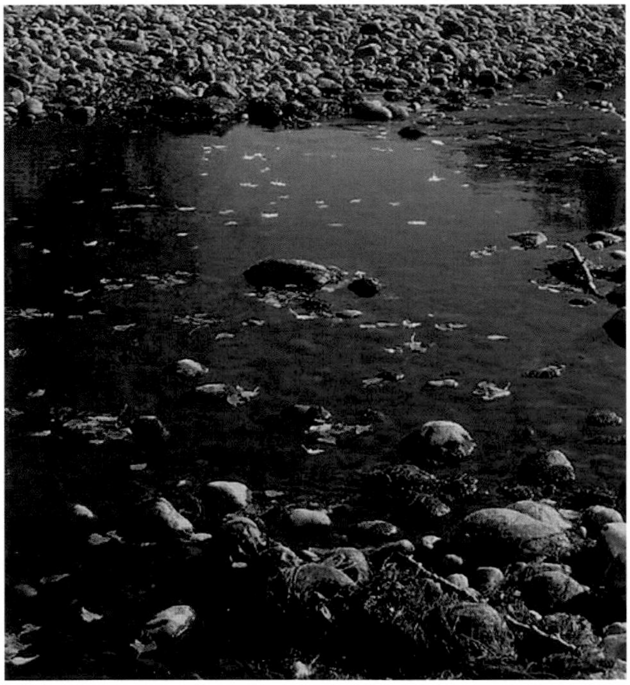

CHAPTER SEVEN

THE RED DEER RIVER SUB-BASIN

Figure 7.1. *Red Deer River Sub-basin*

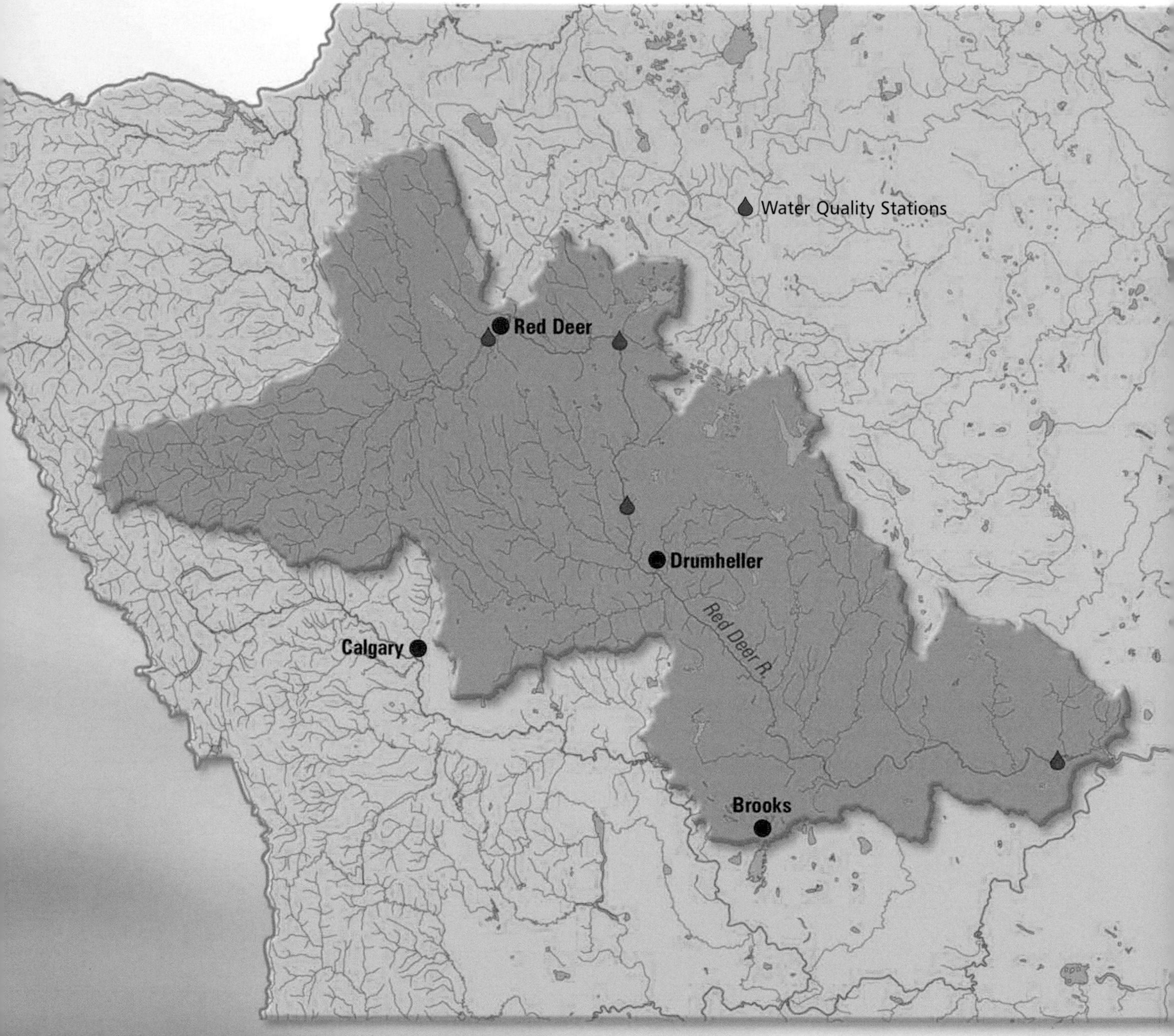

CHAPTER SEVEN
THE RED DEER RIVER SUB-BASIN

The Red Deer River rises in Banff National Park near Lake Louise. The origin of the name is the Cree 'was ka soo', meaning elk. Leaving the mountains, the river flows northeast through the foothills forest of the boreal plain towards the city of Red Deer. It then turns southeast through the prairie ecozone to Dinosaur Provincial Park then turns east, joining the South Saskatchewan River 16 km inside the Saskatchewan boundary.[1] The sub-basin is shown in Figure 7.1.

Sub-basin Summary

Characteristics
- high alpine to plains
- length 806 km
- gross drainage area 50 445 km^2
- effective drainage area 29 139 km^2

Hydrology
- reliable flow on headwaters tributaries and mainstem
- ephemeral flow on plains tributaries
- regulated

Water Quality
- good for headwaters tributaries and the mainstem to Red Deer
- fair to poor for plains tributaries and lakes and fair for the mainstem from Red Deer to the South Saskatchewan River confluence

Biodiversity
- headwaters protected
- riparian zones healthy, but problems

Key Issues
- land use – forestry and agriculture
- municipal and industrial effluents
- interprovincial water apportionment

The water towers portion of the Red Deer River sub-basin is small, although it accounts for more than 50 percent of the water that flows in the sub-basin. Elevations range from 3700 m in the mountains to 1500-1000 m in river valleys. Grasslands and open forests of spruce and fir at the tree line give way to closed forests at lower elevations. Extensive stands of lodgepole pine occupy the lower elevations. With the exception of the headwaters, almost the entire sub-basin is devoted to agricultural production. There is a band of agricultural rangeland in the lower foothills of the sub-basin. The middle sub-basin is cropland while the lower sub-basin is almost entirely rangeland. Overall, about one-half the agricultural area is cropland, with about five percent being summer fallowed in any given year. About 10 percent of the agricultural area is improved pasture with the remainder being natural pasture.[2] One-half of the farms in the sub-basin are cattle operations. Cattle density is particularly high near Brooks.

The Red Deer River sub-basin contains a portion of one national park, eight Alberta provincial parks, and one First Nations reserve. The middle sub-basin is well known for both archaeological and palaeontological resources.

The population of the sub-basin in 2006 was about 270 000 persons. Cities in the sub-basin include Red Deer, Brooks and an extremely small portion of Calgary. The larger towns include Strathmore, Sylvan Lake, Drumheller, Innisfail and Olds. The population of the larger urban centres is increasing rapidly while that of rural areas is stable.

Oil and gas exploration and development and refining operations are extensive, particularly in the lower sub-basin near Brooks. Only the Rocky Mountain headwaters lack oil or gas resources. The sub-basin has significant coal deposits used to support thermal power generation.

HYDROLOGY

The Red Deer River is 806 km long. The mountain headwaters area of the sub-basin is relatively small. The only significant upper sub-basin tributaries are the James and Raven rivers. Important plains tributaries include Medicine, Kneehill and Rosebud creeks. The gross drainage area is 50 445 km^2 and the effective drainage area is 29 139 km^2. Most of the non-contributing area lies in the lower sub-basin.

The annual precipitation in the headwaters valleys of the sub-basin is almost 600 mm, with half of that falling as snow. Precipitation at higher elevations is greater, and a greater percentage of that precipitation falls as snow. Where the river reaches the plains at Red Deer, annual precipitation is less than 500 mm, about 80 percent falling as rain. Annual precipitation continues to decline moving eastward in the sub-basin. Annual precipitation at Empress near the Saskatchewan boundary is only 290 mm, with 72 percent of this falling as rain. Snowmelt and rain during the snowmelt period are the key factors determining annual runoff. Summer rains, while sustaining crops, produce little runoff.

Although the headwaters portion of the Red Deer River accounts for much of the flow in the sub-basin, there is a significant contribution from prairie runoff, as shown by the naturalized flows in Figure 7.2. The first of two flow peaks occurs in April, caused by runoff from the plains tributaries of the sub-basin. The later and higher peak in June or July is from mountain runoff. The contribution of prairie runoff to the annual flow of the Red Deer River means that the flow is not as reliable as that of an almost exclusively mountain-fed stream, such as the North Saskatchewan River.

The Red Deer River is regulated by Dickson Dam in the foothills upstream of Red Deer, constructed in 1983 to provide increased winter flows and some flood control for the city of Red Deer. Since the

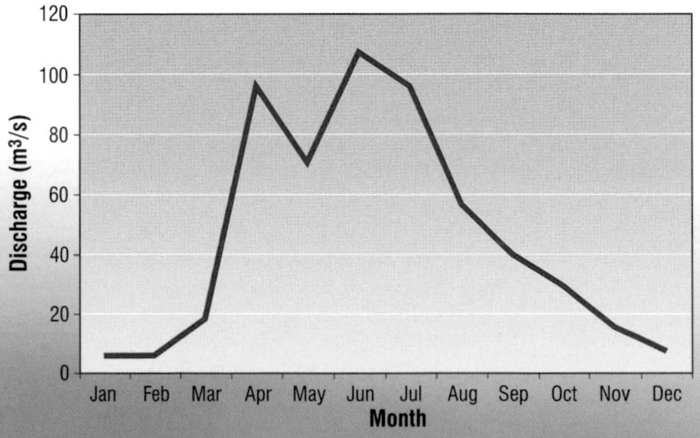

Figure 7.2. Median Monthly Naturalized Flows at Interprovincial Boundary.

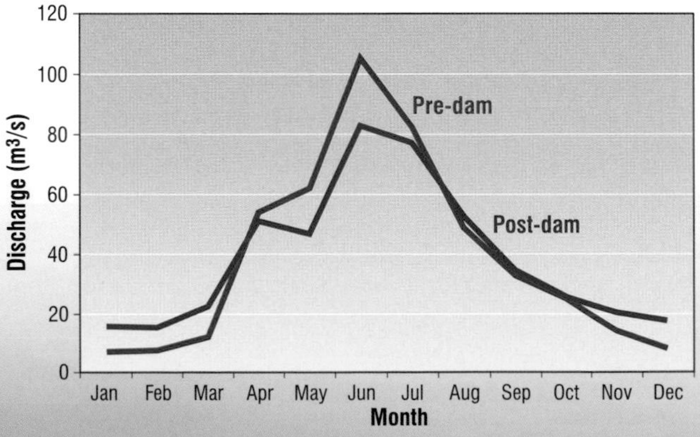

Figure 7.3. Effects of River Regulation on Flows at Red Deer.

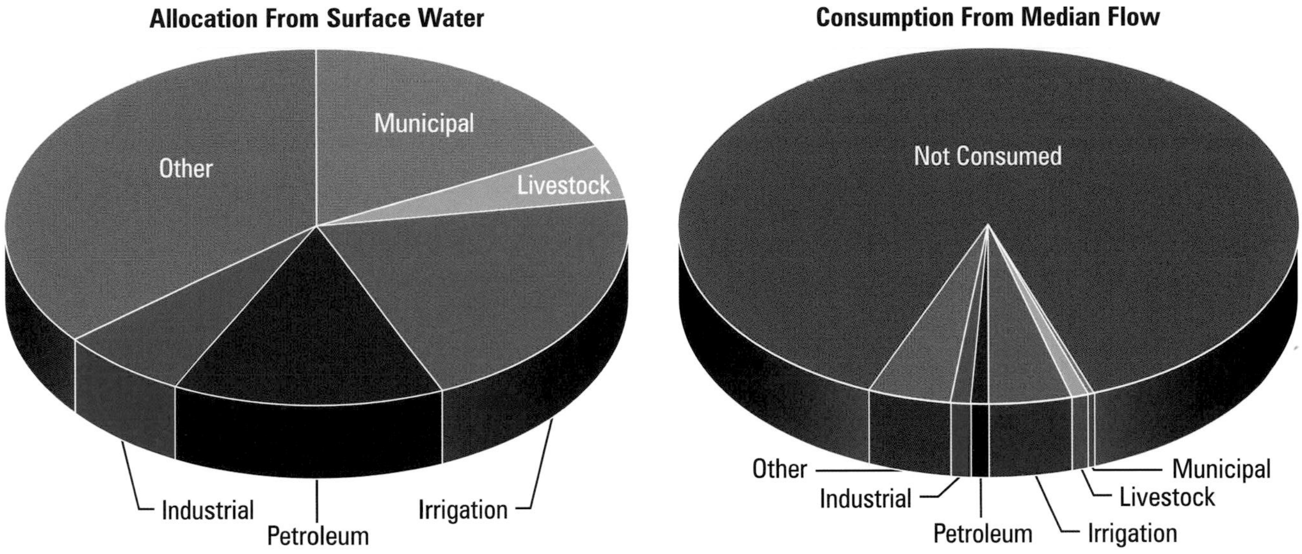

Figure 7.4. Licensed Allocation and Water Consumption from Surface Water.

purpose of the reservoir is water management rather than hydroelectric generation, the flow pattern tends to mimic the natural hydrograph. Generally, winter flows are slightly greater than they would be under natural conditions, while the spring peaks are slightly lower. The reservoir created by the dam, Glennifer Lake, provides recreational uses. The effect of the reservoir on annual flows is shown in Figure 7.3.

Streamflows are monitored at 43 sites in the sub-basin and lake or reservoir levels at 9 sites. The program is carried out by the Water Survey of Canada under a cost-sharing arrangement with Alberta Environment.

WATER USE

The licensed annual water allocation for the Red Deer River sub-basin in 2005 was 335 504 dam^3, and 37 325 dam^3 of this was from groundwater. Under the terms of Alberta's South Saskatchewan Water Management Plan, an initial maximum allocation of 600 000 dam^3 from the Red Deer sub-basin is identified. When allocations in the Red Deer sub-basin reach 550 000 dam^3, a thorough review aimed at identifying the allocation limit will be conducted.[3] Actual consumption from groundwater is 27 380 dam^3. Surface water consumption is now 190 455 dam^3, which is 12 percent of the median naturalized annual flow.[4] Water allocations from surface water and annual water consumption compared to the median are shown in Figure 7.4.

Agricultural water represents about 45 percent of the surface water consumed in the Red Deer sub-basin. Stockwatering makes up 10 percent and private irrigation about 35 percent of total consumption. Water for stockwatering is primarily groundwater, while irrigators use surface water. Almost all of the irrigators are producing forage to support cattle operations. Crawling Valley Reservoir in the lower sub-basin near Bassano was constructed on a glacial meltwater channel in 1983. The reservoir is filled from the Bow River by means of the Eastern Irrigation District North Branch Canal.[5] This diversion from the Bow River is a net increase in the flow of the Red Deer River.

The next largest consumer is the 'other' category, at 35 percent. This represents water used by projects related to flood control, lake stabilization and habitat enhancement. Many of this last group are Ducks Unlimited Canada projects. The next largest water consumer in the sub-basin is the petroleum sector. Much of that consumption is surface water required by gas and petrochemical plants. Water use by the petroleum sector is declining.

Industrial water consumption from surface water is modest. The largest water allocation is for cooling water for the coal-fired generating station at Sheerness. Cooling water for the 760 MW Sheerness station is pumped from the Red Deer River to a cooling pond that also provides the municipal supply for Hanna, which is outside the sub-basin. Most of the water is recycled through the cooling pond.

Municipal water consumption is small. Water allocated to the municipal sector is significant, but consumption is small and most of the water withdrawn returns to the stream. Urban centres depend on surface water while rural and other users rely on groundwater. Brooks and Bassano, while in the Red Deer sub-basin, draw their water from the Bow River. Stettler in the Battle River sub-basin draws its water from the Red Deer River.

The largest single consumer of groundwater is water for livestock, accounting for three-quarters of all groundwater consumption. Groundwater use by other sectors is small.

Any application for a water licence from the Red Deer River received after May 1, 2005 is subject to water conservation objectives. Some licences granted prior to this time contain a 'retrofit provision' that may be used to make the licences subject to water conservation objectives. In the reach from Dickson Dam to the confluence with the Blindman River, immediately downstream of the city of Red Deer, a flow of 45 percent of the natural flow or 16 m^3/s, whichever is greater, must be maintained. Downstream of the Blindman River confluence, the water conservation objective is the same for the November to March period and drops to 45 percent of the natural flow or 10 m^3/s, whichever is less, for the April to October period. These objectives can be compared to the values shown in Figures 7.2 and 7.3. The highest priority for the operation of Dickson dam is to provide a year-round release of 16 m^3/s.[6]

The flows in the Red Deer River are also subject to the PPWB *Master Agreement on Apportionment*. Under the agreement, the waters of the South Saskatchewan River, including the Red Deer River, are treated as one stream for apportionment purposes. The specific arrangements pertaining to the South Saskatchewan River are discussed in Chapter 9.

WATER QUALITY

The waters of the Red Deer River to Glennifer Lake and its headwaters tributaries are mostly unaffected by human activity. The waters are naturally hard and nutrient poor. The water quality is considered as good, although total phosphorous levels are naturally elevated. Downstream of the Glennifer Lake, effects of river regulation are evident. Winter flows are higher than natural and have higher oxygen levels and so are better able to assimilate waste from point and non-point sources. The clear water released from the reservoir scours the stream channel immediately downstream of the dam. The partial suppression of spring peak flows means that flushing flows are reduced. The releases from Dickson Dam also affect the thermal regime of the river.

Water quality is affected by wastewater effluents from Red Deer and Drumheller and by industrial effluents from petrochemical plants near Joffre. Nutrient loading in the lower reaches of the river is significant, primarily from agricultural sources in the plains tributary sub-basins such as the Little Red Deer, Medicine and Blindman rivers. Smaller streams such as Hayes, Ray, Renwick, and Threehills creeks are also affected by nutrient loads. Despite these nutrient inputs, overall water quality is considered to be good upstream of Drumheller and fair downstream to the confluence with the South Saskatchewan River. The lower Red Deer River also receives irrigation return flows from the Western Irrigation District and the Eastern Irrigation District. Pine, Sylvan and Gull lakes, major recreational lakes, are also affected by nutrients originating from septic leachate, recreational use and urban runoff, as well as from agricultural sources. Agricultural runoff also affects the wetlands of the sub-basin.[7]

Table 7.1. Long Term Water Quality Monitoring Sites.

Stream	Location	Agency	Remarks
Red Deer River	at Highway 2	Alberta Environment	Upstream of Red Deer
Red Deer River	Nevis	Alberta Environment	Downstream of Red Deer
Red Deer River	Morrin Bridge	Alberta Environment	Upstream of Drumheller
Red Deer River	Bindloss	Environment Canada	Near Saskatchewan boundary

Based on nutrient levels, the Red Deer River is low in nutrients, or oligotrophic, upstream of Glennifer Lake, oligotrophic to mesotrophic from Glennifer Lake to Drumheller and high in nutrients, or eutrophic, downstream of Drumheller. The natural lakes of the sub-basin tend to be eutrophic or hypereutrophic, particularly in the lower sub-basin.[8]

Water quality is monitored at four locations on the Red Deer River as shown in Table 7.1. Historical monitoring data are available for the reach at Sundre, upstream of Glennifer Lake. There are no long-term monitoring sites on tributary streams, although periodic assessments have been carried out. Assessments of water quality of recreational lakes are also conducted.

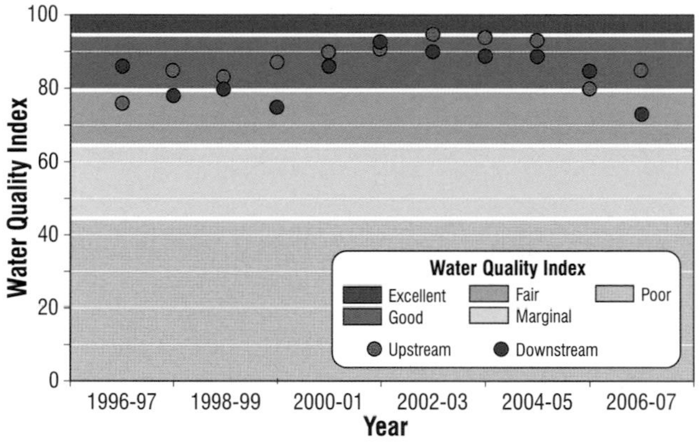

Figure 7.5. Water Quality Index Upstream and Downstream of Red Deer.

Alberta produces a water quality index based on monitoring upstream and downstream of Red Deer. Results drawn from several years of data are shown in Figure 7.5. The effect of improvements to the Red Deer effluent treatment in 2000 is apparent. The principal factor contributing to reduced index values remains elevated nutrient concentrations.

The Prairie Provinces Water Board has developed water quality objectives for the reach from Bindloss to the confluence with the South Saskatchewan River, based on physical, chemical and biological variables. Water samples obtained throughout the year are tested against these objectives. About one percent of the samples have concentrations exceeding the objectives. Although nutrients are the major water quality concern in the Red Deer sub-basin, pesticides are frequently detected.

BIODIVERSITY AND ECOSYSTEMS

The headwaters of the Red Deer River lie in the relatively undisturbed landscape of Banff National Park and the Bighorn Forest Management Unit. The forests of the upper sub-basin provide important habitant for many mammals and migratory songbirds. The sub-basin then passes through parts of the Sundre and Spray Lake Forest Management Areas. In these areas, timber harvesting leads to younger and more fragmented forests that lead to the decline of some species. Petroleum exploration also leads to habitat fragmentation through seismic line cutting, road and pipeline construction. The only part of the sub-basin where riparian health assessments have been carried out is the reach from Glennifer Lake to immediately downstream of Red Deer. Riparian health is deemed to be fair to poor.

Table 7.2. Fish Species in the Red Deer Sub-basin.

Species Type	Common Name
Coldwater Species (5-18°C) ** Introduced Species*	Brook Trout Brown Trout* Bull Trout Lake Whitefish Mountain Whitefish Rainbow Trout
Coolwater Species (10-25°C)	Goldeye Mooneye Northern Pike Sauger Walleye Lake Cisco Yellow Perch Burbot Lake Sturgeon
Non-game Species	Brook Stickleback Emerald Shiner Fathead Minnow Flathead Chub Iowa Darter Lake Chub Longnose Dace Longnose Sucker Mountain Sucker Northern Redbelly Dace Shorthead Redhorse Sucker Pearl Dace Quillback Sucker River Shiner Spottail Shiner Trout-Perch White Sucker

Overall aquatic ecosystem health in the Red Deer sub-basin can be considered as good in the upper portion of the sub-basin and fair in the lower portion. Ecosystem health in the lower sub-basin is degraded by agricultural runoff and irrigation return flows. Full assessment of sediment quality and non-fish biota is not possible because of lack of data.

Fish species of the sub-basin are shown in Table 7.2. Fish populations are generally stable. The conservation flows discussed earlier in this chapter are based in part on the temperature and dissolved oxygen requirements for fish.

The agricultural rangeland and cropland extending from the forested upper sub-basin through to the city of Red Deer is a non-point source of pollutants, particularly nutrients. In general, however, the composition and diversity of benthic invertebrate communities is consistent with a healthy ecosystem upstream of Glennifer Lake. Downstream of the lake, the effects of river regulation are evident as are the effects of municipal and industrial effluents at Red Deer. The species downstream of Red Deer and Joffre tend to include those that are more tolerant of nutrient enrichment. Very sensitive species are not present. Even so, the condition of aquatic communities in the lower sub-basin is reasonably good.[9]

ENDNOTES

[1] Ecological Stratification Working Group 1996. *A National Ecological Framework for Canada.* Canadian Soil Information System (CanCIS), Agriculture and Agrifood Canada. Ottawa, ON.

[2] Alberta Environment 2007a. *Current and Future Water Use in Alberta.* Prepared by AMEC Earth & Environmental. Alberta Environment. Edmonton, AB.

[3] Alberta Environment 2006. *Approved Water Management Plan for the South Saskatchewan River Basin (Alberta).* Alberta Environment. Edmonton, AB.

[4] Alberta Environment 2007a. *supra.*

[5] Prepas, E. and P. Mitchell 1990. *Atlas of Alberta Lakes.* University of Alberta Press. Edmonton, AB.

[6] Alberta Environment 2006. *supra.*

[7] Alberta Environment 2007b. *Information Synthesis and Initial Assessment of the Status and Health of Aquatic Ecosystems in Alberta.* Technical Report 278/279-01. Alberta Environment, Edmonton, AB.

[8] Alberta Environment 2007b. *supra.*

[9] Alberta Environment 2007b. *supra.*

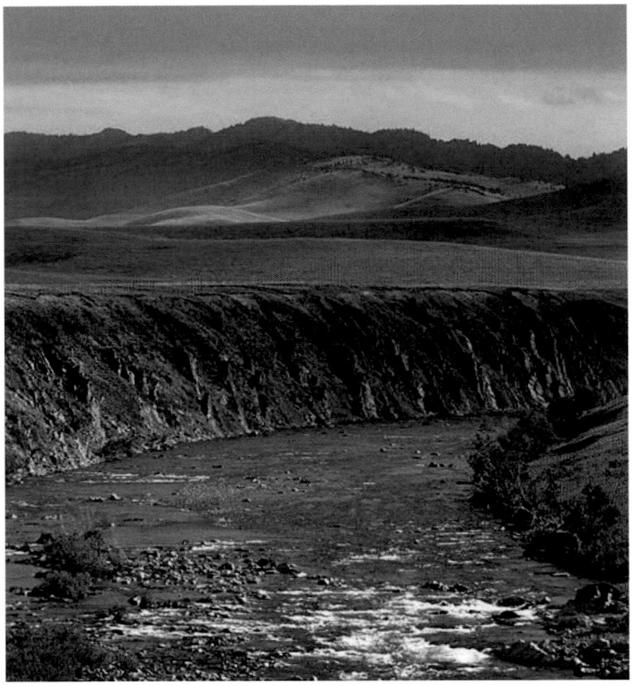

CHAPTER EIGHT
THE BOW AND OLDMAN RIVER SUB-BASINS

Figure 8.1. *The Bow and Oldman River Sub-basins*

CHAPTER EIGHT
THE BOW AND OLDMAN RIVER SUB-BASINS

Bow Sub-basin Summary

Characteristics
- high alpine to plains
- length – 637 km
- gross drainage area – 25 611 km^2
- effective drainage area – 19 304 km^2

Hydrology
- reliable flow on headwaters tributaries and mainstem
- ephemeral flow on plains tributaries
- highly regulated

Water Quality
- excellent for headwaters
- good for lower reaches
- poor for plains tributaries

Biodiversity
- headwaters protected
- riparian zones healthy, but problems

Key Issues
- agricultural land use
- irrigation water use
- municipal effluents
- interprovincial water apportionment
- drought

Oldman Sub-basin Summary

Characteristics
- high alpine to plains
- length – 443 km
- gross drainage area – 28 270 km^2
- effective drainage area – 20 990 km^2

Hydrology
- reliable flow on headwaters tributaries and mainstem
- ephemeral flow on plains tributaries
- highly regulated

Water Quality
- excellent for headwaters
- good for lower mainstem
- poor for plains tributaries

Biodiversity
- riparian zones healthy, but problems
- few remaining wetlands

Key Issues
- agricultural land use
- irrigation water use
- international and interprovincial water apportionment
- drought

The Bow River sub-basin (Figure 8.1) originates in the montane cordillera ecozone on the eastern slopes of the Rocky Mountains. The river itself flows southeasterly through the communities of Lake Louise and Banff. Crossing the foothills forest of the boreal plains, it then emerges onto the prairie, flowing through aspen parkland to Calgary. It then crosses grasslands, meandering southeasterly through an ancient glacial spillway to join the Oldman River. Important mountain tributaries include the Spray, Cascade Kananaskis, Elbow, Sheep, and Highwood rivers. Plains tributaries are few, but include Nose, Fish, West Arrowhead, Arrowhead and Crowfoot creeks.[1]

The steep mountain gradients of about 7 m/km in the mountains become less than 0.5 m/km at the confluence with the Oldman River. The river channel is wide and relatively shallow, and is composed of boulders, cobble and gravel. It has well-developed riffle, run and pool sequences that provide fish habitat.[2]

The Oldman River sub-basin (Figure 8.1) also originates on the eastern slopes of the Rocky Mountains, and makes a rather abrupt transition from mountains to prairie. The Oldman River itself rises near Mount Lyall and flows generally eastward through fescue grasslands and moist mixed grasslands to Lethbridge. It continues to meander through grasslands to its confluence with the Bow River. Important mountain tributaries include the Livingstone, Crowsnest, Castle, Waterton, Belly, and St. Mary rivers. These last three rise in the United States, in Glacier National Park, Montana. In their northward path the Waterton and Belly rivers pass through Waterton Lakes National Park. The Little Bow River is an important plains tributary.

The headwaters of the Bow and Oldman sub-basins descend from alpine tundra through forests of lodgepole pine, spruce, fir and trembling aspen. The undulating prairie consists of open grassland. The high natural fertility and good moisture-holding capacity of the underlying dark soils, high in organic matter, have given rise to productive agriculture. Over 80 percent of these sub-basins is devoted to agriculture. In some cases, there are significant riparian cottonwood forests. Wetland areas in the Bow River sub-basin are much more significant than those in the Oldman sub-basin. According to PFRA data, about 1000 wetlands cover 94 km^2 in the Bow sub-basin, and about 500 cover 10 km^2 in the Oldman sub-basin.

The headwaters of the Bow sub-basin lie within Banff National Park, and in several provincial parks and wilderness areas. As mentioned earlier, some headwaters tributaries of the Oldman sub-basin lie in national parks but, in general, park areas in the upper sub-basin are small. The dominant population centre of the sub-basins is Calgary with a population of over one million, representing 85 percent of the overall population of Bow and Oldman sub-basins. The largest city in the Oldman sub-basin is Lethbridge, with a population of 74 637 in 2006. There are three First Nations reserves in the Bow sub-basin and two in the Oldman sub-basin. The Kainaiwa Reserve, southwest of Lethbridge, is the largest single reserve in the entire Saskatchewan River basin.

HYDROLOGY

The Bow River begins at Bow Glacier at an elevation of 3400 m and drops to an elevation of 740 m at its confluence with the Oldman River. The highest point in the Oldman sub-basin is Mount Cleveland in Montana. The channels of the two rivers have the typical concave longitudinal profile of all the mountain-fed streams of the Saskatchewan River basin. The rivers are significantly regulated by both hydroelectric and water management dams.

The Bow and Oldman sub-basins are subject to the temperature extremes associated with a cold continental climate. They lie in a region where dry westerly chinook winds, warmed by their descent from the mountain slopes, can produce dramatic mid-winter temperature changes. Mid-winter snowmelts in the lower elevations of these sub-basins are not uncommon.

The annual precipitation in the headwaters valleys of the sub-basin is about 500-700 mm, with about half of that falling as snow. Precipitation at higher elevations is even greater, as is the proportion falling as snow. Entering the plains, precipitation drops in the rain shadow of the mountains and decreases even further at the downstream end of the sub-basins. At Calgary, annual precipitation is only 412 mm, with almost 78 percent of that falling as rain. At Lethbridge, annual precipitation is 386 mm, with 70 percent of that falling as rain. About one-half of the annual precipitation falls as rain in the months of May through August. These rains, while sustaining crops, produce very little runoff. It is snowmelt and rain during the snowmelt period that produce the runoff to replenish water supplies and sustain ecosystems.

Mountain runoff accounts for most of the flow in the Bow and Oldman sub-basins. The combined naturalized median monthly flow is shown in Figure 8.2. Both rivers have similar flow characteristics. The small increase in flow in March and April can be attributed to plains runoff, while the pronounced annual peak in June is from the mountain snowmelt.

As mountain-fed streams, the natural flows of the Bow and Oldman rivers themselves are much more reliable than those of plains-fed tributaries. The Bow River has a particularly reliable flow.

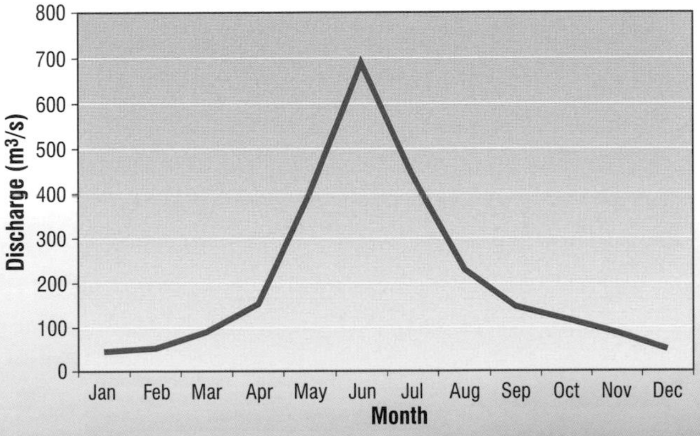

Figure 8.2. Combined Bow and Oldman Median Monthly Naturalized Flows.

Hydroelectric generating stations were installed on the Bow River as early as 1911 to support the growth of the city of Calgary. At present, TransAlta Utilities operates stations at 11 locations in the Bow River headwaters. These stations are used to provide electricity to meet morning and evening power demands. Bearspaw Dam, just upstream of Calgary, acts to smooth short-duration fluctuations in flow caused by the hydroelectric stations. Its reservoir provides one-half of the city's municipal supply. Despite the use of the system for daily peaking, the overall effect on the annual hydrograph is to increase winter flows and reduce summer flows. Increased winter flows facilitate operation of downstream water intakes and assist waste assimilation. Glenmore Reservoir on the Elbow River captures water that supplies about one-half the municipal demand for Calgary. Further downstream, the Western Irrigation District operates a water diversion weir within Calgary, and the Bow River Irrigation District operates a weir at Carseland. A dam at Bassano provides water for the Eastern Irrigation District. These structures significantly reduce the summer flows of the Bow River, so that the flushing flows that enhance ecosystems occur less frequently than before regulation.

Unlike the Bow River, the initial modification of the natural flows of the Oldman sub-basin was driven by agricultural water demands. Irrigation development in the lower Milk River in the Mississippi River basin began with minor diversions in 1887. To meet irrigation water demands, the United States began diverting the St. Mary River, an Oldman River tributary, into the Milk River in 1916. The United States developed Lake Sherburne on Swiftcurrent Creek in 1917 then built a canal to the Milk River with a design capacity of 24 m^3/s. The actual quantity of water that may be diverted in a year is subject to the *Boundary Waters Treaty*. Flow requirements are calculated every 15 days from April to October, and there are no specified minimum flows.

Canada completed major infrastructure developments as well. These included regulation of the Waterton River and diversion of the Waterton

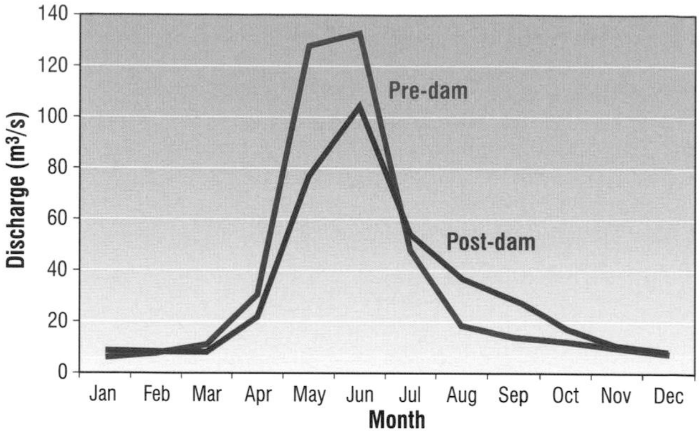

Figure 8.3. Effect of River Regulation on Median Monthly Flows for the Oldman River near Brocket.

and Belly rivers into the St. Mary River. Many water management dams, diversions or conveyance facilities were constructed or expanded in the latter half of the last century. This development culminated with completion of Oldman Dam in 1991. Figure 8.3 shows flows before and after construction of the dam. Downstream flows tend to mimic the natural hydrograph, although flows are reduced because of water withdrawals. Depending on the exact operation of the diversion, this is not always the case elsewhere in these sub-basins.

Streamflows are monitored at 112 sites and lake or reservoir levels at 24 sites in the two sub-basins. The work is carried out for the most part by the Water Survey of Canada under a cost-sharing arrangement with Alberta Environment. The irrigation districts also conduct extensive monitoring within the districts.

WATER USE

The licensed annual surface water allocation in the Bow and Oldman sub-basins in 2005 was 4 792 670 dam^3, and the groundwater allocation was 97 624 dam^3. Almost four million cubic decametres of the surface water allocation relate to licences for irrigated agriculture. Surface water consumption in the sub-basins is calculated to be 2 247 044 dam^3, and groundwater to be 118 040 dam^3.[3] This is 35 percent of the median naturalized flow of the South Saskatchewan River at the Alberta-Saskatchewan boundary – by far the highest water consumption in any sub-basin of the Saskatchewan River basin. Figure 8.4 shows the water allocation and actual water consumption from surface waters. Water consumption in the two sub-basins is almost identical.

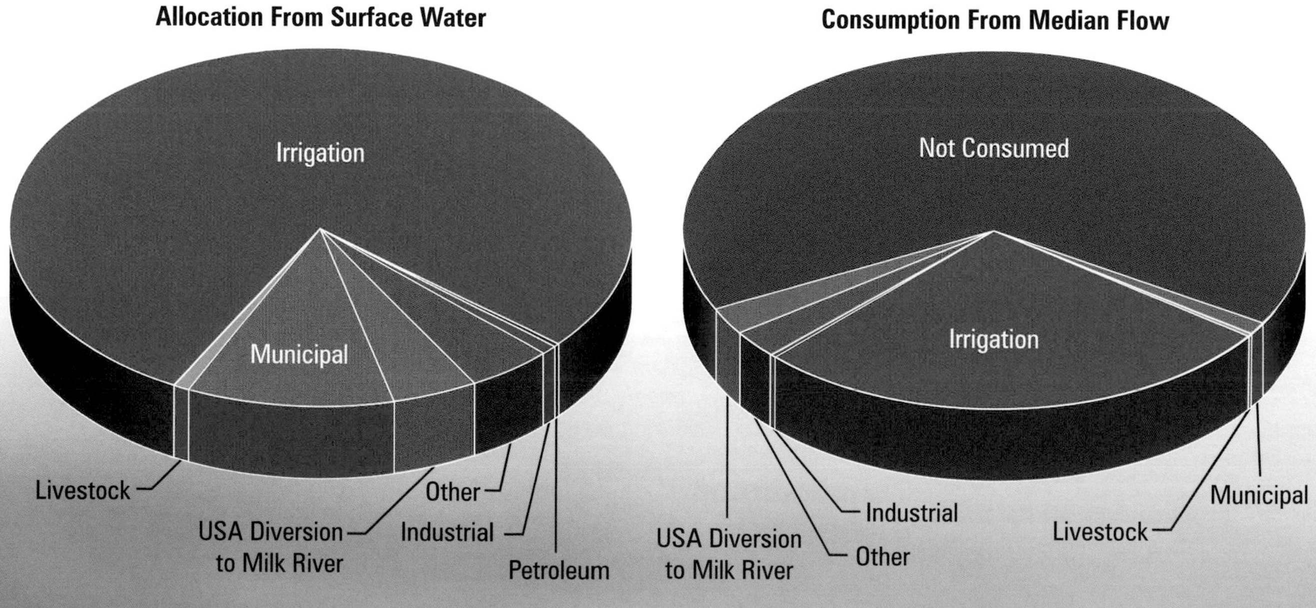

Figure 8.4. Water Allocation and Water Consumption from Surface Water.

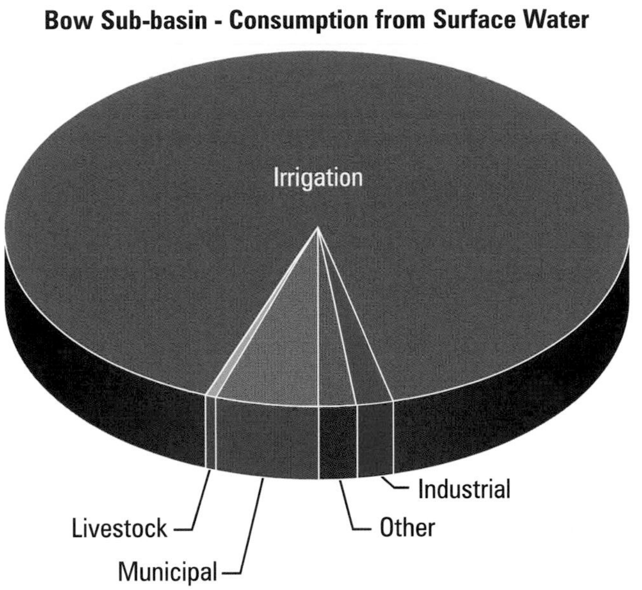

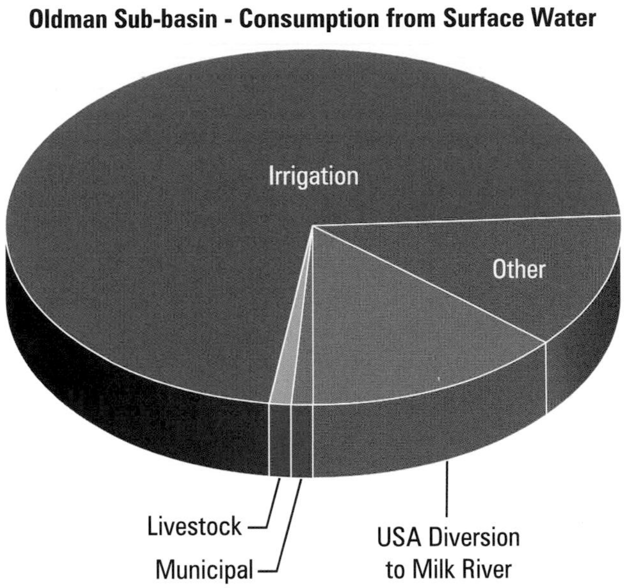

Figure 8.5. Water Consumption from Surface Water in the Bow and Oldman Sub-basins.

Under an Order of the International Joint Commission arising from the *Boundary Waters Treaty* of 1909, the waters of the St. Mary River are shared with the United States, with the American share being diverted to the Milk River.[4] The historical median United States annual entitlement is 228 000 dam^3, while the median annual diversion has been 177 200 dam^3, which represents about 30 percent of the annual streamflow of the St. Mary River, but only about one percent of the Saskatchewan River's annual flow.[5] From a Saskatchewan River basin perspective, all of the waters diverted to the Milk River within Montana are considered to be consumed. The diversion is included in Figure 8.4 and 8.5.

As of 2006, Alberta no longer accepts applications for new surface water allocations from the Bow and Oldman rivers. The Minister of Environment will specify through a Crown Reservation how currently unallocated water will be used. Crown Reservation waters can be allocated only to water conservation objectives; storage of peak flows to mitigate impacts on the aquatic environment; and support to existing licences, including licences pending at the time of the Crown Reservation and allocations for First Nations reserves.[6] Although the waters of the Bow and Oldman sub-basins can be considered as fully allocated, they are not entirely used. Depending on the situation, existing licence holders could expand operations or, under recent legislation, transfer part of an existing licence to another user.

Water consumption from surface water in the Bow and Oldman sub-basins is shown separately in Figure 8.5. Groundwater consumption is very small and is related primarily to stockwatering and domestic use.

Irrigated agriculture is by far the most significant water user in the Bow and Oldman sub-basins. The irrigated area of Alberta is some 6500 km^2, most of that being in these sub-basins. This represents 65 percent of all irrigated agriculture in Canada. Within the 13 irrigation districts in southern Alberta, 5364 km^2 are irrigated. Table 8.1 identifies the districts. Even those districts not physically within the Bow or Oldman sub-basins depend on water infrastructure within the sub-basins for their water supply. There are an additional 1200 km^2 in private irrigation and First Nations irrigation. The project on the Kainaiwa Reserve, which irrigates 100 km^2 using water from the Oldman sub-basin, is the largest private licence holder in Alberta. A map of the Alberta irrigation districts, most of which are in the Bow and Oldman sub-basins, appears in Figure 8.6.[7]

Table 8.1. Irrigation Districts in Alberta.

Map Location	Name	Length of Distribution System (km)	Irrigated Land (km^2)
1	Mountain View	35	4
2	Leavitt	56	19
3	Aetna	27	8
4	United	227	70
5	Magrath	106	45
6	Raymond	247	131
7	Lethbridge Northern	650	495
8	Taber	364	311
9	St. Mary River	1719	1390
10	Ross Creek	20	4
11	Bow River	1058	802
12	Western	1077	274
13	Eastern	1784	1113

Irrigation accounts for about 80 percent of the water consumption in the two sub-basins. The quantity of water consumed in any given year will vary, depending on weather conditions. Return flows from the Western Irrigation District are conveyed by the Rosebud River to the Red Deer River. Water diverted from the Highwood River in the Bow River sub-basin is transferred to the Little Bow River in the Oldman sub-basin. Irrigation water is drawn from surface water; groundwater use is minor. There is still some scope to expand irrigation development within the present water allocations.

The water diverted from the St. Mary River to the Milk River in Montana in a given year depends on the natural flow of the river. It is not an allocation licensed by Alberta; rather, the annual quantity is defined by the *Boundary Waters Treaty*.

The next largest consumer of water is the 'other' sector. Water is allocated for management for flood control and lake stabilization, and for fish, wildlife and habitat enhancement. Most of the licences in the Oldman sub-basin are for water management, while habitat enhancement licences dominate in the Bow sub-basin. Most of the water allocated is consumed by evaporation.

Municipal applications account for the next largest water consumption. Less than five percent of municipal use is from groundwater. The apparent consumption shown for the Bow River in Figure 8.5 relates to city of Calgary licences, but is likely overestimated. Allocations and water consumption related to stockwatering, petroleum and industrial applications are also small. Most of the water allocated for these purposes is consumed.

The flows in the Bow and Oldman are subject to the PPWB *Master Agreement on Apportionment*. Under the agreement, the waters of the South Saskatchewan River, including the Red Deer River, are treated as one stream for apportionment purposes. Because of relatively high water use in the Bow and Oldman sub-basins, the apportionment of the Saskatchewan River at the interprovincial boundary is more complex than for other streams subject to the Master Agreement. This is discussed in Chapter Nine.

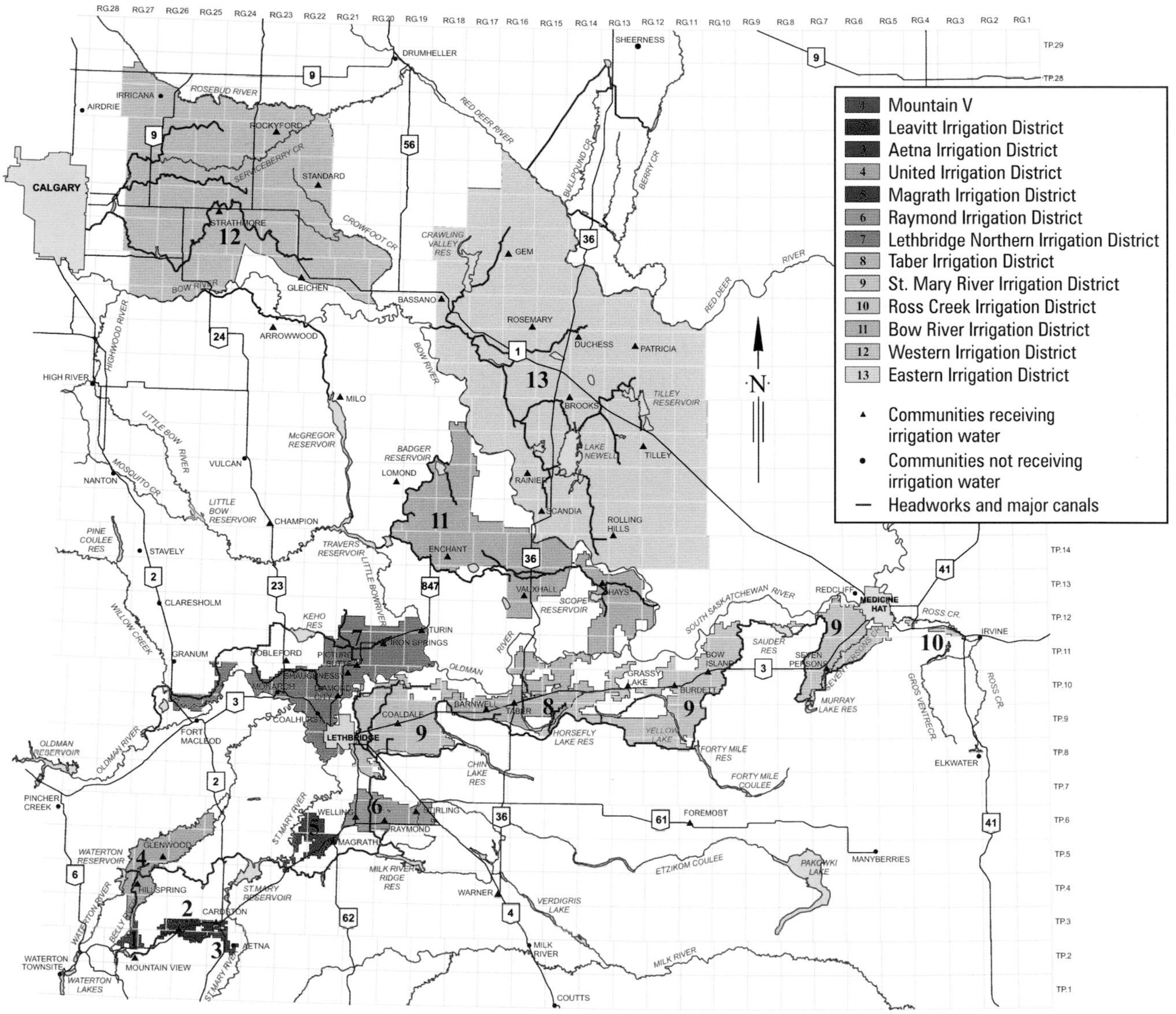

Figure 8.6. Alberta's Irrigation Districts (Alberta Agriculture, Food and Rural Development).

WATER QUALITY

Water quality of the streams, lakes and reservoirs of Bow and Oldman sub-basins is influenced by the landscape through which the streams flow and by human uses. As the headwater tributaries originate in the Rocky Mountains and most of the water flowing in the river constitutes mountain runoff, the water quality of these streams is generally good. This water tends to be naturally hard and nutrient poor. Natural mineralization and nutrient levels gradually increase downstream. On the other hand, the tributaries and small lakes of the plains tend to have water that is naturally highly mineralized and nutrient rich. The natural quality of the waters of the sub-basins is influenced by runoff from agricultural lands, and by municipal and industrial effluents.

Water quality is routinely monitored at several locations on the Bow and Oldman river mainstems, as well as on the Elbow River. Table 8.2 lists these locations. Periodic assessments have also been conducted at other locations. In general, water quality is found to be excellent in headwaters

Table 8.2. Water Quality Monitoring Locations.

Stream	Location	Agency	Remarks
Bow River	Lake Louise	Environment Canada	Upstream of Lake Louise
Bow River	Canmore	Environment Canada	Near National Park Boundary
Bow River	Upstream Exshaw Creek	Alberta Environment	
Bow River	Cochrane	Alberta Environment	Upstream of Calgary
Bow River	Carseland Dam	Alberta Environment	Downstream of dam
Bow River	Cluny	Alberta Environment	
Bow River	Bow City	Alberta Environment	At bridge
Bow River	Ronalane	Alberta Environment	Downstream of Bassano Dam
Elbow River	9th Ave. Bridge, Calgary	Alberta Environment	Downstream of Glenbow Reservoir
Oldman River	Brocket	Alberta Environment	Headwaters
Oldman River	at Highway 3	Alberta Environment	Upstream of Lethbridge
Oldman River	at Highway 36	Alberta Environment	Near confluence with Bow River

reaches and good further downstream. Water quality in the lower reaches of these rivers is influenced by agriculture, irrigation, and natural processes, such as channel erosion.

In the case of the Bow River, there was a noticeable improvement in water quality following the completion of the Banff wastewater treatment plant in 1989.[8] Further improvements aimed at reducing sediments, nutrients and micro-organisms were completed in 2003 at both Lake Louise and Banff.[9] Nutrient reduction measures taken by Calgary have reduced phosphorous loading to the Bow River. Despite the application of full tertiary treatment, the city remains the largest single source of nutrients in the Bow and Oldman sub-basins. These nutrients support aquatic plant growth and increased biological productivity downstream of the city; they can lead to daily fluctuations in dissolved oxygen because of respiration and photosynthesis.[10]

Water quality assessments of three Bow River tributaries have been conducted. The quality of the Ghost River – a mountain-fed stream – is excellent, although there are short-term, high-suspended sediment concentrations at times. The quality of the Elbow River – also a mountain-fed stream – is good near its confluence with the Bow River and better upstream, although there are indications water quality is degrading over time. The water quality of Nose Creek, a plains stream entering the Bow River at Calgary, is poor. Nutrient concentrations are high and bacteria and pesticide concentrations are also elevated.[11] The creek is degraded by both urban and agricultural runoff.

The water quality of the Oldman sub-basin is strongly linked to water withdrawals for irrigation and irrigation return flows, as well as to agricultural runoff caused by summer rains. Eight wastewater treatment plants discharge effluent into the river. Before a wastewater treatment plant upgrade in 1999, Lethbridge was a significant point source. The Oldman River is well oxygenated throughout its length, in part because of winter releases from the Oldman dam. Water quality assessments in the Oldman sub-basin have not been as extensive as those in the Bow sub-basin. The overall water quality of the Oldman River itself is considered excellent in the headwaters and good for the rest of its length. Although limited water quality assessments have been carried out for the St. Mary and Belly rivers, no overall rating is available. The quality can be considered to be good to excellent. The quality of the Little Bow River, where some water quality assessments have been conducted, generally degrades from the headwaters to its confluence with the Oldman River. The quality also varies considerably from year to year, ranging from good to poor.[12]

The upper reaches of the Bow and Oldman rivers and their tributaries are oligotrophic, while the plains tributaries are eutrophic. The Bow mainstem becomes mesotrophic at Calgary, while the Oldman River is considered oligotrophic throughout its length. Plains tributaries in the Bow sub-basin are eutrophic. Chestermere Lake, an off-stream reservoir immediately east of Calgary, is mesotrophic. St. Mary Reservoir in the Oldman sub-basin is oligotrophic. The irrigation reservoirs in the sub-

The Development of Irrigation in the Saskatchewan River Basin

European settlement of the West led to two major demands on available water supplies: irrigation and hydropower. In semi-arid southern Alberta, the first successful irrigation project took place in 1880 when John Glenn irrigated six hectares at Fish Creek south of Calgary. In 1889 the first diversion permit was issued for water from the St. Mary River. Mormon settlers constructed many small-scale projects based on their earlier experience in Utah. They also brought an approach to water allocation that was new to Canada – the concept of an exclusive right to water.

A significant drought and increased demands for irrigation development led to The *North-west Irrigation Act* of 1894. The Act, which applied to the area that is now Alberta, Saskatchewan and part of Manitoba, vested ownership of water in the federal crown and suppressed riparian rights. The ability of the government to grant exclusive rights to water enabled investments in irrigation development. Irrigation in the Milk River basin in southwest Saskatchewan began at roughly the same time but did not extend into the Saskatchewan River basin until later.

Large-scale irrigation got underway with the completion in 1900 of a 184 km canal from the St. Mary River to land near Lethbridge to deliver water to what is now known as the western block of the St. Mary Irrigation District. The Alberta Irrigation Company received a water right for almost the entire flow of the St. Mary River.

In 1903, the Canadian Pacific Railway (CPR) began construction of a weir on the Bow River near Calgary and a system of water delivery canals to what is now the Western Irrigation District. Six years later the CPR diverted the Bow River near Bessano and constructed a water delivery system to what is now the Eastern Irrigation District.

These early irrigation projects eventually failed, in part because of relatively wet weather during this era. In 1914, the Government of Alberta passed legislation that allowed landowners to organize themselves into co-operatives. The Taber Irrigation District, established in 1917, was the first to be organized. The federal and provincial governments supported major capital investments in the districts. With the creation of the Prairie Farm Rehabilitation Administration in 1935, the federal government became a major developer of reservoirs and water delivery systems. The Government of Alberta assumed this role in the 1970s, making major investments in new and refurbished infrastructure.

The irrigation infrastructure in southern Alberta now includes over 50 reservoirs and 8000 km of conveyance channels. The irrigation districts themselves contain 38 off-stream reservoirs. This infrastructure not only meets the needs of irrigators but also provides water to 42 000 people in 50 municipalities and 12 major industrial users. The infrastructure has also been used to create or enhance 350 km^2 of wetland habitat. Small-scale hydro has been added to some irrigation canals.

basins tend to have high flow-through rates, so it is not surprising that their trophic status is the same as their source waters.

Monitoring data have been used to calculate water quality indices for the mainstems of both the Bow and Oldman rivers. Figures 8.7 and 8.8 show the trends in water quality in the downstream reaches of both. Nutrient levels in the Bow River have improved since 1999, while other components of the index remain unchanged. Nutrient levels for the Oldman River have also improved overall, but nutrients and pesticides are still major concerns.

As measures to reduce the impacts of urban wastewater effluents on receiving waters have taken effect, the impacts of stormwater runoff have become more evident. In Calgary, stormwater runoff accounts for about 20 percent of the nutrient load to the Bow River. Unlike some of the other cities in the sub-basin, Calgary's sanitary sewers are separate from the stormwater system. Some stormwater runoff is captured in settling ponds in new developments, and efforts are also underway to reduce runoff, two steps to improving water quality. Stormwater runoff from the relatively impermeable urban environment, if uncontrolled, will be much greater than the runoff from an undeveloped landscape. One examination of Nose Creek in Calgary demonstrated that the increase in runoff due to urbanization was equivalent to a four-fold increase in the catchment area. The increased volume of water leads to increased scour and channel-widening, in turn leading to bank instability and the introduction of much larger sediment loads downstream.[13]

Following the improvements to Lethbridge's wastewater treatment system in 1999, the city has relatively little effect on downstream water quality. The more recent water quality index values are the result of both urban and agricultural runoff or return flows.

BIODIVERSITY AND ECOSYSTEMS

The headwaters of the Bow and Oldman sub-basins lie in a relatively undisturbed landscape. Banff National Park and several provincial parks provide considerable protection for the Bow River headwaters; however, a portion lies within the Spray Lake Forest Management Area. The United States' Glacier National Park, Waterton Lakes National Park and Bob Creek Provincial Park provide some protection for Oldman sub-basin headwaters. Both rivers are highly regulated by dams, weirs and water diversion structures. These structures fragment aquatic habitat, but, at the same time, river regulation provides opportunities to replenish

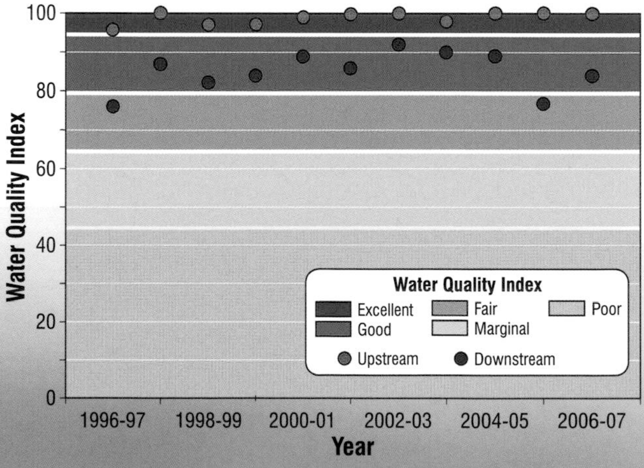

Figure 8.7. Water Quality Index - Bow River Upstream and Downstream of Calgary.

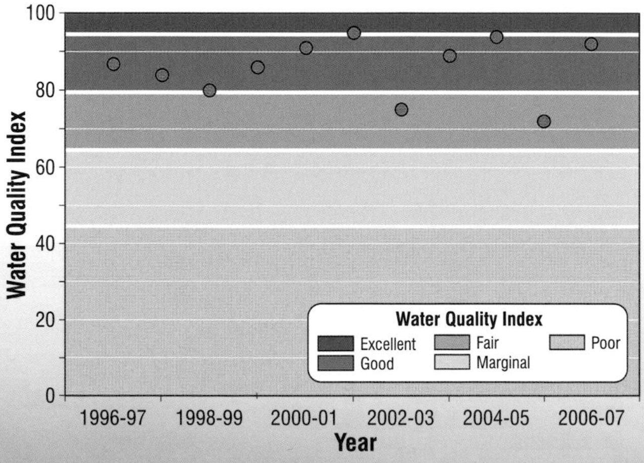

Figure 8.8. Water Quality Index - Oldman River Downstream of Lethbridge.

wetlands in the lower sub-basin. Alberta has established water conservation objectives for these sub-basins – either 45 percent of the naturalized flow, or the instream flow objective plus 10 percent, whichever is greater.[14] In the case of the Bow River below Bassano dam, the objective is 17.1 m^3/s.

The grassy slopes and forests of the sub-alpine portion of the upper part of both sub-basins provide habitat for many mammals, large and small. The foothills forest supports many migratory songbirds and non-migratory birds, such as owls and woodpeckers. Several species are threatened by habitat fragmentation and the loss of old-growth forest. The ecological resources of the upper sub-basin provide extensive outdoor recreation and ecotourism opportunities.

The fish species of the Bow and Oldman sub-basins are shown in Table 8.3. The upper Bow River and its mountain tributaries provide coldwater fish habitat. In the case of the Bow River, this habitat extends to Carseland Weir, where it becomes cool water habitat. Mountain whitefish, rainbow trout, brown trout, and bull trout are common. The Bow River is a renowned rainbow trout fishery. The combination of stable flows downstream of Bearspaw Dam and nutrients from Calgary municipal effluent and Highwood River increases fish production. The lack of fish passage facilities at Bassano dam, much reduced summer flows, high water temperatures, and oxygen-depleting aquatic growth significantly deplete fish stocks.[15]

The Oldman River and its mountain tributaries provide coldwater fish habitat. Mountain whitefish is the most common species in the upper sub-basin. The eastslope sculpin, a threatened species, is found in the St. Mary River. The operation of Oldman Dam, which began in 1991, has led to establishment of a bull trout fishery downstream, a result of the changed water temperature regime caused by the dam. Further downstream, flow reductions at the Lethbridge Northern Irrigation District (LNID) Weir affect the fishery. Although both the LNID Weir and the weir at Lethbridge have fish passage facilities, it is not certain how effective they are. In the lower sub-basin, fish habitat can also be affected by irrigation return flows.[16]

The effect of the city of Calgary on the Bow River has been monitored for many years. In general, the health of aquatic ecosystems is good upstream of the city, is degraded by the city, and then recovers further downstream. Both algal and rooted plant biomass increase downstream of Calgary, then decline from Carseland Weir to the confluence with the Oldman River. Plant biomass declined following

Table 8.3. Fish Species of the Bow and Oldman Rivers.

Species Type	Common Name
Coldwater Species * *Introduced Species*	Brook Trout (Bow) Brown Trout* Bull Trout Cutthroat Trout (Bow) Lake Trout (Bow) Rainbow Trout* Mountain Whitefish
Coolwater Species	Goldeye Mooneye Lake Whitefish Northern Pike Sauger walleye Yellow Perch Burbot Lake Sturgeon
Non-game Species	Brook Stickleback Emerald Shiner Fathead Minnow Lake Chub Longnose Dace Pearl Dace (Oldman) River Shiner Spottail Shiner Longnose Sucker Mountain Sucker Quillback Sucker Shorthead Redhorse Silver Redhorse Spoonhead Sculpin Trout-Perch White Sucker

implementation of tertiary treatment. Benthic invertebrate communities increase as the river moves through Calgary – an effect of increased nutrients from municipal and industrial effluents. Community structure also changes to more pollution-tolerant species. Benthic communities downstream of Calgary were previously affected by a contaminated industrial site, now contained. Benthic communities at the confluence of the Bow and Oldman rivers are similar in composition to those downstream of Calgary. This is a general effect of the nutrient content of the water in this reach. Generally, benthic species in the Bow River are healthy and diverse. Not enough information is available to define the state of the tributary communities.[17]

Assessments of aquatic biomass in the Oldman sub-basin indicate the highest concentrations are in the middle reach of the sub-basin. Dense growth of rooted plants are found downstream of Lethbridge to the confluence with the Bow River, possibly a consequence of both elevated nutrient levels and reduced flushing flows. Benthic communities in the Oldman River are diverse, but there is a tendency to more stress-tolerant communities as we move downstream. It is also evident that the Oldman Dam has perturbed the benthic communities and that they continue to change.[18]

Riparian health of the middle and lower reaches of the principal streams in the Bow and Oldman sub-basins has been assessed under Alberta's Cows and Fishes Program. In general, riparian areas are healthy, but with problems: for example, the presence of undesirable plant species, including invasive species such as purple loosestrife.[19]

Riparian vegetation can also be sensitive to the effects of river regulation. The collapse of the cottonwood population along the lower St. Mary River has been well documented. Consequently, with the completion of Oldman Dam, Alberta implemented an operating plan for the reservoir that closely mimicked the natural hydrograph.[20]

ENDNOTES

[1] Bow River Basin Council 2005. *The 2005 Report on the State of the Bow River Basin.* Bow River Basin Council, Calgary, AB.

[2] Rosenburg *et al.* 2005. Rosenburg, D.M., P.A. Chambers, J.M. Culp, W.G. Franzin, P.A. Nelson, A.G. Salki, M.P. Stainton, R.A. Bodly, and R.W. Newbury 2005. "Nelson and Churchill River Basins". Chapter 19 in *Rivers of North America*, edited by A.C. Benke and C.E. Cushing. Elsevier Academic Press.

[3] Alberta Environment 2007a. *Current and Future Water Use in Alberta.* Prepared by AMEC Earth & Environmental. Alberta Environment. Edmonton, AB

[4] Halliday, R. and G. Faveri 2007. "The St. Mary and Milk Rivers: The 1921 Order Revisited." *Canadian Water Resources Journal.* 32(1): 75–92.

[5] International St. Mary - Milk Rivers Administrative Measures Task Force 2006. *Report to the International Joint Commission.* International Joint Commission, Washington, DC and Ottawa, ON.

[6] Alberta Environment 2006. *Approved Water Management Plan for the South Saskatchewan River Basin (Alberta)*. Alberta Environment. Edmonton, AB.

[7] Alberta Agriculture and Food 2000. *Irrigation in Alberta.* Alberta Agricuture and Food, Edmonton, AB.

[8] Glozier, N.E., R.W. Crosley, L.A. Mottle, and D.B. Donald 2004. *Water Quality and Trends for Banff and Jasper National Parks: 1973-2002.* Environment Canada, Saskatoon, SK.

[9] Bow River Basin Council 2005. *supra*

[10] Alberta Environment 2007b. *Information Synthesis and Initial Assessment of the Status and Health of Aquatic Ecosystems in Alberta.* Technical Report 278/279-01. Alberta Environment, Edmonton, AB.

[11] Alberta Environment 2007b. *ibid*

[12] Alberta Environment 2007b. *ibid*

[13] van Duin, B. and J. Garcia 2005. "Impacts of Urbanization on West Nose Creek – a Canadian Experience". *Water Science and Technology* 53(10): 237-245

[14] Alberta Environment 2006. *supra*

[15] Clipperton, G.K., C.W. Koning, A.G,H. Locke, J.M. Mahoney and B. Quazi 2003. *Instream Flow Needs Determinations for the South Saskatchewan River Basin.* Alberta Environment, Edmonton, AB.

[16] Clipperton *et al.* 2003. *ibid*

[17] Alberta Environment 2007b. *ibid*

[18] Alberta Environment 2007b. *ibid*

[19] Bow River Basin Council 2005. *supra*

[20] Rood, S.B., G.M. Samualson, J.H. Braatne, C.R. Gourley, F.M.R. Highs, and J.M Mahoney 2005. "Managing River Flows to Restore Floodplain Forests." *Frontiers in Ecology and the Environment.* 3:193-201.

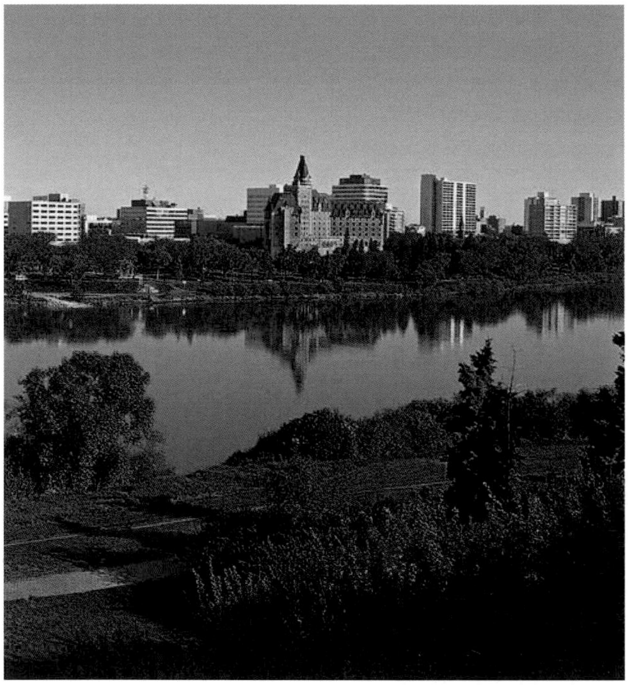

CHAPTER NINE

THE SOUTH SASKATCHEWAN RIVER SUB-BASIN

Figure 9.1. *The South Saskatchewan River Sub-basin*

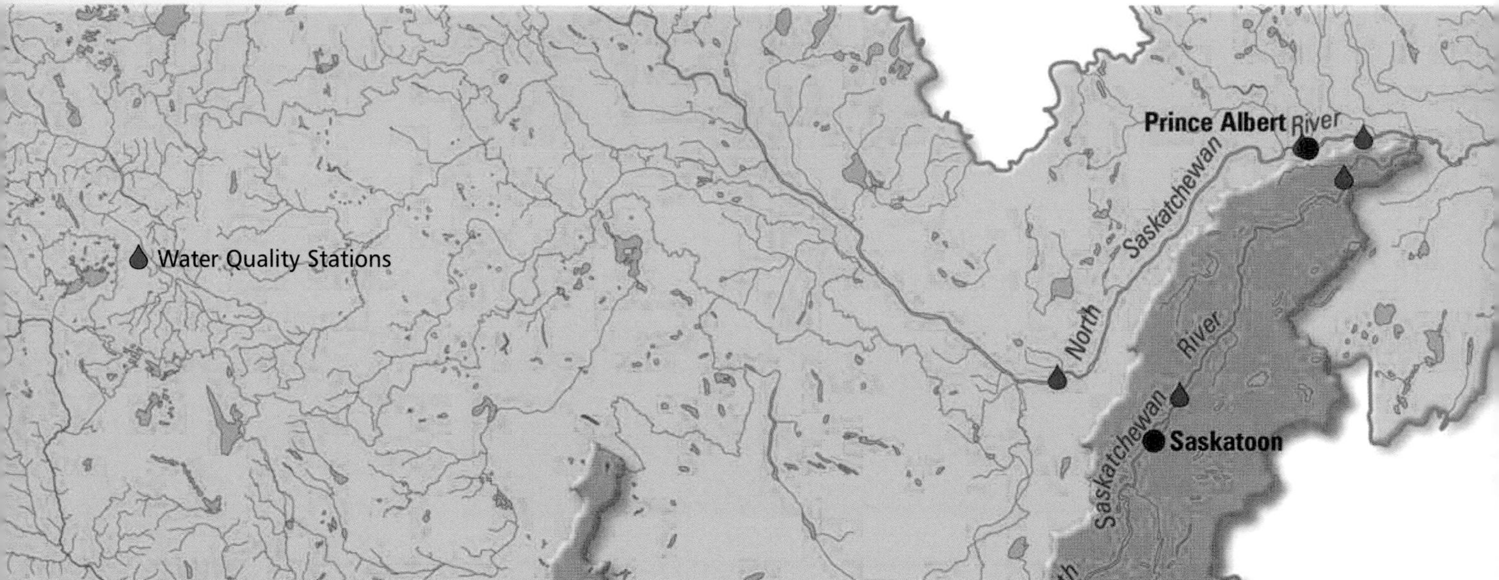

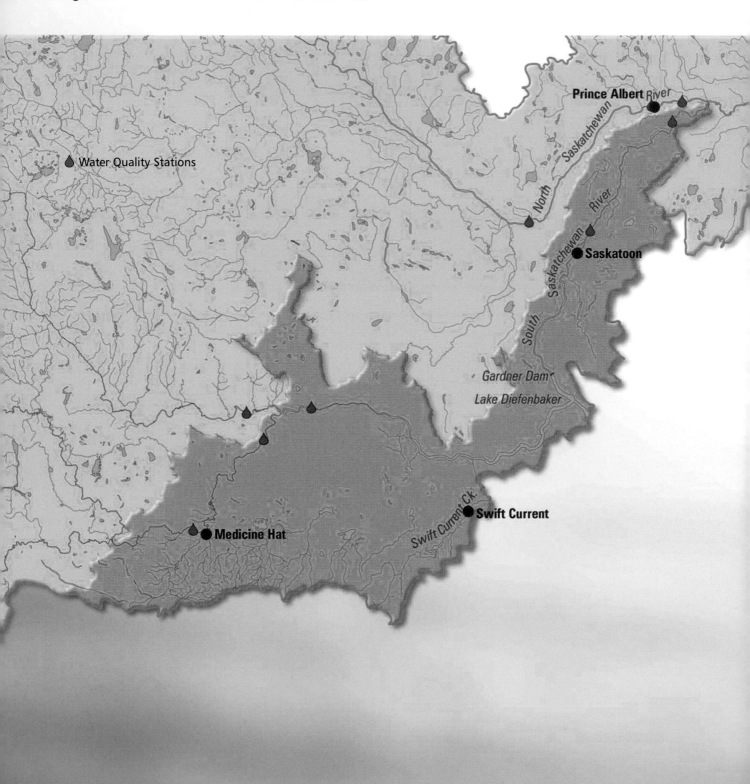

CHAPTER NINE
THE SOUTH SASKATCHEWAN RIVER SUB-BASIN

The South Saskatchewan River sub-basin, shown in Figure 9.1, originates in mixed grasslands at the confluence of the Bow and Oldman rivers. The sub-basin comprises the river reach of the South Saskatchewan River and its associated drainage area. The South Saskatchewan River flows east to Medicine Hat then turns northeast to the Saskatchewan boundary. The river receives some tributary flow from small streams rising on the slopes of the Cypress Hills. Shortly after crossing the interprovincial boundary, it is joined by the Red Deer River.

Sub-basin Summary

Characteristics
- plains to boreal transition
- length – 998 km
- gross drainage area – 59 508 km^2
- effective drainage area – 13 277 km^2

Hydrology
- reliable flow on mainstem
- ephemeral flow on plains tributaries
- highly regulated

Water Quality
- good for mainstem
- poor for plains tributaries

Biodiversity
- riparian zones healthy, but problems
- loss of wetlands

Key Issues
- interprovincial water apportionment
- municipal effluents
- agricultural point sources
- drought
- shoreline erosion, Lake Diefenbaker

Flowing east, the river enters Lake Diefenbaker – a 225 km-long reservoir created by the Gardiner Dam and the Qu'Appelle Dam. This large reservoir has a surface area of 430 km^2 and a shoreline length of 800 km. The river flows northeast from the reservoir through moist mixed grasslands to Saskatoon. It continues through aspen parkland and the boreal plain to its confluence with the North Saskatchewan River.

Open grasslands dominate the upper portion of the sub-basin. Downstream of Gardiner Dam, aspen trees can be found around wetlands, in coulees, and in the river valley. The lower portion of the sub-basin contains aspen groves and natural grasslands, which then give way to continuous forest. The soils of the sub-basin are highly diversified but generally can be considered brown or dark brown. Weakly developed soils along the river valley form significant sand-dune complexes upstream of Lake Diefenbaker. Ninety percent of the sub-basin is taken up by cropland or rangeland, either native or improved pasture.[1]

The sub-basin has a population of about 300 000, with major centres being Medicine Hat, Swift Current and Saskatoon. Canadian Forces Base Suffield – a 2690 km^2 block of unplowed grassland – is on the west bank of the river in Alberta; some of the base extends into the Red Deer River sub-basin. There are four First Nations reserves downstream of Lake Diefenbaker.

Protected areas in this sub-basin include a portion of Cypress Hills Interprovincial Park, three provincial parks on Lake Diefenbaker, two provincial parks downstream of the Lake, and Batoche National Historic Site. A 458 km^2 portion of Canadian Forces Base Suffield is a National Wildlife Area. The riparian woodland of the South Saskatchewan River from the confluence with the Red Deer River to the Leader area is the largest area of deciduous woodland between the Cypress Hills and the aspen parkland. The sub-basin is dotted with small wetlands. PFRA data reveal 121 452 ha of existing wetlands.[2] The lower sub-basin from Outlook to The Forks contains much of the sub-basin's wetland area. There are also significant waterfowl nesting and staging areas in the sub-basin.

Economic activity includes a broad mix of agricultural activities, with both irrigated and dryland crop production, and livestock. Near Saskatoon, there are several dairy operations, while the upper half of the sub-basin features oil and gas production. There are seven potash mines that depend on the sub-basin's water supply, although one is not in the sub-basin.

HYDROLOGY

The South Saskatchewan River sub-basin extends from the confluence of the Bow and Oldman rivers at an elevation of 740 m to its confluence with the North Saskatchewan River at an elevation of 400 m. As described in Chapter Four, almost 90 percent of the flow in the river originates in the water towers. The river channel serves simply as a conveyance channel. There are no large tributaries in over 1000 km of river channel. Tributary inflow in this sub-basin accounts for only two percent of the annual flow, one-half of that being the flow from Swift Current Creek. Some of the small streams originating on the slopes of the Cypress Hills do not join the South Saskatchewan River. They flow into Many Island Lake – a terminal lake. Of the 59 508 km^2 surface area of this sub-basin, only 13 277 km^2 contribute to flow in a median year. The annual hydrograph is typical of the mountain-fed streams of the Saskatchewan River basin: that is, it rises to a June peak because of snowmelt runoff from the mountains.

The annual precipitation through most of this sub-basin ranges from 300 to 350 mm, although it increases to over 400 mm in the boreal transition zone near the confluence with the North Saskatchewan River. About 75 percent of annual precipitation falls as rain, with most of that occurring in May through August. These spring and summer rains contribute little to runoff on the plains. Spring snowmelt drives the plains runoff. Figure 9.2 shows the typical annual hydrograph for Swift Current Creek. The annual runoff produced by the prairie streams is highly variable and unreliable.

Flows entering the South Saskatchewan River sub-basin have been modified by upstream dams and diversions. Within Saskatchewan, the flow of the South Saskatchewan River is significantly modified by Lake Diefenbaker. This large reservoir, completed in 1967, can store more water than all the reservoirs in Alberta combined. The total storage is 9.4 million cubic decameters of water, more than the median annual flow of the river. The live, or usable, storage of the reservoir is 4.3 million cubic decameters. This storage is greater than the combined live storage of all upstream reservoirs. At the time of construction, Lake Diefenbaker was the largest constructed lake in Canada. Gardiner Dam is one of the largest earth-filled dams in the world.

Lake Diefenbaker is operated on an annual cycle, capturing mountain runoff and releasing it during the remainder of the year. Water stored in the reservoir is used for municipal and industrial water needs, irrigation, recreation, hydroelectric generation, and maintenance of downstream flows. The reservoir also provides some flood control for downstream

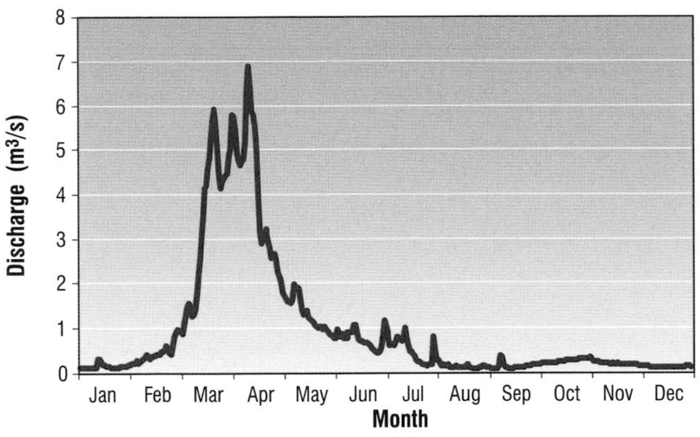

Figure 9.2. Swift Current Creek – Average Daily Flows.

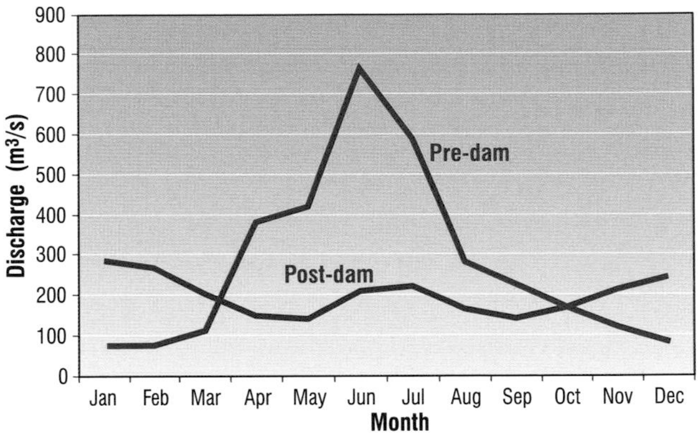

Figure 9.3. Effects of River Regulation Downstream of Gardiner Dam.

communities. Because of hydroelectric installations at Gardiner Dam and downstream on the Saskatchewan River, water is released to meet peak power demands, especially in the winter. The natural hydrograph of the river has therefore been significantly altered as shown in Figure 9.3. Winter flows have increased, which aids assimilation of municipal effluent at Saskatoon. Spring flushing flows are almost entirely absent and overall flow volumes are depleted by upstream diversions. Within this sub-basin, the flows of Swift Current Creek have also been modified by dams and diversions.

Reservoir capacity is affected by sediment inflows, particularly during spring runoff, and by shoreline erosion. These processes may affect the live storage of the reservoir or the unusable storage, known as the dead storage. In the case of Lake Diefenbaker, over a 15-year period following construction, live storage decreased by 1.5 percent. This is made up of a one percent loss from delta formation at the upper end of the reservoir and a half percent loss from shoreline erosion and slumping. Sediments flowing into the reservoir come from the South Saskatchewan River itself; the contribution from Swift Current Creek is negligible.[3]

The effects of climate change on water availability in the South Saskatchewan River have been examined. The climate in 2080 is expected to be warmer and wetter but, for reasons identified in Chapter 12, this does not necessarily lead to increased water supplies. The best estimate of inflow to Lake Diefenbaker for 2080 is for an 8.5 percent reduction in annual inflow. The uncertainty band is wide, however, with the range in inflow values being

"The Greatest Marine Disaster in the History of Saskatoon"

Steamboats rarely used the South Saskatchewan River because the shallow waters made for unreliable service. Not to be deterred, the Medicine Hat hotelier and Scottish nobleman Horatio Ross commissioned a new boat in 1906-07 to connect the newly completed railway at Medicine Hat to points downstream. The sternwheeler, the *S.S. City of Medicine Hat*, was 40 m long and had a draft of only 0.6 m.

On June 7, 1908 the boat proceeded downstream during the high water and tricky currents of the spring flood. It cleared the Grand Trunk Railway Bridge at Saskatoon and was gingerly attempting the passage under the Canadian Northern Railway Bridge when its rudder and sternwheel became entangled in a submerged telegraph line. The captain lost control and the ship drifted downstream striking the pier of the Traffic Bridge. The ship rode up the pier and wrecked. All on board but the ship's engineer clambered on to the bridge. He took to the water and swam to shore downstream. Some remnants of the wreck have been recovered recently.

+8 percent to -22 percent.[4] There is some evidence of declining trends in naturalized flows in the latter half of the 20th Century.[5]

The Water Survey of Canada and the Saskatchewan Watershed Authority monitor streamflows at 24 gauging stations and water levels at 13 stations in this sub-basin. The work is carried out under agreements between Environment Canada and Alberta Environment, and between Environment Canada and the Saskatchewan Watershed Authority.

WATER USE

The licensed water allocation in the South Saskatchewan sub-basin is 1 419 730 dam^3 from surface water and 18 995 dam^3 from groundwater. Most of the licences pertain to the portion of the sub-basin in Saskatchewan. Some 45 percent of that province's population depends on the river for daily needs.[6] For this reach, water consumption in Saskatchewan is ten times greater than consumption in Alberta. Figure 9.4 shows the distribution of water licences from surface water and the actual water consumption, compared to the median annual naturalized flow.

There are some unusual licences that account for the atypical distribution of licences shown in Figure 9.4. The largest single water licence is for the Queen Elizabeth thermal power generating station at Saskatoon. Although the licence is for 427 108 dam^3, the station rarely withdraws more than 75 000 dam^3. Of that, about five percent is consumed. Medicine Hat holds a licence of 162 820 dam^3 for municipal purposes, but much of that water is used as cooling water for a city-owned thermal generating station.[7] As is the case for Saskatoon, consumption is low.

Another large licence in this reach relates to evaporation from Lake Diefenbaker. An annual allotment of 184 143 dam^3 is identified to replace evaporative losses from the reservoir. This reflects the difference between precipitation directly on the lake and evaporation in a typical year, which is about 270 000 dam^3. This annual evaporative loss is similar to the annual consumptive surface water uses in the North Saskatchewan River sub-basin combined.

Water is diverted from Lake Diefenbaker to the Qu'Appelle River at the Qu'Appelle Dam. The licensed diversion, based on the total of individual downstream licences, is about 165 000 dam^3 a year; the average

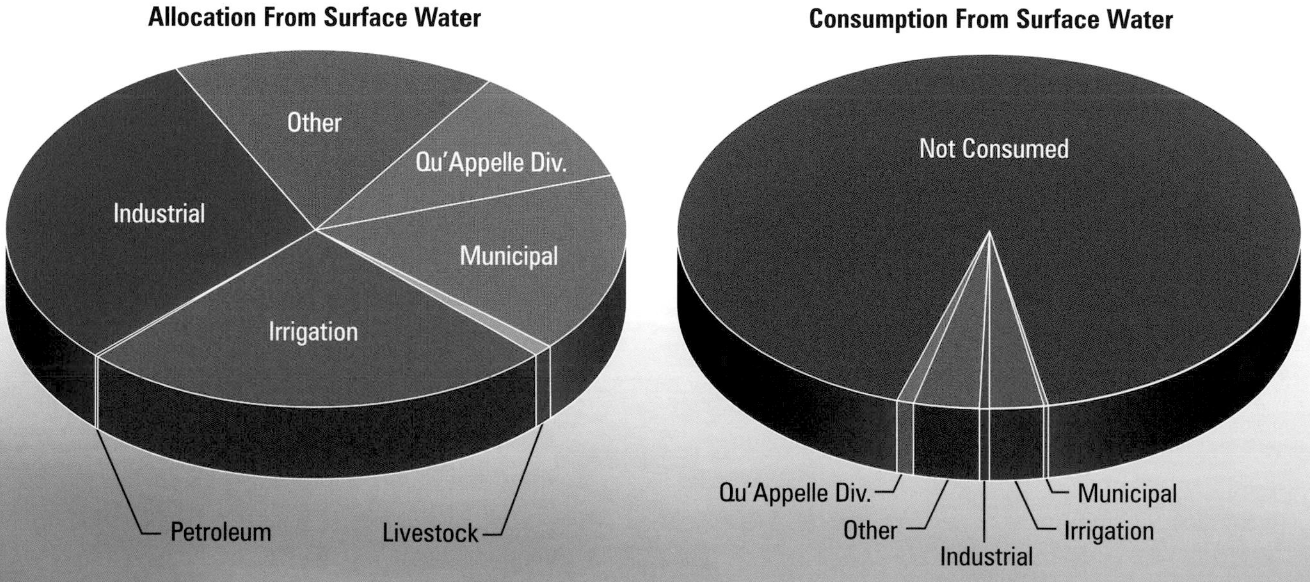

Figure 9.4. Water Allocation and Water Consumption from Surface Water.

quantity diverted annually over the last 20 years is 78 840 dam^3. The annual diversion depends on water needs. The water is used for municipal, industrial, agricultural, and lake stabilization purposes; none of it returns to the Saskatchewan River basin. This diversion represents a loss to the South Saskatchewan sub-basin and is treated as a consumptive use in this chapter. In fact, not all of the water diverted is consumed; some of it reaches Lake Winnipeg by way of the Assiniboine and Red rivers.

The largest conventional water consumption in the sub-basin is irrigated agriculture, with needs met almost exclusively from surface water. The Ross Creek Irrigation District is the only irrigation district in Alberta supplied by the South Saskatchewan River. The St. Mary Irrigation District upstream of Medicine Hat is supplied from headworks in the Bow-Oldman sub-basin. In Saskatchewan, 12 irrigation districts depend on water from Lake Diefenbaker, as listed in Table 9.1. One of these is the 1427 km^2 South Saskatchewan Irrigation District near Outlook. Three are outside the sub-basin but are supplied by the Qu'Appelle Diversion. Two districts draw water directly from the South Saskatchewan River.[8] There are also private irrigators in the sub-basin. The irrigated areas in the South Saskatchewan sub-basin and the Bow and Oldman sub-basins together comprise almost three-quarters of the irrigated area in Canada.[9]

The water needs of the South Saskatchewan Irrigation District are met by the Saskatoon Southeast Water Supply System (SSEWS). This diversion from Lake Diefenbaker consists of a lift station, five reservoirs, and connecting channels. The system also supplies private irrigators, stabilizes the level of Blackstrap Lake for recreation, supports waterfowl habitat, and meets municipal and industrial needs. Although some of the diverted water reaches Last Mountain Lake in the Qu'Appelle River system, most of the water is used within the South Saskatchewan sub-basin.

Table 9.1. Irrigation Districts Supplied by the South Saskatchewan River.

Source	Name	Irrigated Land (km^2)
South Saskatchewan River	Ross Creek	4
South Saskatchewan River	Chesterfield	–
Lake Diefenbaker	South Saskatchewan River	1427
Lake Diefenbaker	Riverhurst	40
Lake Diefenbaker	Lucky Lake	37
Lake Diefenbaker	Macrorie	10
Lake Diefenbaker	Grainland	9
Lake Diefenbaker	Miry Creek	6
Lake Diefenbaker	River Lake	4
Lake Diefenbaker	Thunder Creek	6
Lake Diefenbaker	Saskatoon Southeast Water Supply	71
Qu'Appelle Diversion	Brownlee	8
Qu'Appelle Diversion	Disley South and West	4
Qu'Appelle Diversion	Rocky Lake	9
South Saskatchewan River	Moon Lake	6

Industrial users in the sub-basin consist primarily of fertilizer plants in Alberta and potash mines and a fertilizer plant in Saskatchewan. These facilities use surface water and consume much of the water they withdraw. The most significant consumptive use of groundwater in the sub-basin is in petroleum-related operations in Saskatchewan. Overall, water use by the petroleum sector is relatively small.

As in other parts of the Saskatchewan River basin, water allocations for municipal purposes are large but since most of the water withdrawn is returned to the river, consumption is small. Allocations for municipal purposes tend to be from surface water, although there are some Saskatchewan communities such as Kindersley that depend on groundwater. The town of Bow Island draws its water from the Oldman River.

Other water allocations include water management and habitat enhancement. The previously-mentioned allocation for Lake Diefenbaker evaporation dominates this use. All of the water allocated is consumed.

The breakdowns of water licences and water consumption in the South Saskatchewan River sub-basin discussed previously are for the sub-basin from the confluence of the Bow and Oldman rivers to The Forks. Figure 9.5 shows the licensed allocation and water consumption for the larger sub-basin including the Bow and Oldman river sub-basins. The dominant role of irrigated agriculture is evident. Surface water consumption represents a significant portion of the naturalized median annual flow of the river.

The flows in the South Saskatchewan River are subject to the PPWB *Master Agreement on Apportionment*. Because of relatively high water use in the Bow and Oldman sub-basins, the apportionment of the South Saskatchewan River at the interprovincial boundary is more complex than for other streams subject to the Master Agreement.

In general, the Master Agreement requires that Alberta pass on 50 percent of the natural flow originating in the province to Saskatchewan. In the case of the South Saskatchewan River, however, Alberta has the right to divert or store 2 589 000 dam^3, irrespective of the natural flow in the river. This is in recognition of the extensive water developments, primarily irrigation, that had taken place in Alberta prior to the signing of the Master Agreement in 1969. In doing so, Alberta cannot

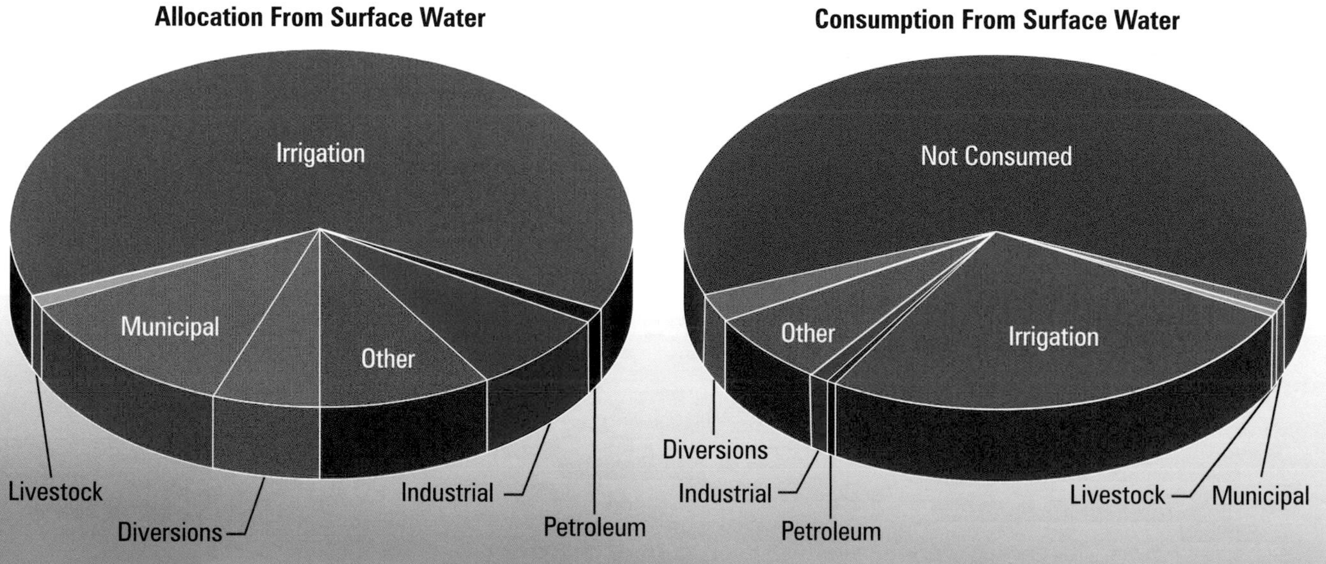

Figure 9.5. Surface Water Allocation and Consumption for the South Saskatchewan River Sub-basin plus the Bow and Oldman River Sub-basins.

reduce the flow in the South Saskatchewan River upstream of its confluence with the Red Deer River below 42.5 m^3/s, except when one-half the naturalized flow would be less than this. If the annual flow is distributed evenly enough that the 42.5 m^3/s flow criterion is met, Alberta and Saskatchewan would share the annual volume equally up to 2 680 000 dam^3. Once the naturalized flow has exceeded that amount, Alberta could use its prior allocation of 2 589 000 dam^3. When the natural flow exceeds 5 180 000 dam^3, any additional flow would be divided equally between the two provinces. The median annual flow in the South Saskatchewan River below the junction with the Red Deer River is 8 661 000 dam^3.

Despite the complexity of these arrangements, there are only four years since 1912 when Alberta's prior allocation provision would have been triggered. In all other years, Saskatchewan would have received at least 50 percent of the natural flow.[10] On average Alberta delivers 78 percent of the combined natural flow of the South Saskatchewan and Red Deer rivers to Saskatchewan.[11]

WATER QUALITY

The quality of the South Saskatchewan River upstream of the confluence with the Red Deer River is governed almost exclusively by the quantity and quality of the waters received from the Bow and Oldman sub-basins. Overall reductions in flow caused by upstream regulation and diversion, combined with the effects of land management practices, influence water quality. Water quality in the South Saskatchewan River reflects the cumulative impacts on the upper sub-basin. The quality is generally good, as is the water quality from the confluence with the Red Deer River to Lake Diefenbaker. Effluents from Medicine Hat do not influence overall water quality. Long-term monitoring at the PPWB site near the Saskatchewan boundary does not indicate any trends in water quality.[12]

Water quality in Lake Diefenbaker is considered good, as is water quality downstream to the confluence with the North Saskatchewan River. Water quality trends are few, although there is some decrease in nutrient loadings. In the channels carrying irrigation return flows, water quality is typically degraded by

A Naval Battle on the South Saskatchewan River

In 1885, the sternwheeler *S.S. Northcote*, a veteran of North Saskatchewan River shipping, was called into service during the Battle of Batoche. The boat had overwintered in Medicine Hat. In mid-April it left Saskatchewan Landing with troops, a field hospital, munitions, provisions and forage. The boat towed two supply barges. Water levels were low and the boat ran aground several times before reaching Major-General Middleton's camp upstream of Batoche village on May 5.

At 06:00 am on May 7, the *Northcote*, carrying 50 riflemen and still towing two barges, pulled anchor and turned downstream as part of a coordinated attack. She tooted her whistle at 07:40 as a signal to Middleton and continued downstream. Coming abreast of Batoche, the boat came under heavy fire and was unable to anchor because of the strong current produced by now rising water levels.

Seizing the moment, the Métis commander, Gabriel Dumont, ordered the ferry cables lowered. The cables caught the *Northcote's* smokestacks, at the same time taking out the boat's signalling whistle. The boat was unable to set its anchor until it had drifted some distance downstream. The civilian crew declined to rejoin the battle. The boat continued further downstream to take on supplies. It finally returned to Batoche on May 12 to find that Middleton had seized the village earlier that day. The *Northcote's* engagement in the only naval battle on the prairies had lasted a little over an hour. The boat was beached at Cumberland House towards the end of 1886 and never sailed again.

Table 9.2. Long Term Water Quality Monitoring Locations.

Stream	Location	Agency	Remarks
South Saskatchewan River	Medicine Hat	Alberta Environment	Upstream of Medicine Hat
South Saskatchewan River	at Highway 41	Environment Canada	PPWB site near Saskatchewan boundary
South Saskatchewan River	at Leader	Saskatchewan Environment	Upstream of Lake Diefenbaker
South Saskatchewan River	Clarkboro East	Saskatchewan Environment	Downstream of Saskatoon
South Saskatchewan River	Clarkboro West	Saskatchewan Environment	Downstream of Saskatoon
South Saskatchewan River	at Muskoday	Saskatchewan Environment	near confluence with North Saskatchewan River

nutrients, sediments and pesticides. Saskatoon treats its municipal effluent to tertiary standards, including nutrient reduction; nonetheless, the city increases nutrient levels downstream.

Under the PPWB Master Agreement, except in drought conditions, Alberta is required to maintain a flow of at least 42.5 m^3/s in the Saskatchewan River channel. Alberta has a water conservation flow objective of 42.5 m^3/s on the South Saskatchewan River and one of 10 m^3/s on the Red Deer River. Saskatchewan, in turn, is committed to releasing at least 42.5 m^3/s from Gardiner Dam. The normal summer target flow is 60 to 150 m^3/s.[13] Minimum flow in the South Saskatchewan River means the water is generally well-oxygenated and the overall good water quality is maintained.

Water quality is routinely monitored at several locations in this sub-basin, as listed in Table 9.2.

The mainstem of the South Saskatchewan River is mesotrophic. Elkwater Lake and Spruce Coulee Reservoir near the Cypress Hills are eutrophic and mesotrophic, respectively.

Monitoring data have been used to calculate water quality indices for the South Saskatchewan River, shown in Figure 9.6. PPWB maintains water quality objectives at the interprovincial boundary. These objectives are aimed at protecting all downstream water uses including aquatic life. Monitoring results are compared with the objectives quarterly. If the objectives are exceeded, a report and recommended course of action is prepared for the PPWB. The PPWB then makes a recommendation on how to resolve the problem to member agencies.

Saskatoon is the largest city in this sub-basin and can be expected to have some effect on downstream water quality. Upgraded effluent treatment has led to improved nutrient reduction in recent years. Figure 9.7 shows the water quality index upstream and downstream of the city. The effect of nutrient reduction measures since 2000 is apparent.

BIODIVERSITY AND ECOSYSTEMS

Algal biomass increases in the South Saskatchewan River moving downstream because of increased availability of plant nutrients. The dominant form is filamentous green algae, which tends to peak in the summer. Rooted aquatic plants, macrophytes, tend to increase sharply below municipal effluent outfalls.[14]

Midges and mayflies dominate invertebrate populations of the South Saskatchewan River. Populations tend to be related to food resources and the temperature regime. Benthic invertebrate populations tend to be low and vary considerably from year to year, depending on river flow.

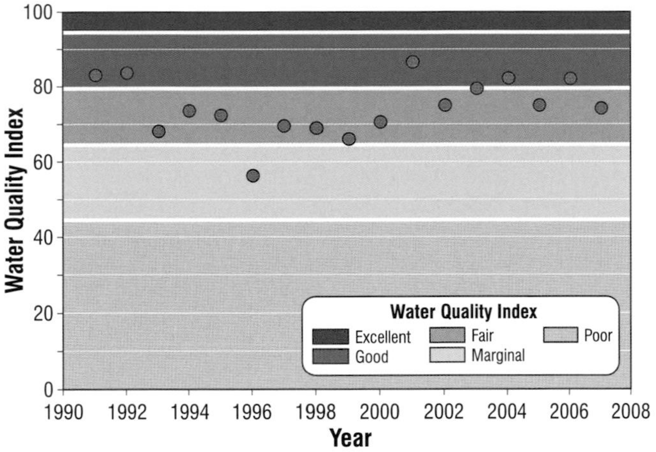

Figure 9.6. Water Quality Index at Interprovincial Boundary.

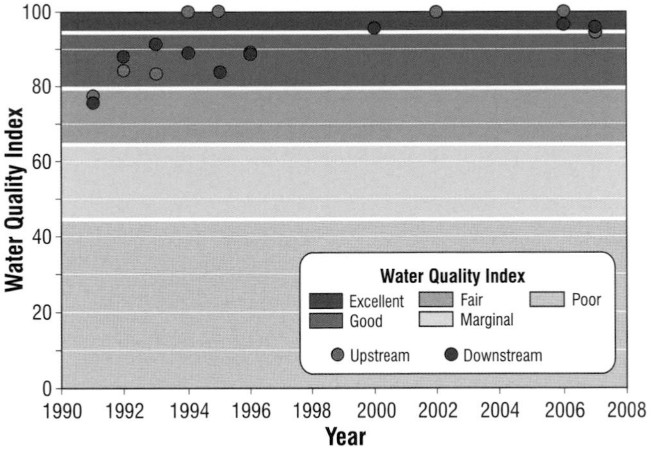

Figure 9.7. Water Quality Index Upstream and Downstream of Saskatoon.

The fish species found in the South Saskatchewan River and its tributaries are shown in Table 9.3. Upstream of Lake Diefenbaker goldeye, sauger, walleye, and lake sturgeon are common.[15] Well-developed riffle, run and pool sequences provide habitat.[16] The bed of the South Saskatchewan River tends to be composed of gravel, sand and silt. The development of Lake Diefenbaker destroyed the riverine fishery but a highly productive reservoir fishery has evolved. Fish species in the reservoir include walleye, northern pike, sauger, burbot, goldeye, whitefish, rainbow trout, and lake sturgeon. There is also a rainbow trout farm on the lake. The reach from Gardiner Dam to Saskatoon is not particularly good fish habitat, in part because of effects of the dam. The river's thermal regime has been altered and nutrient content is low. Riffle habitat is rare. From Saskatoon to the confluence with the North Saskatchewan River, pike, walleye, and several species of sucker dominate.

Table 9.3. Fish Species of the South Saskatchewan River.

Species Type	Common Name
Coldwater Species ** Introduced Species*	Brown Trout* Mountain Whitefish
Coolwater Species	Goldeye Mooneye Lake Whitefish Northern Pike Sauger Walleye Yellow Perch Burbot Lake Sturgeon
Non-game Species	Emerald Shiner Fathead Minnow Flathead Chub Lake Chub Longnose Dace River Shiner Spottail Shiner Longnose Sucker Quillback Shorthead Redhorse Silver Redhorse Spoonhead Sculpin Trout-Perch White Sucker

There is no longer a commercial fishery on Lake Diefenbaker. An aquaculture operation produces almost one million kilograms of rainbow trout annually.

Alberta's conservation flows and riparian flows downstream from Lake Diefenbaker help sustain ecosystems on the main stem of the South Saskatchewan River: that is, water quality, fish habitat, and riparian vegetation are supported. Elsewhere in the sub-basin riparian zones tend to be healthy, but with problems. Invasive species such as purple loosestrife are a concern. These riparian zones provide important habitat for nesting and staging of waterfowl. Galloway Bay on Lake Diefenbaker is an internationally recognized staging area on the mid-continent flyway.

Shoreline erosion around Lake Diefenbaker has led to broad sand and gravel beaches that provide nesting habitat for the endangered piping plover – a medium-sized shorebird, similar in appearance to the common killdeer. Lake Diefenbaker has frequently supported the largest single-site population of piping plover in the world. The lake is considered a globally significant Important Bird Area, and may be designated a Western Hemisphere Shorebird Reserve Network site. The piping plover is very susceptible to water level increases during the critical nesting and brooding season. Rapid increases can flood nests and reduce brooding habitat. Reservoir operations have been modified to the extent possible to accommodate the piping plover.[17, 18] During high flows in 2005, when rapid reservoir rises were forecast, eggs were taken from nests and hatched, and the young birds were later released to the lake. This practice has been repeated, when required, in subsequent years.

ENDNOTES

1 Saskatchewan Watershed Authority 2007. *Background Report, South Saskatchewan River Watershed*. Saskatchewan Watershed Authority. Regina, SK.

2 Martz, L., R. Armstrong and E. Pietroniro 2007. *Climate Change and Water, SSRB Final Technical Report*, L. Martz, J. Bruneau and J.T. Rolfe eds., Saskatoon, SK.

3 Yuzyk, T.R. 1983. *Lake Diefenbaker, Saskatchewan: A Case Study of Reservoir Sedimentation*. Water Survey of Canada, Environment Canada. Ottawa, ON.

4 Martz, L., J. Bruneau and J.T. Rolfe (eds.) 2007. *Climate Change and Water. SSRB Final Technical Report*. University of Saskatchewan, Saskatoon, SK.

5 Bruce, J.P., H. Martin, P. Colucci, G. McBean, J. McDougall, D. Shrubsole, J. Whalley, R. Halliday, M. Alden, L. Mortsch and B. Mills 2003. *Climate Change Impacts on Boundary and Transboundary Water Management*. A Climate Change Action Fund Project. Project A458/402, Natural Resources Canada, Ottawa.

6 Johnson, D. and J. Gerhart 2005. "Source Water Protection and Water Management in the South Saskatchewan River Basin in Saskatchewan." *Proceedings, Canadian Water Resources Association National Conference*, Banff, AB.

7 Alberta Environment 2007a. *Current and Future Water Use in Alberta*. Prepared by AMEC Earth & Environmental. Alberta Environment. Edmonton, AB.

8 Saskatchewan Watershed Authority 2007. *supra.*

9 Brace Centre 2005. *Analysis of Issues Constraining Irrigation Development in Canada and the Role of Agriculture and Agri-Food Canada*. Brace Centre for Water Resources Management, McGill University, Montreal, QC.

10 Saskatchewan Watershed Authority 2007. *supra.*

11 Johnson and Gerhart 2005. *supra.*

12 Alberta Environment 2007b. *Information Synthesis and Initial Assessment of the Status and Health of Aquatic Ecosystems in Alberta*. Technical Report 278/279-01. Alberta Environment, Edmonton, AB.

13 Johnson and Gerhart 2005. *supra.*

14 Rosenburg *et al.* 2005. Rosenburg, D.M., P.A. Chambers, J.M. Culp, W.G. Franzin, P.A. Nelson, A.G. Salki, M.P. Stainton, R.A. Bodly, and R.W. Newbury 2005. "Nelson and Churchill River Basins". Chapter 19 in *Rivers of North America*, edited by A.C. Benke and C.E. Cushing. Elsevier Academic Press.

15 Saskatchewan Watershed Authority 2007. supra

16 Rosenburg *et al.* 2005. *supra.*

17 Environment Canada and Saskatchewan Water Corporation 1991. *Canada-Saskatchewan South Saskatchewan River Basin Study, Final Report*. Environment Canada, Regina and Saskatchewan Water Corporation, Moose Jaw, SK

18 Johnson and Gerhart 2005. *supra.*

CHAPTER TEN
THE SASKATCHEWAN RIVER SUB-BASIN

Figure 10.1. *The Saskatchewan River Sub-basin*

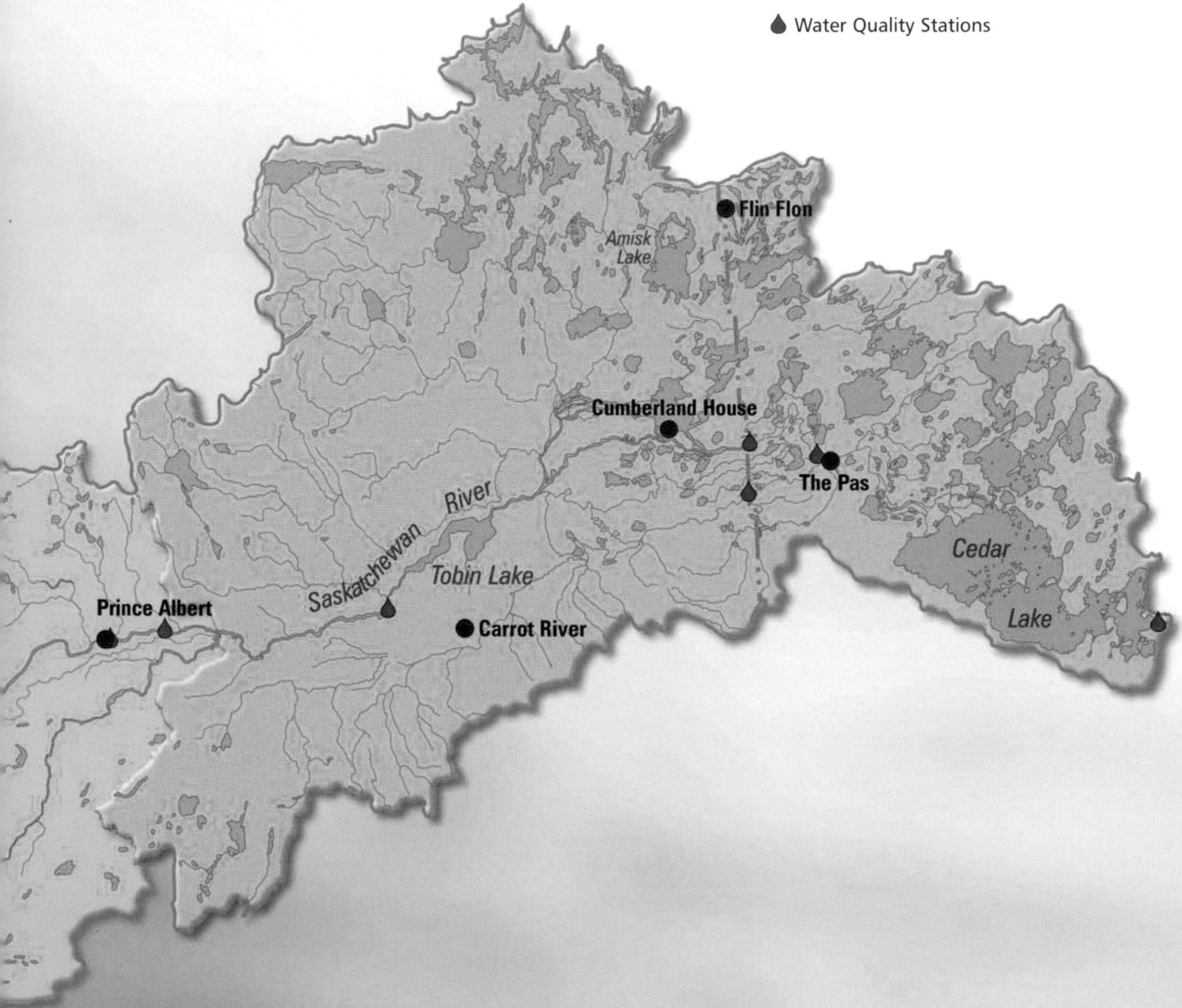

CHAPTER TEN
THE SASKATCHEWAN RIVER SUB-BASIN

The Saskatchewan River sub-basin begins at the confluence of the North and South Saskatchewan rivers (The Forks), southeast of Prince Albert, Saskatchewan. The sub-basin extends generally eastward through Nipawin and Cumberland House to Manitoba. Crossing into Manitoba, it continues east through The Pas and joins Lake Winnipeg near Grand Rapids. The most significant northern tributaries of the Saskatchewan River are the Torch and Sturgeon-Weir rivers. The Torch River rises on the boreal plain and flows east to Cumberland Lake.

Sub-basin Summary

Characteristics
- boreal transition to boreal shield
- length – 642 km
- gross drainage area – 81 680 km^2
- effective drainage area – 76 384 km^2
- Saskatchewan River Delta – 190 km-long, 9950 km^2 in area

Hydrology
- reliable flow on mainstem and on tributaries
- regulated mainstem

Water Quality
- - fair to good throughout the sub-basin

Biodiversity
- riparian zones healthy
- drying of Saskatchewan River Delta affects waterfowl
- lake sturgeon important

Key Issues
- ecological integrity of the Saskatchewan River Delta
- effects of river regulation
- nutrient and contaminant loading to Lake Winnipeg

The Carrot River, the most significant southern tributary, rises in the boreal plain and flows east to join the Saskatchewan River near The Pas. Some tributaries of the Carrot River rise in the Pasquia Hills, as does the Pasquia River, which also joins the Saskatchewan River near The Pas. Figure 10.1 shows the entire sub-basin.

The Saskatchewan River sub-basin lies almost entirely in the boreal plain ecozone. A portion of the northern headwaters of the sub-basin lies in the boreal shield.

The upper portion of the sub-basin, from The Forks to the head of the Saskatchewan River Delta, is a hummocky to kettled plain, covered in glacial till and relatively level lacustrine deposits. This part of the sub-basin forms the transition from farmland to deciduous forest. There are a large number of small lakes, ponds, and sloughs occupying shallow depressions.[1]

Trembling aspen with secondary quantities of balsam poplar, along with a thick understory, is the predominant vegetation. White spruce and balsam fir also occur. Poorly drained sites are usually covered with sedges, willow, some black spruce, and tamarack.

The lower sub-basin is a relatively flat, low-lying region occupied for the most part by the Saskatchewan River Delta. This area is covered almost entirely by level to ridged glacial till, lacustrine silts and clays, and extensive peat deposits. There are local areas of limestone bedrock outcroppings. The cold and poorly drained fens and bogs are covered with tamarack and black spruce. The mixed deciduous and coniferous forest is composed of stands of trembling aspen and balsam poplar. White and black spruce and balsam fir also occur.

The Pasquia Hills in the southern portion of the sub-basin are up to 400 m higher than the surrounding land. Stands of trembling aspen and balsam poplar with white and black spruce, and balsam fir are most

Gateway to the West

Samuel Hearne established Cumberland House on behalf of the Hudson's Bay Company (HBC) in 1774 close to its current location. This is the basin's oldest permanent community. It was noted at the time that the Northwest Company (NWC), based in Montreal, had already established a fort near what is now known as Cumberland Lake. The competitive atmosphere existing between the HBC and NWC apparently led Samuel Hearne to name his post Cumberland House, fully knowing how the predominantly Scottish NWC would react to naming a post after the English duke who had slaughtered so many of Scots, following the Battle of Culloden in 1746.

Charles John Brydges, Land Commissioner for the Hudson's Bay Company, travelled in the area in 1879 and noted:

> *I left Prince Albert in a York Boat on the 3rd September, and came down the Saskatchewan. Between the forks of that river and Lake Winnipeg, the country on the north side is useless for agricultural purposes. It is rocky land full of lakes and muskeg. In fact I may say that there is no good land between Prince Albert and Grand Rapids on the north side, altho' it is rather better between the former place and Fort a la Corne than below the latter. From La Corne downwards the country to the north is very largely under water, and from what Indians and our own people have told me, this bad land extends very far indeed to the north.*

In 1880, Mr Brydges described 'the improvements necessary to make a satisfactory navigation of the Saskatchewan River.' He requested:

- An additional steamer of large capacity, which the HBC would build if other improvements would be made by the Government of Canada, specifically
  - Piers at the head of two rapids south of Cedar Lake called *Roche Rouge* and *Demi-Charge*.
  - The building of wing dams and removal of boulders at Cole's [La Colle] Falls and Tobin's Rapids. 'At both these places great risk is run and in low water it is quite impossible to ascend them.'
  - He further notes 'I think you are aware that we already have a tramway at Grand Rapids (built in 1877), enabling us to carry passengers and freight round the rapid, upwards of four miles in length and which is quite impassable for any steamer.'

Steamboat activity on the Saskatchewan River was significant by the early 1880s. The *Northcote* and *Lily* were already steaming the Saskatchewan when, in 1882, they were joined by the *Marquis*, the *Manitoba* and the *North West*. Each of these last three vessels had to be warped up the Grand Rapids cataract (a 26 m drop in 7 km), a task that took close to two weeks for all three boats to ascend successfully.

abundant. Poorly drained fens and bogs are covered with tamarack and black spruce. The hills contain deep valleys and a large number of small lakes, ponds, and sloughs occupying shallow depressions. The hills are covered by glacial and lacustrine deposits. Well-drained gray soils are dominant.

The Precambrian Shield in the northern part of the sub-basin consists of ridged to hummocky bedrock, forming sloping uplands and lowlands. Local relief is rarely more than 25 m. Exposed bedrock is common. Soils composed of glacial and lacustrine deposits tend to be thin, although there are some deep peatlands. Lakes of various sizes drain into the river systems. Predominant vegetation consists of closed stands of black spruce and jack pine, shrubs and a ground cover of mosses and lichens. Discontinuous permafrost is common.

Agricultural land-use in the basin includes production of grains, oilseeds and forage in the lower basin and near The Pas. Pulpwood, local saw-log forestry, and a dimension lumber industry operate in the eastern part of the sub-basin. Other land-use activities include trapping, hunting, fishing and tourism. The lower Saskatchewan River Delta also supports commercial fishing. Principal communities in the sub-basin are Flin Flon and The Pas. There are many First Nations reserves and several Métis communities in the sub-basin.

Few protected lands are found within this sub-basin. Clearwater Provincial Park and wildlife areas in the lower Saskatchewan River Delta are examples. The sub-basin also has some privately held conservation lands.

SASKATCHEWAN RIVER DELTA

The Saskatchewan River Delta, shown in Figure 10.2, is the largest inland freshwater delta in North America. The delta was formed during the retreat of glacial Lake Agassiz some 10 000 years ago. A portion of the 6800 km^2 upper delta is commonly called the Cumberland Delta or Cumberland Marsh. This part of the delta is now dominated by a single channel and has forested natural levees. Separated by The Pas moraine, the 3150 km^2 lower delta is much younger and still behaves like a delta. That is, its sediment front is actively advancing into Cedar Lake.

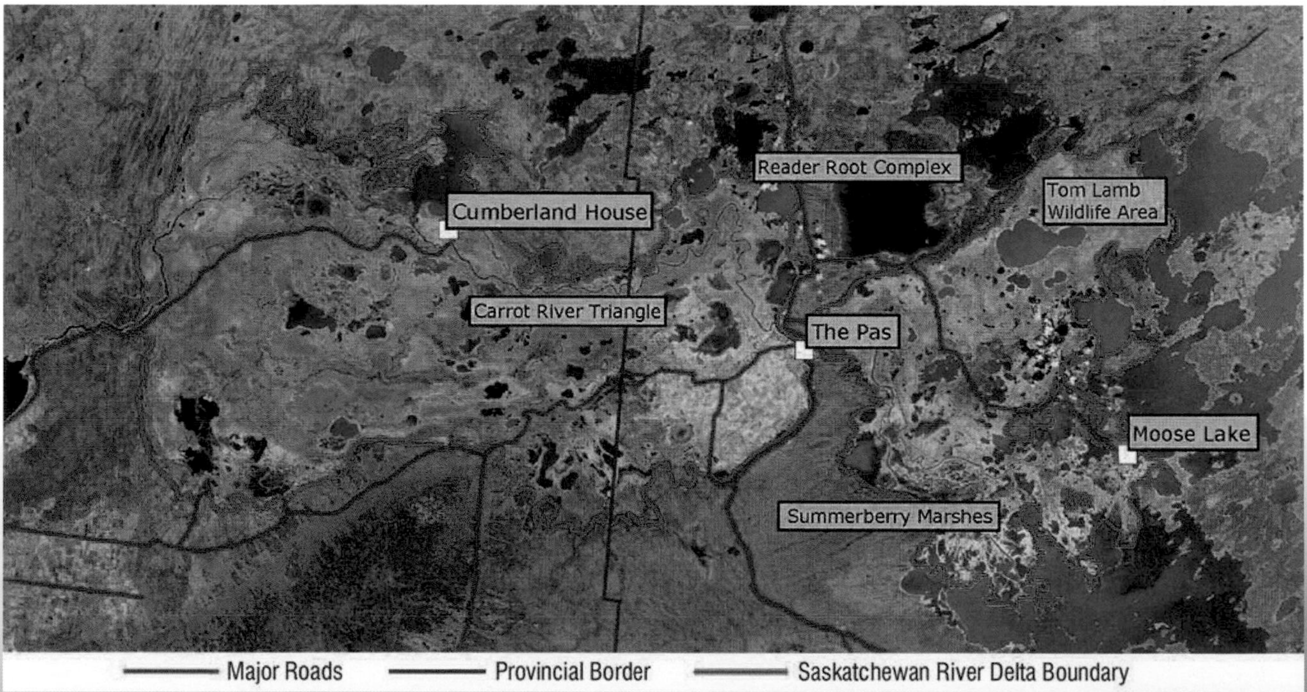

Figure 10.2. The Saskatchewan River Delta *(courtesy of Ducks Unlimited Canada).*

Since the earliest days of human settlement, people have been drawn to the Saskatchewan River Delta. The fertile plain of the delta supports numerous species of water birds, in addition to many mammals and fish species. The Saskatchewan River was the principal transportation corridor for aboriginal people and served as the means by which European explorers entered the interior plains. The delta featured a number of Cree in-gathering sites, where people came together in the spring or fall. Some of these sites had been used for thousands of years, and early fur traders established their posts near these sites. The Pas is one of many such settlements. Cumberland House is not.

The Saskatchewan River Delta has been modified by both natural and human-induced change. A massive change took place in the 1870s, when the course of Saskatchewan River switched from its dominant channel and established a new one, a process known as avulsion. Prior to this time, the Saskatchewan River flowed in a well-developed meandering channel that passed just slightly south of Cumberland Lake. The avulsion, which local knowledge attributes to an ice jam, directed the river and its sediment load north, towards the Torch River. The Torch River channel was unable to contain the new flow. The river now passes through a complex network of new channels and flows into Cumberland Lake. It then leaves the lake, through three channels, to rejoin the Saskatchewan River. Over time, the river will undoubtedly re-establish a single dominant meandering channel.[2] The channel changes brought about by the avulsion eventually put an end to the sternwheeler riverboat traffic on the Saskatchewan River, as the boats were unable to pass through the new channels.[3] The new trans-continental railways doubtless played a part as well.[4]

The avulsion significantly changed the character of Cumberland Lake. The surface area has been reduced from 219 km^2 to 171 km^2, largely on account of delta development at the entrance of the new channels. Although the lakebed has not changed, the lake has decreased in depth from six metres, according to Hudson's Bay Company records, to two metres in the 1950s, to one or two metres today. The physical and ecological changes in the delta are of great concern to local residents. In addition to the effects of the avulsion, the delta has also been affected by completion of the E.B. Campbell Dam in 1963, approximately 30 km upstream of the delta, and Grand Rapids Dam in 1968, downstream of the delta.

The E.B. Campbell Dam, which created Tobin Lake, has modified the flow, sediment and thermal regimes downstream on the Saskatchewan River. The delta is also affected by the lingering effects of the 1870s avulsion and by changing climate. One possible effect of river regulation on the delta is that reduced ice jam frequency may have decreased frequency of overtopping of the natural levees of the channels and flooding of perched basins. This could lead to drying out of the delta.[5] As the delta becomes drier, foliage becomes denser and less suitable for some species. Increased fire suppression also plays a role in vegetative change. Changes in climate variables could lead to drying, although an analysis of evaporation at The Pas shows no trend over several decades.[6] Effects of the dam on the lake sturgeon population of the Saskatchewan River are important, as the sturgeon spawn in the tailrace of the dam.

The Grand Rapids Dam raised water levels on Cedar Lake in the lower delta by 3.5 to 4 m. The reservoir affects up to 2500 km^2 of the lower delta. While the reservoir can affect habitat for water birds and mammals, the key concern is with fish habitat. The commercial fishery on Cedar Lake is the only such fishery in the entire Saskatchewan basin. After a decline in the 1980s, the fishery has now rebounded.

Many control structures and other works have been constructed in the Saskatchewan River Delta. The original structures were built to enhance muskrat populations and to aid forestry transportation. (Water levels in the delta were very low in the 1930s.) By far the most significant works have been those carried out by Ducks Unlimited Canada (DUC) since the 1940s to improve habitat for waterfowl populations. The delta represents DUC's largest single project in North America. The delta is recognized as a Canadian

Important Bird Area of global significance. More than half of the delta consists of wetlands. It is a significant waterfowl-producing area and is critically important to migrating waterfowl and other water birds. Within the Cumberland Marsh – the upper delta – there are now 42 control structures, 60 km of dikes and 90 km of channels regulating water levels in a 1300 km^2 area. There are a further 57 structures in the lower delta aimed at enhancing habitat in three wildlife management areas.[7] Since these works were constructed for waterfowl and muskrat enhancement, fish passage facilities are a relatively recent addition. The muskrat harvest has plummeted since the 1950s, but beaver numbers have increased. There were almost no beaver in the lower delta in the 1940s.

Outside of The Pas, First Nations represent about 20 percent of the population of the delta and a further 78 percent are Métis. Many depend on the hunting, fishing and trapping opportunities provided by the delta. Their long occupancy of the delta and the traditional values imbued in specific species such as lake sturgeon are culturally important.

The first grain grown in the Saskatchewan River basin was in 1751 near The Pas in the lower delta. Within the lower delta is a 550 km^2 area lying between the Carrot and Pasquia rivers, reclaimed for agriculture in the mid-1950s. The project was developed by PFRA with construction of four polders, perimeter dikes, and pumping stations. The land is seeded to grains and oilseeds and yields exceed the provincial average, except in wet years. About 300 km^2 is currently in production.

The delta also has significant forestry resources, discussed in the following section.

FORESTRY

Forestry has a long history in this sub-basin. There has been a forestry industry in the region surrounding The Pas for generations. Similarly, in the eastern part of Saskatchewan, we find a considerable history. Current conditions in the forestry industry, however, have led to a halting of all industrial forestry activities within the Saskatchewan portion of the sub-basin.

Saskatchewan manages its forestry activity through:

- A Forest Management Agreement (FMA) that confers harvesting rights for a specific timber volume for a defined area. This is a 20-year agreement.
- Forest Management Plans (FMPs), which are 20-year plans renewable every ten years. These plans include the licensee's strategies for inventory, harvesting, renewal and access.
- Annual Operating Plans (AOPs), which are five-year plans updated annually detailing how the FMP will be implemented.
- In addition, Saskatchewan also may issue Term Supply Licences (TSLs) that allow harvest of specific products for up to ten years, or a Forest Product Permit that has effect for less than a year but would allow for the harvest of a specific non-timber forest product.[8]

Saskatchewan crown lands, including provincial forests, are subject to an ecosystem-based, comprehensive-planning process. Plans emerging from that process provide a framework for integrated resources management and use. Two land-use planning areas split the Saskatchewan River Delta – the Pasquia/Porcupine to the south and the Amisk-Atik to the north.

Manitoba has divided its forested areas into forest management units (FMU). Each FMU consists of common forest conditions that can be managed as one unit. The forest inventory within each FMU is analyzed to determine annual allowable cuts of softwood and hardwood species. Although there are several FMUs in the sub-basin in Manitoba, harvesting is administered under a single forest management licence, issued to Tolko Industries. Manitoba manages its forestry activity through:

- A Forestry Management Licence (FML) that is granted for a period of not more than 20 years but may be renewed. The FML describes the land upon which trees may be cut, the volume that may be harvested, and other terms and conditions. There are three FMLs in Manitoba, one of which (that held by Tolko) includes land in the Saskatchewan River basin.

- The holders of an FML are obliged to prepare long-term (20-year) Forest Management Plans (FMPs).
- Annual Operating Plans (AOPs) describing in detail how the licence holder will implement their FMP for the current year and providing a broader understanding of their activities for the following two years.[9]

While lumber markets have plummeted and the Tolko sawmill at The Pas is operating only one shift, five days a week (about 40% of the level of production in the mill as recently as two years ago), production of sack kraft paper continues at a high level. Tolko's annual allowable cut (AAC) in the part of the Saskatchewan River basin they are licensed to utilize is approximately 350 000 m^3. Of that, Tolko regularly harvests only about two-thirds of the AAC. Given that conditions are such that timber volume is about 130 m^3/ha, Tolko is harvesting approximately 2700 ha annually.

The boreal forests of the sub-basin are subject to natural disturbances such as fire, disease, and insects that are part of a healthy forest ecosystem. Indeed, fire is the principal factor controlling species composition and age structure of the forest. Insects are part of the food chain for many bird species, while disease outbreaks are part of the natural evolution of the forest. As forests become more intensively used and harvested, there is a desire to suppress outbreaks of fire, insects or disease. This, in turn, may affect the long-term health of forest ecosystems. Increasing efforts are made to harvest timber so that patterns of natural disturbance are mimicked. Increasingly, fires that do not threaten human settlements may be allowed to burn.

HYDROLOGY

The Saskatchewan River reach extends 642 km from The Forks at elevation 400 m to Lake Winnipeg at elevation 217 m. Unlike the upstream parts of the Saskatchewan River basin, this reach exhibits the conventional pattern of tributaries joining larger streams, like a randomly branching pattern of tree roots. More than 90 percent of the sub-basin contributes to streamflow in a median year. Non-contributory surface drainage, for the most part, lies in boreal wetlands. Boreal fens have considerable sub-surface flow and may indeed contribute flow to the surface water system.

The annual precipitation throughout much of this sub-basin ranges from 425 mm in the west to 450 mm in the east. Precipitation is a little higher in the northern Precambrian Shield portion of the sub-basin. About three-quarters of the annual precipitation falls as rain, with much of that occurring in June through September.

Runoff in the sub-basin is driven by snowmelt and precipitation during the snowmelt period. Figure 10.3 shows the hydrograph of naturalized flows for the Saskatchewan River at The Pas. The peak flow occurs in July as a result of mountain runoff, but the effects of earlier runoff from the tributaries of the lower sub-basin are evident. The figure also shows the median recorded flows since 1965. The differences between recorded flow and naturalized flow demonstrates the cumulative effects of river regulation and surface water consumption in the entire Saskatchewan basin upstream of The Pas. Note, for example, that the recorded plains runoff peak in May is typically higher than the July mountain runoff peak.

One of the major tributaries, the Carrot River, originates in the Waterhen Marsh in east central Saskatchewan and flows northeast for about 400 km, to join the Saskatchewan River near The Pas. (The Waterhen Marsh project, initiated in 1938, was the first Ducks Unlimited Canada project in Saskatchewan). Its largest tributaries include the Leather River, and Goosehunting, Melfort and Burntout creeks. Figure 10.4 provides an example of the median monthly tributary inflow for the Carrot River. Tributary flows for this sub-basin typically peak in May.

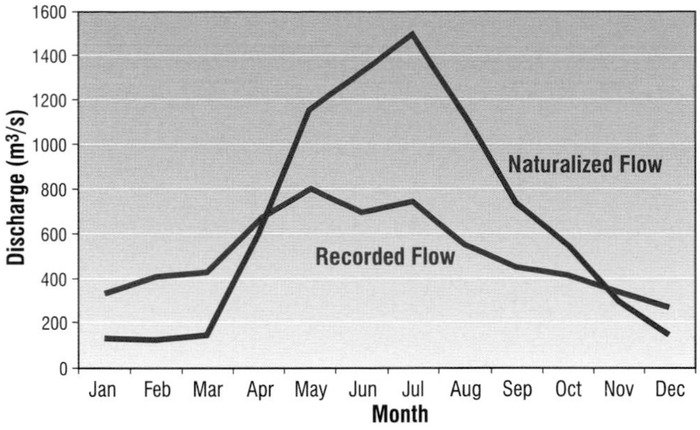

Figure 10.3. Median Monthly Naturalized Flow for Saskatchewan River at The Pas.

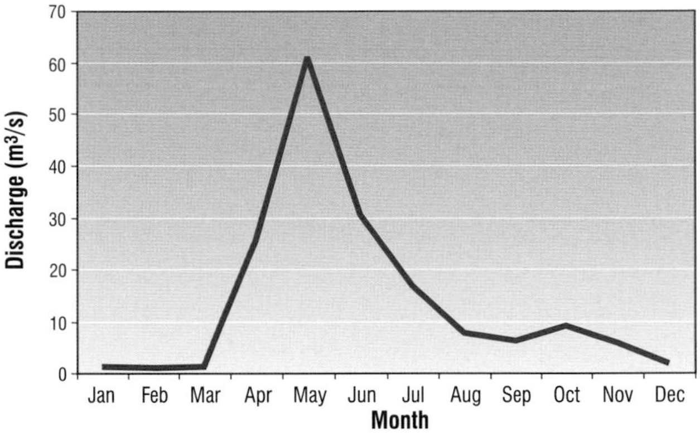

Figure 10.4. An Example of Tributary Flow for the Carrot River.

Although tributary flows in this sub-basin tend to be more reliable than flows of the plains tributaries further upstream, they are still not as reliable as the flows of the mainstem.

The mainstem of the Saskatchewan River is highly regulated. The North Saskatchewan River upstream of The Forks is regulated by two projects, while the South Saskatchewan River is regulated by many projects. SaskPower's Nipawin and E.B. Campbell Generating Stations on the Saskatchewan River provide additional regulation.

At Nipawin, the Francois-Findlay Dam, commissioned in 1985, creates Codette Lake but the project is essentially a run-of-the-river facility, benefiting from upstream regulation. The E.B. Campbell Dam, commissioned in 1963, stores a significant quantity of water in Tobin Lake. The E.B. Campbell Generating Station is used to provide automatic generation control for the entire SaskPower system, by maintaining frequency and matching generation to load demands. Because of this operational characteristic of the generating station, daily water level fluctuations downstream of the dam are highly variable. In the early days of operation, flows downstream of the dam would drop to near zero on weekends. Because of concerns from downstream communities, the operating plan was changed in September 2004 to maintain a minimum flow of 75 m^3/s. Figure 10.5 shows the flow variations below this generating station.

The reservoir traps sediments as well as nutrients and contaminants bound to those sediments. Cumberland Lake, formerly a place where river sediments have been deposited, has become a source of sediments. The relatively clear water released from the reservoir leads to degradation or down-cutting of the river channel downstream. This effect extends some 40 km downstream: that is, into the Saskatchewan River Delta.

The Saskatchewan River flows are smoothed by the passage of the river through Cumberland Lake. Further downstream, just before the river joins Lake Winnipeg is Manitoba Hydro's Grand Rapids Generating Station. The station provided automatic generation control for the entire Manitoba Hydro network. This means that downstream water level fluctuations are considerable.

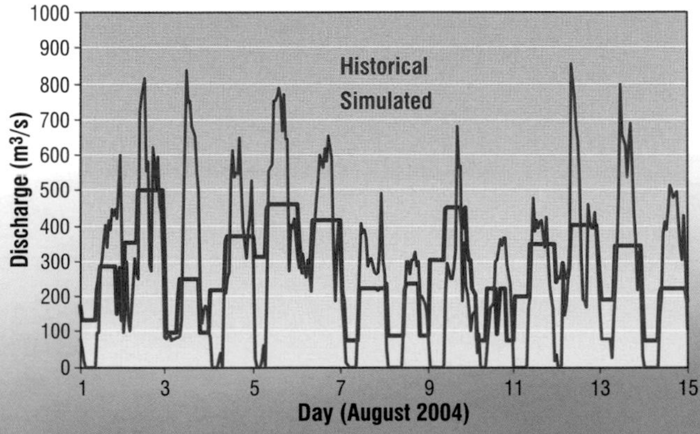

Figure 10.5. Effect of 75 m^3/s Downstream Flow Constraint at E.B. Campbell Dam.

Under most circumstances, the Grand Rapids Dam completely regulates the Saskatchewan River. The usable storage in Cedar Lake is about double that in Lake Diefenbaker although the reservoir rarely reaches it full supply level.

The Saskatchewan River has been affected significantly by river regulation and by upstream water consumption. While recorded flows have trended downward, there is no apparent trend in the naturalized flows of the river.[10] That is, the reduced flows in the river are attributable to increased water consumption, not decreased supply.

Water levels and streamflows are monitored at gauging stations in this sub-basin by the Saskatchewan Watershed Authority, Environment Canada, Manitoba Hydro and Manitoba Water Stewardship. There are 34 gauging stations, 16 of which are streamflow stations.

WATER USE

The licensed water allocation in the Saskatchewan sub-basin is 470 578 dam^3 from surface water and 9499 dam^3 from groundwater. Figure 10.6 shows the distribution of water licences from surface water. Water consumption is very low in comparison to overall supply.

Allocation From Surface Water

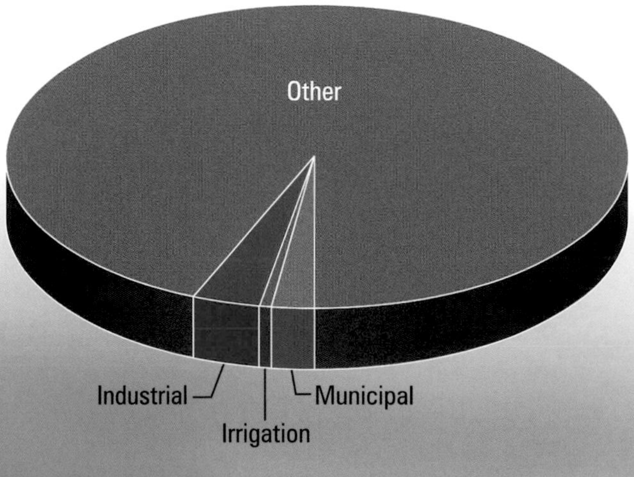

Figure 10.6. Licensed Withdrawal from Surface Water.

Roughly half of the groundwater-pumping is for drainage at the Nipawin Generating Station, and this water is returned to the Saskatchewan River. Most of the remaining groundwater allocation is for municipal purposes, and much of that also returns to surface waters.

The only significant surface water allocation – the 'other' sector in Figure 10.6 – in the Saskatchewan sub-basin is for lake stabilization and habitat enhancement. Many of the latter projects are DUC developments. The water allocated to this category is consumed by losses to groundwater or evaporation. The only significant industrial demand is for the Tolko Industries pulp and paper mill at The Pas; much of this water is consumed. Most of the water allocated to municipal purposes returns to surface water.

The flows in the Saskatchewan River are subject to the PPWB *Master Agreement on Apportionment*. The Master Agreement requires that Saskatchewan pass half of the natural flow received from Alberta to Manitoba, plus half the natural flow that originates in the basin within Saskatchewan. In practice, the quantity of water originating in Saskatchewan is small compared to that received from Alberta.
The Saskatchewan River tributaries that rise in Saskatchewan and flow across the interprovincial boundary, before joining the Saskatchewan River, are considered separately under the Master Agreement. If water uses in Saskatchewan on say, the Carrot River, became significant, the natural flow would be divided equally between Saskatchewan and Manitoba.

WATER QUALITY

Water quality is routinely monitored at several locations in this sub-basin. Table 10.1 lists these locations.

Long-term monitoring data have been used to produce an overall water quality index for the Saskatchewan River at the interprovincial boundary. This index is shown in Figure 10.7. Water quality at this location is strongly influenced by flow conditions, as there are few point sources of contamination. High flow conditions,

Table 10.1. Long Term Water Quality Monitoring Locations.

Stream	Location	Agency	Remarks
Saskatchewan River	at interprovincial boundary	Environment Canada	PPWB site near Manitoba boundary
Saskatchewan River	at The Pas	Manitoba Water Stewardship	upstream of Carrot River
Cedar Lake		Manitoba Water Stewardship	
Saskatchewan River	at Grand Rapids	Manitoba Water Stewardship	
Carrot River	near Turnberry	Environment Canada	near Manitoba boundary

for example, may result in contributions of water usually retained in the marshes of the Saskatchewan River Delta to the flow of the Saskatchewan River. These waters tend to have higher concentrations of mineral, nutrients, and total dissolved solids.

Water quality in the mainstem of the Saskatchewan River is generally fair to good. Phosphorus and nitrogen are nutrients of considerable concern, with respect to water quality in Lake Winnipeg. Although trends in nitrogen concentrations have not been analyzed, those for phosphorus concentrations along the Saskatchewan River system have been produced. There has been no significant trend in phosphorus concentrations along the mainstem of the Saskatchewan River during the period 1974 through 1999. However, there was a significant increase in phosphorus concentrations in the Carrot River, near Turnberry, during that same period. The phosphorus concentrations at Grand Rapids, just before the flow enters Lake Winnipeg, tend to be lower than further upstream, suggesting phosphorus assimilation by vegetation in Summerberry Marsh and other wetlands above Cedar Lake and, particularly, retention within Cedar Lake itself. Although the concentrations of nutrients in the Saskatchewan River are not particularly high, the volume of flow means that nutrient loadings to Lake Winnipeg are still significant.

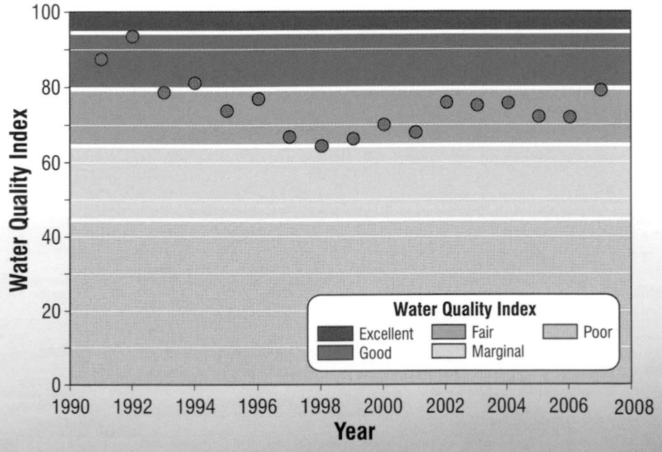

Figure 10.7. General Water Quality Index for the Saskatchewan River.

BIODIVERSITY AND ECOSYSTEMS

Although the relatively high flows of the Saskatchewan River and the small numbers of people living in this sub-basin may suggest environmental stress in the sub-basin is low, ecosystems have been altered because of river regulation. Forest harvesting has also altered the terrestrial landscape. Large mammals such as black bear and moose occur throughout the sub-basin. White-tailed deer and coyote are common in the upper sub-basin while other mammals such as wolves, lynx, and snowshoe hare occur in the lower basin. The upper sub-basin provides critical habitat for large numbers of neotropical migrant bird species, as well as ruffed grouse and waterfowl. Bird species in the lower sub-basin include raven, common loon, spruce grouse, bald eagle, gray jay, hawk owl, and waterfowl. The Saskatchewan River Delta is an enormously productive ecosystem. More than 50 plant species have been identified and 48 fish species.[11] Aquatic mammals such as beaver, muskrat, mink and otter are found throughout the delta. Water birds include ducks, geese, swans, shorebirds, grebes, terns, and gulls. Yellow rails – a species of concern – are present during the breeding season. The delta has been recognized as a globally significant Canadian Important Bird Area. This is based on population numbers of several species of waterfowl. The delta, for example, has about 10 percent of the world's population of ring-necked ducks. The upper delta is also ranked as nationally important for migratory birds, one of only two such areas in the basin.[12]

With the exception of the Saskatchewan River Delta, very little information is available concerning the algae, plants and invertebrates of the sub-basin. There are no indications that populations are unhealthy, except for effects of river regulation.

The terrestrial and aquatic ecosystems of the lower basin may be affected by acid deposition, caused by sulphur and nitrogen compounds. Fortunately, agricultural soils are not sensitive to acid deposition. Only the forested upland of the boreal shield north of the Saskatchewan River is sensitive to acid deposition and currently receives atmospheric loads that exceed critical loads.[13] Sulphur dioxide and various nitrogen oxides originating in Alberta oilsands developments, and carried eastward by prevailing winds, are the primary source of the problem. Sulphur dioxide emissions from a smelter at Flin Flon also contribute.

The main stem of the Saskatchewan River is noted for fish species such as burbot, goldeye, lake sturgeon, northern pike, perch sauger, and walleye. Tobin Lake is considered a major destination for those who seek trophy-sized pike and walleye. The commercial fishery in Cedar Lake is dependent on species such as walleye and goldeye and to a lesser extent, whitefish, sauger, and pike.

Although lake sturgeon occur throughout the North and South Saskatchewan rivers and the Saskatchewan River, its numbers have been declining and the species is considered endangered. The species is long-lived but reproduces slowly. Since sturgeon migrate up to 100 km, they are threatened by habit fragmentation from construction of dams and control structures. Mortality tends to be higher in flood years. The sturgeon population downstream of E.B. Campbell Dam is of particular interest because of long association with the people of Cumberland House and The Pas. About 3 to12 percent of the population is harvested annually by aboriginal people. Sturgeon spawn at several locations in the Saskatchewan River Delta, as well as below the dam. Fish hatcheries at Grand Rapids and Fort Qu'Appelle are used to support stocking programs.

ENDNOTES

1 Ecological Stratification Working Group 1996. *A National Ecological Framework for Canada*. Canadian Soil Information System (CanSIS), Agriculture and Agri-Food Canada, Ottawa, ON.

2 Smith, N.D., R.L. Slingerland, M. Pérez-Arlucea, and G.S. Morozova 1998. "The 1870s Avulsion of the Saskatchewan River." *Canadian Journal of Earth Sciences,* 35:453-466

3 Peel, B. 1972. *Steamboats on the Saskatchewan*. Western Producer Books, Saskatoon, SK.

4 Yee, B. 1994. "The Saskatchewan River Delta Ecosystem: Old problems, New Approaches." *Water: A Resource in Transition*. Proceedings 47th CWRA National Conference.

5 Prowse, T.D. and M. Conly 1998. "Effects of Climatic Variability and Flow Regulation on Ice-jam Flooding of a Northern Delta." *Hydrological Processes,* 12: 1589-1610.

6 Hesch, N.M. and D.H. Burn 2005. *Analysis of Trends in Evaporation – Phase 1*. Report to the Prairie Farm Rehabilitation Administration. University of Waterloo, Waterloo, ON.

7 Reader, R. 2008. "Water Control in the Saskatchewan River Delta." Saskatchewan River Delta Symposium, April 1-3, 2008, Saskatoon, SK.

8 Saskatchewan Environment – Forestry. http://www.environment.gov.sk.ca

9 Manitoba Conservation – Forestry. http://www.gov.mb.ca/conservation/forestry

10 Bruce, J.P., H. Martin, P. Colucci, G. McBean, J. McDougall, D. Shrubsole, J. Whalley, R. Halliday, M. Alden, L. Mortsch and B. Mills 2003. *Climate Change Impacts on Boundary and Transboundary Water Management*. A Climate Change Action Fund Project. Project A458/402, Natural Resources Canada, Ottawa.

11 Rosenburg *et al.* 2005. Rosenburg, D.M., P.A. Chambers, J.M. Culp, W.G. Franzin, P.A. Nelson, A.G. Salki, M.P. Stainton, R.A. Bodly, and R.W. Newbury 2005. "Nelson and Churchill River Basins". Chapter 19 in *Rivers of North America*, edited by A.C. Benke and C.E. Cushing. Elsevier Academic Press.

12 Poston, B., D. Ealey, P. Taylor, and G.B. McKeating 1990. *Priority Migratory Bird Habitats of Canada's Prairie Provinces*. Environment Canada, Edmonton, AB.

13 Aherne, J. and S.A. Watmough 2006. *Calculating Critical Loads of Acid Deposition for Forest Soils in Manitoba and Saskatchewan*. Report to the Canadian Council of Ministers of the Environment. Trent University, Peterborough, ON.

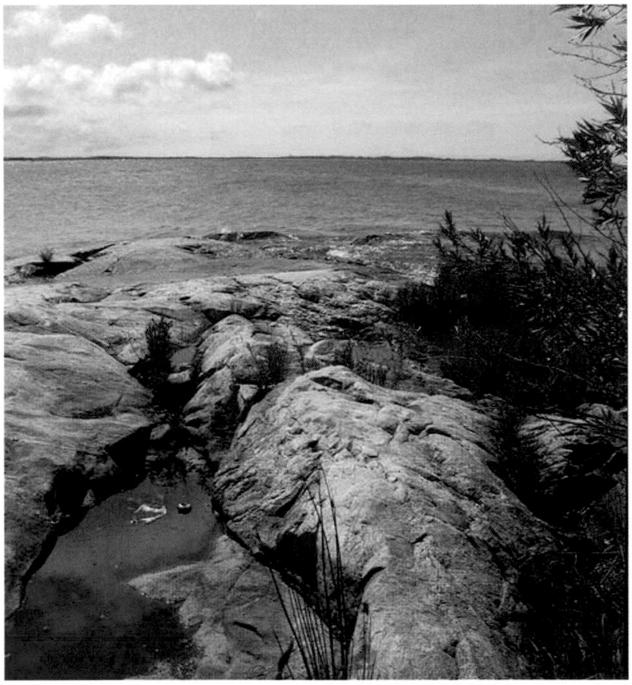

CHAPTER ELEVEN
LAKE WINNIPEG

Figure 11.1. *Lake Winnipeg Basin*

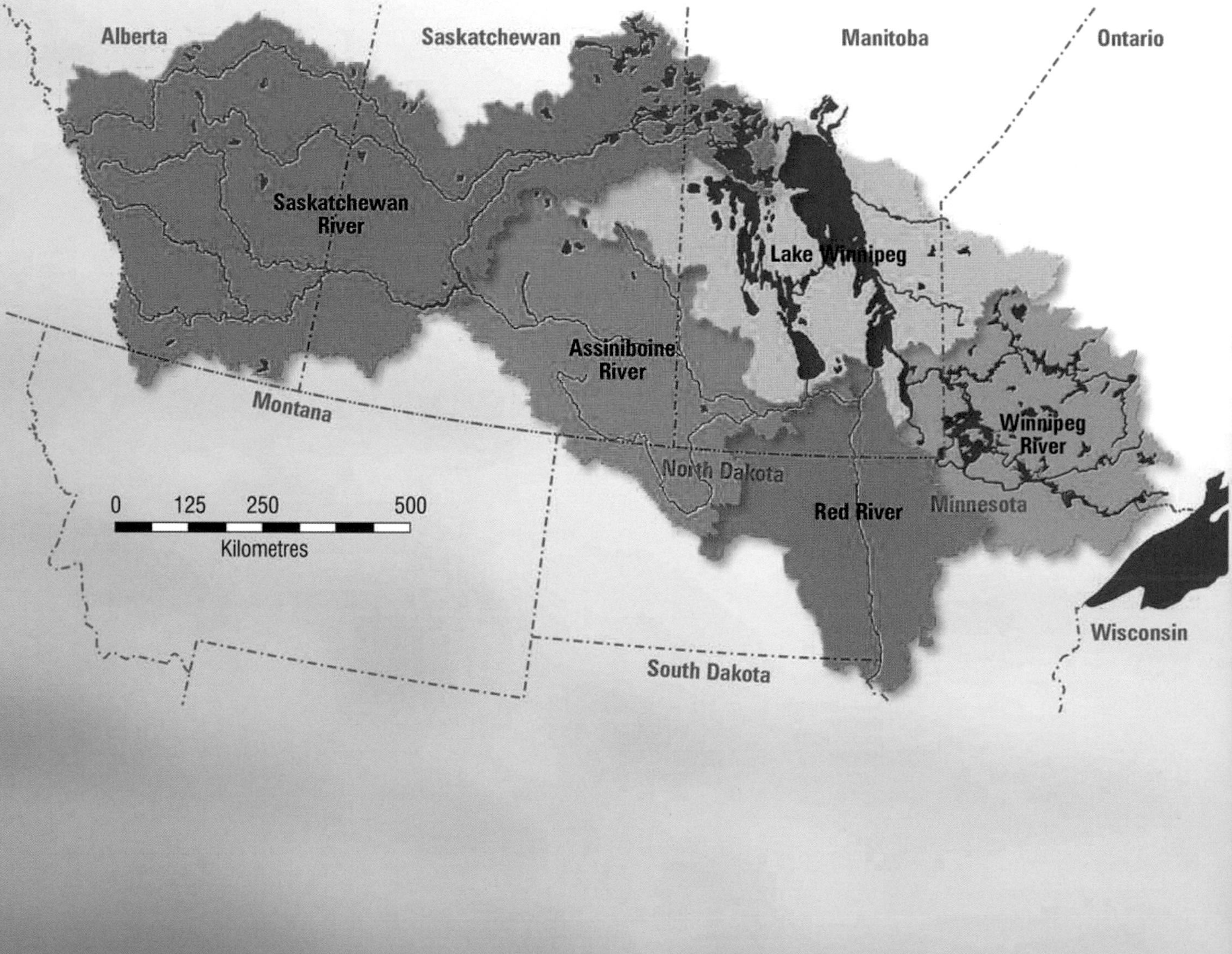

CHAPTER ELEVEN
LAKE WINNIPEG

Lake Winnipeg is made up of remnants of glacial Lake Agassiz, a lake that covered much of Manitoba and parts of other provinces and American states from about 13 000 years ago until about 8000 years ago. The northern basin of Lake Winnipeg became hydrologically detached from Lake Agassiz about 7700 years ago. The original course of the Saskatchewan River bypassed Lake Winnipeg. Instead, the river flowed toward the Nelson River and entered the receding Lake Agassiz through the Minago River.

Sub-basin Summary

Characteristics
- boreal plain to boreal shield
- world's 11th largest lake
- area – 23 750 km^2
- length – 436 km
- gross drainage area – 1 025 900 km^2

Hydrology
- reliable inflow
- average level – 217.4 m
- both inflow and outflow regulated
- regulated range in water level is smaller than natural range

Water Quality
- fair

Biodiversity
- healthy, but with problems

Key Issues
- eutrophication
- effects of lake regulation on water quality
- invasive species
- climate change
- natural shoreline erosion

At least 2500 years ago, the river breached a till barrier between what is now Cross Bay and Cedar Lake, and began flowing to Lake Winnipeg.[1] The lake drains northward to Hudson Bay through the Nelson River. Water levels are controlled by a bedrock narrows at Jenpeg, now the site of a hydroelectric dam.[2]

Lake Winnipeg is the 11th largest body of freshwater (measured by surface area) in the world, with a surface area of 23 750 km^2. The lakebed is flat and shallow with an average depth of 9.7 m in the south basin and 16 m in the larger north basin. Strong currents in the narrows between the north and south basins near Black Island have removed bottom sediments, creating the lake's maximum depth of over 60 m. It is 436 km in length and varies in width from a minimum of 2.5 km at the narrows up to 40 kilometres in the south basin, and as wide as 111 km in the north basin. The shoreline length is 1760 km. The total volume of water in the lake is small compared with its surface area. On average, the water is exchanged in the lake every three to five years. The equivalent time for Lake Superior is 191 years and for Okanagan Lake, 53 years.

The rebounding of the earth's surface due to the loss of the Laurentide ice sheet – about one kilometre thick at Lake Winnipeg – continues to occur across the whole lake. With the rebound hinged to the northeast of Lake Winnipeg, the north end of the Lake is rebounding more quickly than the south. The effect on the south basin is to increase water levels at a rate of about 200 mm each century, leading to shoreline erosion.

The length of the lake means there are significant climate variations from one end to the other. At the south end, the mean annual temperature is about 1.9°C, while toward the north end it is 0.5°C. Similarly, precipitation varies from an annual mean of 589 mm toward the south end to 483 mm toward the north end.

Water flowing into and through Lake Winnipeg serves over six million people in its drainage basin. There are a number of communities on or near the lake, including 11 First Nations communities.

THE LAKE WINNIPEG WATERSHED

The watershed encompasses 953 000 km^2 and extends from within 20 km of Lake Superior to the headwaters of the Saskatchewan River in the Rocky Mountains, and thus includes parts of four provinces and four states. (Figure 11.1) It is the second largest watershed in Canada after the Mackenzie River Basin. Lake Winnipeg's drainage basin to surface area ratio, at 40:1, is the largest of any of the great lakes of the world. This large catchment area raises concern that the loadings of nutrients, contaminants and sediments entering the lake through natural processes and human activities may be greater than the lake's natural capacity to process these materials.

Approximately 65 million hectares of agricultural land is found within the basin – 55 million of that within Canada. More than half is under crop production. At the same time, the Canadian portion of the watershed supports 17 million livestock, made up of approximately equal numbers of cattle and pigs and a few hundred thousand sheep.

Water Sources

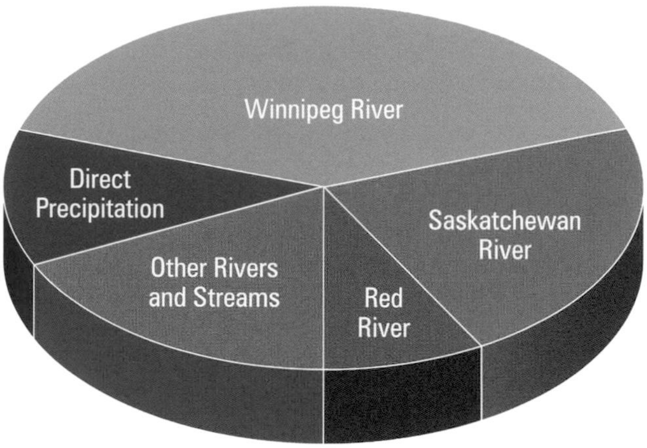

Figure 11.2. Sources of Water Entering Lake Winnipeg.

Major inflows to the lake arrive via the Winnipeg River, the Saskatchewan River and the Red River, as well as from a number of smaller rivers. Their proportions of the total inflow to the lake are shown in Figure 11.2. Approximately 45 percent of the annual inflow to Lake Winnipeg occurs during the April to July period.

Lake Winnipeg is bounded on the west by the boreal plain ecozone and on the east by the boreal shield. To the east of the lake, and for much of the lake bottom, the terrain is underlain with the hummocky and undulating bedrock of the Precambrian Shield. The dominant landcover is dense coniferous boreal forest of spruce and balsam fir; wetlands cover about 25 percent of the landscape. To the west of the lake, the flat interlake plain is underlain by sedimentary limestone. Moving from north to south, the closed boreal forest gives way to farmland.[3]

Under the lake itself, Lake Agassiz clays are up to 50 m deep in the southern basin and over 100 m deep in the northern basin. More recent sediment deposits rarely exceed 10 m in depth.[4]

LAKE CHARACTERISTICS

The water chemistry of the lake reflects the diverse geology of this huge basin and the similarly diverse human activities prevalent, not only in the Saskatchewan basin, but also in the basins of the Red River and the Winnipeg River. The Winnipeg River largely drains the Precambrian Shield to the southeast of the lake. The Saskatchewan River, both north and south branches, rises on the eastern edges of the Rocky Mountains but then flows through the prairie landscape and agricultural lands until within a few hundred kilometres of its mouth, just below Grand Rapids. The Red River and its tributaries, like the Assiniboine River, flow through prairie landscapes almost exclusively. The size of the inflows to the lake is such that the water renewal time for the south basin is about 0.4 to 0.8 years, while the renewal time for the entire lake is 2.9 to 4.3 years. The short renewal time and the shallow depth of the south basin mean that its waters are well mixed.

During the 20th century, water transparency generally increased in the north basin. This is attributed to the damming of the Saskatchewan River and the consequent removal of sediment from the Saskatchewan River inflows. Meanwhile, in the south basin, water transparency has steadily declined. Phosphorus, nitrogen and carbon concentrations have increased. Zooplankton abundance has multiplied. The north basin algal species have adjusted and more blue-green algae are now in evidence. Phosphorus retention in the lake, as a percentage of the annual loading, has tripled since 1973.

Lake Winnipeg is operated as a reservoir for generating hydroelectric energy at dams along the Nelson River, which drains Lake Winnipeg into Hudson Bay. This has the effect of stabilizing lake elevations and altering typical outflows by decreasing outflow during spring and summer and increasing outflow during fall and winter. The total range of water levels on the lake is also limited to less than half the natural and historical range. The current licensed range of Lake Winnipeg is 216.8 m to 218 m above sea level, while before regulation fluctuations were from approximately 216.3 m to 218.9 m – almost a metre and a half greater. The licensed range can be exceeded during very high or very low flow periods. The upper level was exceeded as recently as 2005.

HISTORICAL AND CURRENT RESIDENTS

Archaeological evidence indicates that native North Americans were resident in areas surrounding the lake approximately 8000 years ago. The Cree moved into the Lake Winnipeg basin about 2000 years ago, followed by the Ojibway in the 1700s. The first permanent European settlers on the shores of Lake Winnipeg were the Icelanders who arrived in 1875. The Icelanders were followed by Ukrainian, German, Hungarian, and Polish immigrants. (Although the land granted to Lord Selkirk in 1811 by the Hudson's Bay Company included part of the western shore of Lake Winnipeg, the Selkirk colonists settled primarily at the junction of the Red and Assiniboine rivers. The Hudson's Bay Company repurchased the land in the 1830s from Selkirk's estate.)

The combined permanent population of the communities around the lake is more than 23 000. In addition, there are over 10 000 cottages or seasonal residences rimming the south basin of the lake. The population is increasing in communities such as Gimli and Winnipeg Beach, which are considered good seasonal residential or holiday areas and good communities for retirement.

LAKE WINNIPEG AND THE ECONOMY

The lake has a significant influence on provincial and regional economies. Commercial fishing has been a major industry on the lake for over 125 years. The harvest typically exceeds six million kilograms a year, which makes it the largest freshwater commercial fishery in Canada, west of the Great Lakes. Walleye and whitefish are the dominant species harvested but sauger and goldeye are also an important part of the

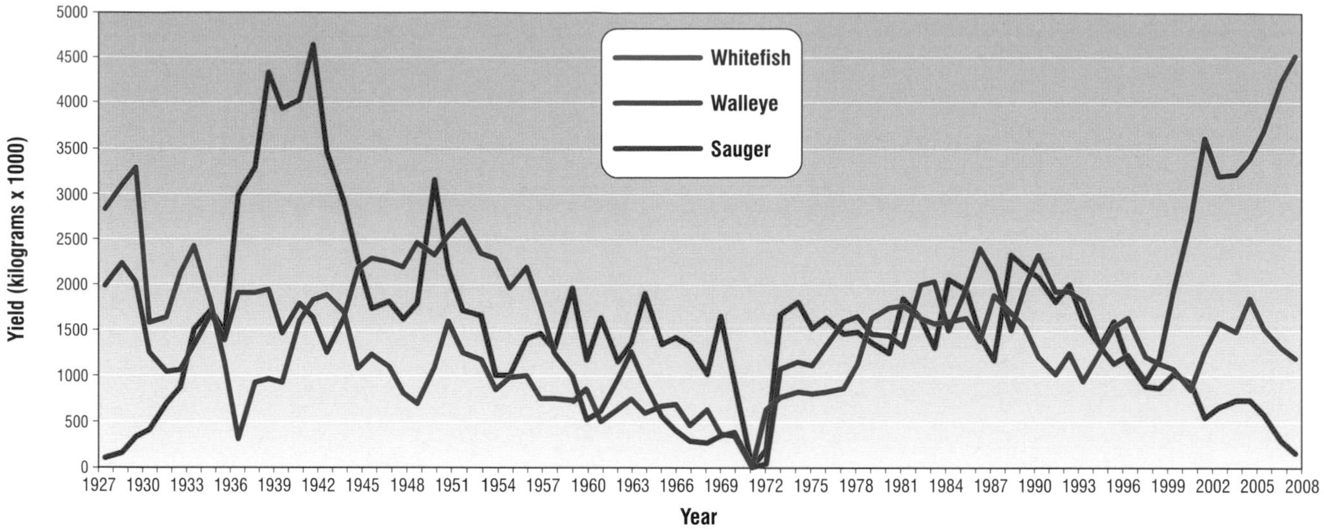

Figure 11.3. Commercial Fisheries Yield from Lake Winnipeg (Manitoba Water Stewardship).

harvest. Indeed, Lake Winnipeg's walleye harvest is the largest in North America. Annual returns are in the order of $20 million and support the livelihoods of approximately 1000 commercial fishers, 80 percent of whom are of First Nations or Métis ancestry.[5]
In addition, the fishery is a major source of income to those employed in packing, processing or transporting the fish. A plot of the commercial yield from Lake Winnipeg is shown in Figure 11.3.

Subsistence fishing is an important source of food for those living in fishing communities. Fishing is also important to the traditional life of First Nations people.

Significant income is generated from recreation and tourism around the south basin of the lake. There are eight provincial parks. Grand Beach and Winnipeg Beach are two of the busiest, often with a combined half a million visits per year. Fifteen harbours provide berthing for commercial and recreational craft. The largest, Gimli, has a capacity of 220 boats. Recreation and tourism expenditures are in the range of $110 million a year. Recreational fishing on the Red and Winnipeg rivers, close to Lake Winnipeg, is estimated at about $17 million of direct expenditures per year.

Manitoba Hydro's use of Lake Winnipeg as a reservoir helps the crown corporation to generate several hundred million dollars in energy export sales each year. Regulation of flows out of the lake assists Manitoba Hydro to optimize power generation in the large hydroelectric generating stations downstream on the Nelson River.

CHALLENGES AND SOLUTIONS FOR LAKE WINNIPEG

From a water quality perspective, Lake Winnipeg is in crisis. Nutrient loading and invasive species are particular challenges, although the lake is vulnerable to other water quality threats.

Nutrients

Phosphorus and nitrogen inputs to Lake Winnipeg have been climbing, resulting in significant algal blooms in both basins. In fact, the lake is identified as the most eutrophic of the world's major lakes. The environmental consequence of this situation is major, and deterioration of the lake's condition can be expected to have a similar effect on local and downstream economies.

The impacts of eutrophication can include:

- Changes to the water quality in the lake
- Changes in the numbers and types of organisms in the lake
- Reduction in dissolved oxygen leading to fish kills and reductions in other species
- Release of toxins harmful to either or both aquatic species and human health.

Nutrient inflow concentrations have been examined, with the following findings:

- A significant increase in median concentrations of total phosphorus and total nitrogen in the Red River at Selkirk for the period 1978 to 1999 inclusive. In addition, the annual flows to Lake Winnipeg from the Red River during the last decade have been the highest in almost 90 years of record.
- A significant increase in median concentrations of total phosphorus for the period 1972 to1999 inclusive for the Winnipeg River measured at Pointe du Bois.
- No significant trend in total phosphorus concentrations in the Saskatchewan River below Grand Rapids for the period 1973 to 1997 inclusive.[6]

The increased inflow of nutrients is linked to human activities, including use of household cleaning products, run-off from urban residential and commercial properties, municipal sewage, particularly from communities where tertiary treatment is not implemented, livestock manure, use of commercial or synthetic fertilizers, and other land management practices, such as drainage, which hasten the flow of water off the land. The decrease of wetlands on the agricultural landscape also leads to faster run-off from snowmelt and rainfall, and, consequentially, greater movement of soil and nutrients off the landscape. Wetland restoration can play a role in reducing nutrient runoff. The occurrence, intensity and extent of algal blooms may be exacerbated by climate change. Higher air temperatures will lead to greater warming of the lake, while increased evaporation will cause changes in the concentrations of nutrients in the water.

Blooms of blue-green algae clog fishing nets and water intakes, and the related toxins are harmful or fatal to various life forms in the lake. Effects of the algal blooms include changes in fish species and quantities of species available for harvesting, and reduced species diversity.

Interaction of three factors contributes to the rapid pace of eutrophication of Lake Winnipeg:

- Excessive inputs of phosphorus, coming from the watershed
- Regulation of the lake as a reservoir, which holds back water during the most productive growing periods
- Lower sediment loads in the Saskatchewan River due to impoundments. This means clearer water and more light penetration, and consequent greater algal growth.

Phosphorus loadings to Lake Winnipeg are shown in Figure 11.4. Phosphorus and nitrogen loadings to the lake originate from point sources, such as the city of Winnipeg wastewater outflows (and countless other wastewater treatment facilities, whether municipal or

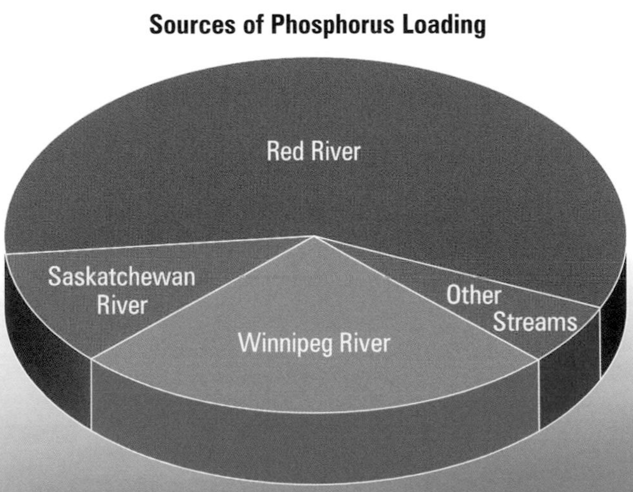

Figure 11.4. Sources of Phosphorus Loading to Lake Winnipeg.[8]

industrial), and non-point sources, such as run-off from all soils, but particularly from agricultural lands. Fifty-three percent of the phosphorous entering the lake is from non-Manitoba sources. The city of Winnipeg on average contributes seven percent of the phosphorus loading to Lake Winnipeg. The contribution from agricultural land in Manitoba is estimated to be 5% of the nitrogen load and 15% of the phosphorus load to Lake Winnipeg.[7]

There is debate about how to bring Lake Winnipeg closer to natural conditions, in terms of its ecological state. Both nitrogen and phosphorus are required for accelerated eutrophication to occur. However, the ratio of nitrogen to phosphorus is quite important. The phosphorus content of commercial fertilizers has thrown the natural ratio out of balance. The simplest way to restore the appropriate ratio is to reduce the runoff of phosphorus from the landscape and from communities. Measures that reduce nitrogen in runoff serve to limit ammonia toxicity, particularly in tributary streams. In reducing nitrogen, the importance of the ratio must be considered or extra high rates of algal growth will continue.

Regulation of lake levels and outflows from the lake may result in enhanced algal growth and accumulation of that biomass. As a consequence, nitrogen and phosphorus are accumulating in the sediments of the lake and lower concentrations are leaving the lake via the Nelson River. This may mean that even when nutrient inflows to the lake are reduced, there will still be a reservoir of nutrients bound to sediments available to support rapid algal growth.

Invasive Species

The spread of invasive species can cause habitat change, competition for food, and even local extinction of indigenous species.[9] A number of species introduced into the lake are having considerable impact on habitat and/or indigenous fish species on the lake. A few key examples are:

- **Rainbow smelt** – this is a small fish first documented in Lake Winnipeg in 1990. It apparently arrived from northwestern Ontario via the Winnipeg River. It is a voracious predator that multiplies rapidly and competes with native species, such as the emerald shiner, for food. It has become the most abundant bait fish in the north basin of Lake Winnipeg. It is also a primary food choice for the walleye population and tends to be linked to the seven-year high walleye harvests from the lake. Its effects are 1) to put competitive pressure on the emerald shiner, and 2) to cause palatability and spoilage issues related to walleye and sauger catches.
- **Asian carp tapeworm** – has recently been found in emerald shiners in Lake Winnipeg. In other locations, effects have been severe on other fishes higher in the food chain as it is spread by ingestion. Thus, the walleye and sauger populations may be threatened by this parasite's entry to the lake.
- **Common carp** – this species is, of course, not a new invasive. It has been observed in southern Manitoba waters for over a century. The carp tends to stir up bottom sediments causing turbidity issues. It can slowly cause small islands in marshes to disappear over time, such as in Netley Marsh at the south end of the lake, as it causes sediments to be eroded and carried away. The carp is also a heavy feeder on vegetation in marshes, destroying habitat for other species.
- **White bass** – a species introduced into North Dakota in 1953 that had moved downstream to Lake Winnipeg as early as 1963. It is in competition with pike, walleye and sauger for emerald shiners and zooplankton.
- ***Eubosmina coregoni*** – is a zooplankton first identified in Lake Winnipeg in 1999. It is of Eurasian origin and has quickly become the most abundant zooplankton in the north basin of the lake. It appears to be replacing native species, thus affecting the overall ecology of the lake.
- **Hybrid cattail** – an invasive from Europe began to hybridize with the North American cattails nearly two centuries ago. The hybrid is described as more robust and a better competitor than either its native or imported parent. It invades wetlands and ponds, reduces biodiversity, and displaces species more desirable for wildlife habitat. This has

happened in the Netley Marsh at the south end of Lake Winnipeg, significantly reducing the productivity and diversity of the marsh.

There are a number of well-known invasives that have not yet arrived in Lake Winnipeg but which threaten to if preventative measures are not put in place:

- **Rusty crayfish** – a bigger, more robust crayfish than the native species, which has been found in Lake of the Woods, the upper Winnipeg River and in Falcon Lake (2007). It has come to the basin from Ohio and tends to be spread by bait bucket release. Should the rusty crayfish make it to Lake Winnipeg, it can be expected to replace the native crayfish and damage the commercial fishery as it eats fish caught in nets and can cause huge damage to the netted fish in a very short time.
- **Zebra mussel** – is moving towards Lake Winnipeg from the Great Lakes and the Mississippi River, where it has caused billions of dollars in damage by clogging infrastructure and reducing the recreational value of waterways. It has a significant effect on aquatic ecosystems.
- **Viral hemoragic septicaemia** – a virus which has been found in the states to the southeast of Manitoba. When it has become established in native fish populations it has been disastrous to those populations.

Most of the invasive species that affect Lake Winnipeg negatively have arrived from the southeast and not from the Saskatchewan River basin or via the Saskatchewan River. Nonetheless, this does not mean watershed planners and managers should not pay due attention to control or removal of invasive species within the Saskatchewan River basin. Some may cause issues within the individual sub-basins. Others may migrate to Lake Winnipeg and cause issues there.

One example is grass carp. This species has been introduced into the drainage ditches in Alberta to control aquatic plants. The fish introduced have been genetically modified to eliminate the possibility of reproducing, which reduces the risk to other ecosystems. This is not to say the risk has been entirely eliminated.

Another concern is, of course, that Lake Winnipeg may become a source of invasive species that then begin to migrate upstream into the Saskatchewan River basin. While downstream migration of an invasive species is of primary concern, species that are moved for use as bait fish, for example, can quickly establish themselves in an entirely new watershed. Whether movement is upstream or downstream thus becomes almost irrelevant. All sub-basins need to be cognizant of threats posed to them or by them when it comes to invasive species, and must manage their portion of the basin accordingly.

Other Vulnerabilities

Additional challenges to the health of Lake Winnipeg, though still in need of quantification include:

- Persistent organic pollutants – which include DDT, PAHs, PCBs and dioxins that can last in biological organisms for quite some time. Some may disrupt normal functioning of organisms (endocrine disruptors). The Saskatchewan and Red river basins are largely agricultural, and pesticides used in agricultural production will find their way to the lake during the spring runoff or during summer rainstorms. The Red River Flood of 1997 resulted in significant inputs of persistent organic pollutants to the south basin of the lake.
- Pharmaceuticals and personal care products – which include antibiotics and other pharmaceuticals and disinfectants. Some are endocrine disruptors and can result in impacts on organism development and reproduction. Another concern is the enhancement of antibiotic-resistant bacteria.
- One species of snail and five species of fish in Lake Winnipeg are designated either as endangered, threatened, or of special concern.
- Wetland habitat is substantially reduced due to the control of lake levels within a reduced range.
- The cumulative effects of landscape change and climate changes on water supply to Lake Winnipeg.

Lake Winnipeg Action Plan

Several programs are aimed at improving scientific understanding of Lake Winnipeg and to reducing nutrient loadings to the lake. In 2003 Manitoba announced a plan to reduce nitrogen and phosphorous loads to Lake Winnipeg to pre-1970s levels. The plan is aimed at protecting riparian growth along the Red and Assiniboine rivers, ensuring appropriate fertilizer application, introducing new effluent regulations, reducing shoreline erosion on Lake Winnipeg, and engaging other jurisdictions in Lake Winnipeg nutrient management. As a federal contribution to meeting the challenges to the sustainability of Lake Winnipeg ecosystems, recent federal budgets have allocated $18 million to a Lake Winnipeg Basin Initiative. Through federal-provincial mechanisms, federal funding will be directed to reduction of harmful algae blooms, improved recreational water quality, restoration of the ecological integrity of Lake Winnipeg, and a sustainable fishery. Federal funding will support research information and monitoring, and facilitate governance and stewardship.

ENDNOTES

[1] McMartin, I. 1996. "Lake Agassiz Beaches and Reconstruction of Lower Lake Levels in the Shield Margin Area, Northwest of Lake Winnipeg." in *Lake Winnipeg Project: Cruise report and Scientific Results*. Todd, B.J., C.F.M. Lewis, and L.H. Thorleifson, editors. Geological Survey of Canada Open File 3113. Ottawa, ON.

[2] Lewis, C.F.M., D.L. Forbes, B.J. Todd, E Nielsen, L.H. Thorleifson, P.J. Henderson, I. McMartin, T.W. Anderson, R.N. Betcher, W.M. Buhay, S.M. Burbridge, C.J. Schroëder-Adams, J.W. King, K. Moran, C. Gibson, C.A. Jarrett, H.J. King, W.L. Lockhart, W.M. Last, G.L.D. Matile, J. Risberg, C.G. Rodrigues, A.M. Telka, and R.E. Vance 2001. "Uplift-driven Expansion Delayed by Middle Holocene Desiccation in Lake Winnipeg, Manitoba, Canada." *Geology* 29:8 743-746.

[3] Agriculture and Agri-Food Canada and Environment Canada 1996. *A National Ecological Framework for Canada*. Ottawa, ON.

[4] Todd, B.J., C.F.M. Lewis, and L.H. Thorleifson 1996. *Lake Winnipeg Project: Cruise report and Scientific Results*. Geological Survey of Canada Open File 3113. Ottawa, ON.

[5] Lake Winnipeg Stewardship Board 2006. Reducing Nutrient Loading to Lake Winnipeg and its Watershed: Our Collective Responsibility and Commitment to Action. Report to the Minister of Water Stewardship. Winnipeg, MB.

[6] Manitoba Conservation 2001. Long-term Trends in Total Nitrogen and Total Phosphorus Concentrations in Manitoba Streams. Report No. 2001-0. Winnipeg, MB.

[7] Lake Winnipeg Stewardship Board 2006. *supra.*

[8] Lake Winnipeg Implementation Committee 2007. *Restoring the Health of Lake Winnipeg*. Lake Winnipeg Implementation Committee. Winnipeg, MB.

[9] Personal Communication – Wendy Ralley, Water Quality Specialist, Manitoba Water Stewardship.

CHAPTER TWELVE
BASIN-WIDE VULNERABILITIES

CHAPTER TWELVE
BASIN-WIDE VULNERABILITIES

The Saskatchewan River basin has been profoundly altered by human activities such as agricultural development, drainage, forest harvesting, oil and gas exploration and development, and mining. Natural streamflows have been altered because of these landscape changes, and through construction of dams and diversions. The basin is also vulnerable to stresses that may originate beyond its boundary. Changes and environmental stresses introduced by human activity will ultimately affect the environmental quality of the basin's receiving water body, Lake Winnipeg.

Key vulnerabilities of the basin are related to physical and ecological effects of landscape modification, water supplies to meet human and other needs, effects of urban development on water quality, natural hazards such as floods and droughts, and invasive species. The challenge for integrated water resources management is to attempt to balance human and environmental needs within this diverse river basin. This implies a need for a more robust institutional framework to meet future challenges.

LANDSCAPE MODIFICATION

The landscape of the Saskatchewan River basin has completely changed in the last 150 years. Natural grasslands and parkland forests have given way to agricultural development, foothills forests have been disturbed by oils and gas exploration, as well as by timber harvesting, and wetlands have been drained. Expansion of urban centres and growth of transportation networks to support those centres continue to transform the natural landscape.

Landscape changes also affect the hydrologic regime of the basin, through changes in storage of surface and groundwater, and in modifications to flow patterns. Physical and hydrological changes lead to biological change, through changes in aquatic, riparian and terrestrial habitat.

Wetlands are critically important to the lifecycle of ducks, geese, swans, and other waterbirds. They also provide food and habitat for fish, shorebirds and mammals. Wetlands modify effects of hydrologic events, recharge or receive groundwater, and filter sediments and contaminants. Wetlands make up a significant portion of the land surface of the prairie and boreal lands of the basin. Landscape changes threaten the wetlands of the plains and of the boreal forest. Wetlands conservation programs are aimed at protecting critical wetlands, mapping other wetlands and related upland habitat, and identifying best management practices for resource development.

Riparian areas adjacent to wetlands, lakes and streams provide unique ecosystems and are important to landscape health. Riparian health can be affected, not only by human activity, but also by natural phenomena such as floods and droughts. Riparian health may be assessed by measuring a standard suite of physical and vegetative parameters at selected sites. Sites where 80 percent of the parameters show little impairment of riparian function are considered healthy. Sites with some impairment are considered healthy, but with problems, and sites with severe impairment are considered unhealthy.[1] In general, about one-half of the riparian areas of the basin can be considered healthy, but with problems. Many human influences have been identified, and more work is needed to present a thorough assessment of riparian health.

Agriculture

The soils of the prairies developed under grassland vegetation, which supported substantial populations of numerous animal species. At the same time, sloughs and potholes dotted the landscape, providing habitat for birds and other wildlife. Trees in river valleys also provided sanctuary. The vegetation of the region varied from short grasses in the drier sections, to tall grasses in areas of increased rainfall, to reeds and sedges in low-lying areas.

Agricultural development has irrevocably altered the natural landscape of prairie Canada, affecting both physical attributes and biological resources.
As agriculture became more intensive and farm equipment increased in size, wetlands were drained, trees removed, and grasslands cultivated. Only one percent of the tall grass prairie, 18 percent of the short-grass prairie, 25 percent of the mixed grass prairie, and 25 percent of the aspen parkland remain.[2] Over 70 percent of pre-settlement wetlands have been drained or altered to the point of no longer functioning as wetlands ecosystems. As a result, habitat for many plant and animal species has been lost to a grains and forage monoculture. Remaining areas of unaltered wildlife habitat have become progressively more fragmented, more isolated, and often too small to sustain viable populations of once abundant species.

Grazing by cattle and other domestic animals reduces plant cover and the supply of food and shelter for meadow and grassland species of mammals, birds and invertebrates. On the other hand, some forms of wildlife thrive under conditions arising from agriculture. Farm shelterbelts and abandoned farmsteads provide cover for numerous species of birds. Other species have benefited from increased feeding opportunities provided by agricultural crops.

While the area devoted to farming in the Prairie Provinces has not increased over the last two decades, land use continues to evolve. Since 1981, there has been a dramatic decrease in the practice of summer fallowing, from 20 percent to 7 percent of the area in farms in Alberta and Saskatchewan.[3] This decrease in summer fallow is almost entirely taken up by an increase in area under crops. Cropped areas now cover 52 percent of the farm area of the two provinces. Significant changes in cropping practices have also occurred during this same period, with an ever-increasing number of farmers adopting zero or minimum till. In general, current tillage practices improve soil moisture for crop growth, but lead to less runoff.

Another significant trend is that farmers increasingly rent the land they farm rather than owning it. Stewardship of agricultural land, therefore, becomes a joint responsibility of the owner and renter.

The environmental sustainability of farmed areas of the Saskatchewan River basin cannot be considered without first considering the factors that affect environmental, social and economic aspects of agricultural production. These factors include protecting quality and productivity of farmed soils; reducing soil erosion and salinity; conserving and restoring soil organic matter; protecting quality of surface and groundwater; preserving and restoring riparian zones; and maintaining or improving the quality of rangelands.[4] Careful attention to these factors will inevitably lead to a better match of land use to land capability. Enhancing the sustainability of agriculture production can, with care, improve environmental performance.

Forestry

While most of the Saskatchewan River basin is agricultural land, the western and northern parts of the basin include the western boreal forest. The forests of the Saskatchewan River basin include the foothills forest in Alberta, parkland forests of the North Saskatchewan River sub-basin in Alberta and Saskatchewan, as well as the boreal forest of the lower Saskatchewan River sub-basin in Saskatchewan and Manitoba. The foothills forest of the eastern slopes of the Rocky Mountains is a unique part of the boreal forest. The conifer forest at higher elevations consists of stands of spruce, pine and fir. The mixed-wood forest at lower elevations contains hardwoods and conifers and significant wetlands.

Beyond the boundaries of the national parks and designated wilderness areas, the foothills forest is extensively logged. Harvesting old-growth forests reduces unique habitat. The oil and gas sector also has a major effect on the foothills forest by cutting seismic lines, constructing roads and pipelines, and installing extraction facilities. Construction of access roads and other linear features fragments habit. The old growth lodgepole pine stands of this region are particularly threatened by the current outbreak of mountain pine beetle. This could spread to other pines. Changes in composition and age structure of the foothills forest will alter runoff from these forests. In general, decreases in the average age of a forest will lead to increases in runoff.

The parkland forest or boreal transition forest is a mix of trees – largely poplar – shrubs and wetlands in Alberta and Saskatchewan. It is highly productive habitat for birds, mammals and plants. Over time, agricultural expansion has led to conversion of this transition forest to cropped land. In general, this has led to wetland drainage, loss of habitat, decreased biodiversity and hydrological change. The spruce and pine forests in portions of this forest are also subject to logging pressures.

While the boreal forest of the lower Saskatchewan River basin has generally been modified by forest harvesting, the forest of the Precambrian Shield portions of the lower basin in Saskatchewan and Manitoba has been relatively untouched by human activity. The principal disturbances have been road construction and mining, although there is some logging in the Manitoba portion of the shield.

Urban Development

Urban centres in the Saskatchewan River basin are growing rapidly and much of that growth is low-density, automobile-dependent, suburban development. The preference for a suburban life style comes with costs – environmental, social and economic. Loss of wildlife habitat, relatively high water use for lawn watering, and damage to receiving waters from stormwater runoff are some of the environmental costs. Other effects include loss of productive farmland, increased cost of water and transportation infrastructure, and socio-economic fragmentation. Some cities are considering Smart Growth concepts as a means of ensuring more sustainable urban growth patterns.[5]

WATER SUPPLY

In 1900, the first of many projects that would alter timing and quantity of the flows in the Saskatchewan River basin was in operation. This was the Great Irrigation Canal, used to divert water from the St. Mary River southeast of Cardston to the Lethbridge area. In 1910, a weir was constructed on the Bow River in Calgary to divert water for irrigation. A hydroelectric project at Horseshoe Falls on the Bow River in 1911 provided electricity to Calgary. These were just the first of many projects, particularly in the Oldman and Bow river basins, that store or divert water for irrigation and power generation. Today, there are over 30 such projects in the basin, the vast majority being found in the South Saskatchewan basin.

The dams and diversions of the basin make a major contribution to the economic vitality of the basin. Water supplies permit irrigation development, enable value-added agricultural processing, sustain urban centres, and promote industrial growth. They also help mitigate, to some degree, the environmental consequences of human developments.

Considering the basin as a whole, water supplies are sufficient to meet reasonable needs, if managed wisely. The management challenge differs in different parts of the basin. The quantity of water consumed in the North Saskatchewan River basin in a typical year is small. Under the terms of existing water allocations, that quantity could be double its current size. Even then, this would be small compared to the reliable water supply. Water consumption is also very small downstream on the Saskatchewan River.

The South Saskatchewan River basin is a different matter, however. About 35 percent of the naturalized flow is consumed in a median year. The Bow and Oldman sub-basins can be considered fully allocated. Alberta has placed a cap on new water licences in those sub-basins. The current water-supply situation prompts questions about water supplies under future climate scenarios, and raises concerns about environmental effects of existing and proposed dams and diversions.

Water supplies originating with the mountain-fed principal streams of the basin are much more reliable than those of the plains-fed tributaries. For these streams, reliable flow tends to be small so potential investments in water infrastructure tend not to meet economic tests. As much of the land producing plains-runoff is agricultural, land-use change alters runoff.

CLIMATE CHANGE

Climate change is a global problem that will affect the Saskatchewan River basin. The hydrological effects of climate change should be considered within the context of natural variability. There is considerable climatic and hydrological variability in the Saskatchewan River basin, both within years and between years, and basin residents and aquatic ecosystems have adapted to this variability. Water management authorities take this into account in developing programs and projects. Adaptation to the effects of climate change has to be considered in addition to adaptation to natural variability.

Recent climate change scenarios for 2050 for the mountain headwaters of the South Saskatchewan River indicate increases in annual mean temperature of 2.0°C and of 9.5 percent in total precipitation. Winters are projected to be wetter and warmer; springs, wetter and somewhat warmer; summers drier and much warmer; and autumns wetter and warmer. For 2080, equivalent annual figures indicate a temperature increase of 3.8 degrees and a precipitation increase of 15.2 percent.[6] Scenarios for the plains portion of the basin tend to show similar temperature increases, but both increases and decreases in annual precipitation. Trend analysis of temperature and precipitation from the recent past tend to show increased temperatures and no consistent trend in precipitation.

A recent review of trends in temperature and precipitation that included the plains portion of the basin indicated that from 1951 to 2004 average daily maximum temperatures increased by about one-fifth of a Celsius degree each decade, and that average daily minimum temperatures increased somewhat more than this. Over the same period, annual snowfall amounts declined throughout the basin, while annual rainfall increased. In Saskatchewan, there was an overall increase in annual precipitation, while Alberta and Manitoba showed annual decreases.[7]

A reasonable climate scenario for the Saskatchewan River basin could be based on the certainty of continued warming, the possibility of increased mountain precipitation, and the likelihood of seasonal changes in precipitation, even if annual plains precipitation remains the same. The relationship between this scenario, or any other, and future water supplies is difficult to determine. Water supplies in the basin are highly dependent on snowmelt. Increased temperatures will inevitably lead to an increased percentage of annual precipitation falling as rain rather than snow.

Projecting runoff under climate change is complicated by the fact that precipitation also recharges groundwater, which, in turn, can sustain streamflow during low flow periods. Considering the more reliable mountain runoff, there are very few current trends suggesting declining annual runoff, although spring snowmelt is occurring earlier now than in the past. Runoff from the water towers is also affected by the state of the forests on the eastern slopes of the Rockies. In general, younger forest stands yield more runoff than mature stands. Streams originating on the plains are showing decreases in spring runoff and annual runoff. These reductions could be the effect of changes in land-use practices, such as conservation tillage, as well as a response to changing climate.

Even if future average water supply conditions are within the ability of basin residents to adapt, climate change could lead to a higher probability of extreme conditions, such as floods and drought. The economic effects of the 2001-2002 drought in the basin were considerable, and potential effects of a widespread decadal drought are staggering to contemplate.

DAMS AND DIVERSIONS

Dams and weirs constructed in the basin have several important effects. First, they change the portion of the river channel where the project is constructed from a river environment to a lake environment. Reservoirs inevitably change distribution and abundance of aquatic biota. Nutrients leached from flooded soils may actually increase biological productivity, albeit for species different from the original dominant inhabitants.[8] Even when a project provides little storage, such as a run-of-the-river hydro-facility, dams and weirs fragment the natural ecosystem by providing barriers to migration of aquatic species and disrupting riparian habitat.

Reservoirs store water during the spring runoff and release it for later use. In the Saskatchewan River basin, hydroelectric stations tend to be used to meet peak load requirements, while thermal generation is used to meet base loads. Although peak power demands occur on a daily basis, hydroelectric stations tend to reverse the high and low cycles of the natural hydrograph. As overall electricity demand is greater in the winter than in the summer, river flows can be higher than natural in the winter and lower in the summer. While hydroelectric projects consume no water other than losses to evaporation, they do significantly alter the flow pattern. Because irrigation water demands are in the summer, flow conditions downstream may in some cases mimic those of the natural hydrograph when water is released from storage for use downstream. Irrigation water demands, however, are significant enough to reduce downstream flows, thus raising concerns about instream flow requirements for aquatic life.

River channels immediately downstream of a dam will tend to scour because the water discharged from the reservoir carries less sediment than the pre-project water. Further downstream, the absence of a spring peak flow (except under very high runoff conditions) reduces the natural flushing of sediments deposited in the river channel, thus changing the character of the river channel. In particular, permanent vegetation is likely to develop in areas now subject to decreased annual flooding. Conversely, riparian vegetation, such as cottonwood trees, requires periodic flooding to sustain new growth. Decreased flooding inevitably leads to loss of the riparian forest. Some aquatic species are sustained by periodic flushing of the channel.

Reservoirs also affect the thermal regime of the river. Summer releases tend to be cooler than normal, while winter releases are warmer. Water temperatures will affect the distribution of fish species downstream of a reservoir. Changes in the winter flow regime will change ice conditions in the stream and affect the winter aquatic ecology.[9]

The physical, biogeochemical, and biological processes within the reservoir will affect water quality in the reservoir and downstream. The degree to which water quality is affected will depend on factors such as the surface-to-volume ratio and depth of the reservoir, surficial geology and soils of the catchment, sedimentation rates, magnitude and timing of flows entering the reservoir, and biological productivity of the reservoir.

MUNICIPAL WATER AND WASTEWATER

Continued urban growth and the related demand for water services such as water supply, wastewater treatment, and drainage pose a considerable challenge. All the urban centres in the basin provide treated water and some level of wastewater treatment to household, industrial, commercial, and institutional users. The cost of providing these services is recovered through water charges and municipal taxes. Two of the key challenges for the Saskatchewan River basin are providing safe drinking water and reducing effects of wastewater effluents on downstream communities and ecosystems.

Water Supply

Almost all the water used in the cities of the basin is surface water. Groundwater tends to be used only by smaller communities and farmsteads. Although urban water withdrawals are large, household water consumption in the basin is relatively small. The reason for this is that almost all the domestic water used indoors returns to the aquatic system as wastewater; only water used outdoors tends to be consumed. If one includes stormwater runoff as part of the contribution of urban centres to streamflow, most urban centres in the basin return more surface water to the natural system than they withdraw. Urban centres also tend to be net contributors to the groundwater system, as water tables in urban areas can be as much as five metres higher than those in undeveloped areas. There are several reasons for this, the most important being excessive lawn watering.[10]

The main advantage of urban water conservation, therefore, lies not so much in saving water, as in postponing the need for capital investments in water supply and wastewater treatment systems. Calgary, for example, has a goal of decreasing per capita water consumption by 30 percent in 30 years.[11] Water-use efficiency goals of this magnitude are readily achievable; Denver uses about the same quantity of water today as it did in the 1960s, despite a 65 percent increase in population. Reduced water withdrawals also benefit the aquatic health of the streams receiving municipal effluents, by enabling more effective operation of wastewater treatment systems.

Safe drinking water and public health and environmental consequences of municipal effluents are shared concerns among municipal, provincial, and federal governments. The federal government has little direct authority over drinking water supplies, except in the case of federal lands such as First Nations reserves. Provincial governments have primary jurisdiction and responsibility for drinking water quality. However, a federal/provincial/ territorial government committee on drinking water standards develops and maintains *Guidelines for Drinking Water Quality*.[12] The committee takes into account health assessments (both domestic and international), treatment costs, and other economic factors. The *Guidelines* specify maximum acceptable concentrations of substances known to or suspected of causing health effects.

Public concerns about safe drinking water can be addressed through source water protection, effective water treatment, a secure distribution system, and robust operating and control systems. Larger centres have the skilled personnel and financial resources to design, build, operate, and maintain a satisfactory water supply system. This is not always the case for smaller centres and First Nations reserves. Difficulties lie not only in the need to secure resources and skills to implement a water supply system, but also in particular problems related to protecting and enhancing local source waters, including meeting the need for innovative small-scale systems.[13] In fact, rural water supplies in the basin rarely meet health and aesthetic objectives. The United States Environmental Protection Agency has observed that municipal water systems serving more than 20 000 people tend to be safer than smaller systems.

Wastewater

Municipal wastewater consists of human and other organic waste, suspended solids, nutrients, microorganisms, and various household and industrial chemicals. It may also contain stormwater runoff in centres where combined sewers are still in use. All cities in the basin treat their wastewater before discharging it to the natural system. The treatment process reduces contaminant levels of the effluent, but the sheer volume of effluents discharged annually to the environment make urban wastewater an environmental concern. Effluent suppresses oxygen levels in the stream and may contain suspended solids, nutrients, organic chemicals such as pesticides, and metals. Other contaminants may include pharmaceuticals, personal care products, endocrine-disrupting compounds, and brominated flame retardants. These effluents affect the quality of the receiving waters as well as the quality of the sediments in the stream, in turn affecting the plants and animals of the ecosystem. Effluents may also lead to human health and economic effects.[14, 15]

Generally, municipal wastewaters are treated through a progression of processes usually identified as preliminary, primary, secondary, tertiary, and quaternary. These processes incrementally remove increasing amounts of suspended solids from the effluent stream and reduce the oxygen demands of the effluent. Sewage lagoons provide a level of treatment similar to secondary treatment. Some wastewater treatment systems in the basin also include nutrient reduction. Effluents are disinfected before release to the environment. All municipal effluents in the basin receive at least secondary treatment. Banff, Calgary and Saskatoon perform advanced nutrient reduction.

Stormwater

Prior to the 1940s, cities constructed combined sewers to convey sanitary and stormwater runoff to receiving streams. Even as wastewater treatment facilities were in development, combined sewers continued to discharge untreated sewage to receiving waters during high-runoff events. These combined sewers still exist in the central cores of some cities in the basin. Cities are modifying infrastructure to reduce overflow incidents. The City of Edmonton, for example, is increasing capture and treatment of wet weather flows in the combined sewer system from 56 to 86 percent, and reducing average annual overflow incidents from 89 to 46.

Recognizing problems associated with combined sewers, cities developed sewer systems exclusively for stormwater runoff. Early systems were aimed, primarily, at reducing property damages from flooding and allowing traffic to move during storms. Some of these systems caused physical damage to conveyance channels and to downstream properties, and little consideration was given to effects of stormwater runoff on aquatic resources or wildlife habitat.

Stormwater detention ponds were developed in the 1970s as a means of reducing physical damage from urban runoff, and as a means of enhancing environmental values. They have met with varying degrees of success. They will, in general, reduce downstream damages while maintaining reasonable quality water in the pond.

Stormwater runoff contains much lower levels of contaminants than sewage effluent, but flows of stormwater are much greater than those of sewage effluent and are often confined to pulses of flow during wet weather. These flow pulses contain contaminants from streets and parking lots. As wastewater treatment systems improve, effects of stormwater runoff on receiving waters become more apparent. Treatment of stormwater runoff will become an increasing requirement in the basin.

NATURAL HAZARDS

The Saskatchewan River basin is subject to both floods and droughts. Floods and droughts are primarily natural events, although they can be modified, both positively and negatively, by human activity. These phenomena affect natural ecosystems and human settlement. Although the effects of smaller floods and droughts can be mitigated, there is always the risk of a flood event exceeding the design capacity of the infrastructure, or of a drought exceeding the coping range of aquatic ecosystems, individual water users or infrastructure.

Floods

Many urban communities in the basin are in river valleys. During spring runoff and intense summer rainstorms, these communities can be flooded. Although loss of life is rare in Canadian floods, financial and other losses associated with flooding are significant. Entire communities may be disrupted for lengthy periods following a flood.

The traditional approach to reducing flood damages was through construction of structural measures such as dams, dikes, and diversions. These measures are costly to build and maintain, and may lead to a false sense of security for floodplain residents. They may also have significant environmental consequences. Current approaches tend to be non-structural: that is, the flood hazard in a community is determined, high risk property is identified, and zoning implemented to reduce the threat of flood damages. This often leads to floodplains being used for parks and other low-impact uses, rather than for homes and industries. Flood-risk areas have been determined for urban communities in the basin, and maps showing that risk are available from provincial authorities. Basin communities where at least some portion of the community is subject to flooding from streams or lakes are shown in Tables 12.1 and 12.2. The tables also identify communities where flood-risk areas have been mapped and zoned.

Rural areas of the Saskatchewan River basin are subject to flooding hazards, leading to losses in agricultural productivity and other economic losses. Damages can sometimes be reduced through operation of water infrastructure, but often adjustments to help upstream lands lead to flooding of downstream lands and vice versa.

Provincial governments produce flood forecasts and warnings so that emergency response personnel and the public can take appropriate action during a flood. Maintaining meteorological and hydrometric monitoring networks to support flood forecasting can be a problem.

Table 12.1. Alberta Communities Having a Flood Hazard.

Community	Stream	Mapped	Designated	Zoned
Airdrie	Nose Creek	✓		
Alix	Parlby Creek			
Birchwood Village Greens	Buck Lake			
	Modeste Creek			
Black Diamond/Turner Valley	Sheep River	✓	1996	✓
Bragg Creek	Elbow River	✓		
Calgary	Bow River	✓	1996	✓
	Elbow River	✓		
	Nose Creek	Draft, under review		
Camrose	Camrose Creek	✓	1995	✓
Canmore	Bow River	✓	1994	✓
Carbon	Kneehills Creek	✓		
Cardston	Lee Creek	✓	1994	✓
Cochrane	Bow River	✓	1991	✓
Coleman/Blairmore	Crowsnest River	✓		
Didsbury	Rosebud River	✓		
Drayton Valley	West Creek			
Drumheller	Red Deer River	✓		
Eckville	Medicine River	✓		
Edmonton	North Sask. River	✓		
Fort Macleod	Oldman River	✓	1992	✓
High River	Highwood River	✓		
Lacombe	Wolf Creek	✓	1998	✓
Lamont	Lamont Creek	✓		
Lethbridge	Oldman River	✓		
Markerville	Medicine River	✓		
Medicine Hat	South Saskatchewan River	✓	1991	✓
Millet	Pipestone Creek	✓		
M.D. of Bighorn	Bow River	✓	1998	✓
M.D. of Rockyview	Elbow River	✓		
Okotoks	Sheep River	✓	2000	✓
Penhold	Waskasoo Creek	Draft, under review		
Pincher Creek	Pincher Creek	✓	1994	✓
	Kettles Creek	✓	1994	✓
Ponoka	Battle River	✓	1994	✓
Priddis	Fish Creek	✓		
Radway	Namepi Creek			
Red Deer	Red Deer River	✓	1996	✓
	Waskasoo Creek	✓	1995	✓
Rochester	Tawatinaw River	✓		
Rocky Mountain House	North Saskatchewan River	Draft, under review		
Rosebud	Rosebud River			
St. Albert	Sturgeon River	✓	1991	✓
Stettler	Red Willow Creek	✓		
Sundre	Red Deer River	✓	2003	✓
Thorsby	Weed Creek	underway		
Two Hills	Vermilion River	Draft, under review		
Vegreville	Vermilion River	✓	1997	✓

Table 12.2. Saskatchewan and Manitoba Communities Having a Flood Hazard.

Community	Stream	Mapped	Designated	Zoned
Aborfield	Burntout Brook			
Battleford/North Battleford	North Saskatchewan River, Battle River	✓	1990	✓
Carrot River	Emmons Creek	✓		
Cumberland House	Saskatchewan River	partial		
Martensville	Opimihaw Creek tributary			
Melfort	Melfort Creek	✓	1988	✓
Prince Albert	North Saskatchewan River	✓		
Rosthern	Rosthern Creek			
Saskatoon	South Saskatchewan River	✓		✓
Swift Current	Swift Current Creek	✓		
Tisdale	Doghide River	✓	1989	✓
Zenon Park	Burntout Brook tributary			
RMs of Corman Park, Vanscoy Dundurn, Montrose	South Saskatchewan River	partial		
The Pas, Manitoba	Saskatchewan River	partial		

Drought

Unlike other natural hazards that can affect the basin, drought is a slow-onset phenomenon. In fact, definitions of drought vary considerably and the precise beginning and end of a drought period may be difficult to determine. All droughts begin with a deficiency in precipitation extending over a significant length of time, known as a climatological drought. If this deficiency leads to lack of availability of soil water to support agricultural activities, an agricultural drought exists. With continuing precipitation deficits, streamflows, lakes, reservoirs, and aquifers may become depleted, leading to hydrological drought. Finally, effects of meteorological, agricultural and hydrological droughts on human activity may affect human activity so significantly that we can speak of a socioeconomic drought.[16] The economic impact of the 2001-2002 nation-wide drought in Canada, if taken as one event, would constitute the largest natural disaster in Canadian history.[17]

Defining a drought requires consideration of three elements: intensity, duration and spatial coverage. In North America, the Palmer Drought Severity Index (PDSI) is frequently used to indicate the extent and severity of drought, and reconstructed PDSIs have been produced for many severe events over many decades. PDSI maps do not take into account water storage and supply factors and are, therefore, a better indication of climatological rather than hydrological drought. Efforts have been made to produce indices of surface water availability based on precipitation, streamflow, reservoir storage, and so on. While useful, different drought indices will provide different results. In terms of informing the public and water users, a consistent approach is probably more important than a 'right' approach. Products from the Prairie Farm Rehabilitation Administration's Drought Watch are good examples of this consistent approach.

The 20th century was climatologically benign compared to other recent centuries.[18] While significant droughts have taken place, for example in the 1930s, they may not have been as severe as those of previous centuries. Examination of proxy climate data using tree ring reconstruction indicates, for example, that droughts of varying intensity may have persisted in the Cypress Hills (Alberta and Saskatchewan) for almost the entire 1688-1692, 1792-1804, and 1887-1896 periods. Considering the

South Saskatchewan River, low-flow periods in the 1560s to 1570s, the first two decades of the 1700s, and the mid-1800s have been identified.[19] (Captain John Palliser's expedition of 1857-59 during this last drought is famous for declaring the southern prairies as not suitable for agricultural settlement.) Hudson's Bay Company traders at Edmonton House on the North Saskatchewan River observed that in the spring of 1796 there was 'no water in the river.'[20]

Nonetheless, the 20th century featured three major prairie drought events. The first was during the period 1917-1926, the second during the 1930s, and the third during the 1980s. The 2001-02 drought was unusual for its broad spatial coverage and intensity. Farm income on the prairies was negative or zero for the first time in 25 years.[21]

A return to the more extreme climates of previous centuries may raise the prospect of decadal droughts. Planning for a decadal drought in the entire Saskatchewan River basin is very conservative. Consider, for example that in 1981, a very dry year in southern Saskatchewan, there was a significant flood threat on the North Saskatchewan River and flows in the Saskatchewan basin as a whole were well above normal. A simplistic account of the spatial coverage of low-flow years in western Canada can be seen in Table 12.3. The table compares the low-flow years for two mountain-fed streams, one stream originating in the Cypress Hills, and two prairie streams. The Souris River record did not start until 1930, but the others start in 1912 or shortly after. The scatter in the low-flow years is very evident; the only frequently occurring years are 1931, 1977, and 1988.

Drought preparedness can be a difficult task because of the slow-onset nature of the problem and the lack of agreement on drought definitions and preparedness methodologies. Current approaches use risk management approaches to define the problem and to determine the public-policy response.
A drought-preparedness plan is much preferred to taking a crisis-management approach to drought response. Alberta's Drought Risk Management Plan is an example of drought-preparedness planning.

INVASIVE SPECIES

Invasive species are animals, plants or micro-organisms originating in other countries, or from other ecosystems outside the basin. They are characterized by an ability to reproduce and spread rapidly, as well as by having negative attributes that affect natural systems, crops and people. They often have no natural enemies to limit their reproduction, and spread where they are introduced. Invasive species threaten the environment by causing habitat loss for native species or by out-competing them. They threaten the

Table 12.3. Comparison of Low Flow Years in Prairie Canada.

Rank	South Saskatchewan*	North Saskatchewan*	Battle River*	Battle Creek*	Souris River*	Red River
1	2001	1942	1930	1949	1988	1934
2	1941	1941	1961	1931	1937	1931
3	1931	1975	2004	2001	1931	1935
4	1977	2001	1931	1984	1940	1939
5	1984	1988	1977	2000	1932	1933
6	1988	2002	1929	1977	1961	1937
7	1944	1929	1945	1961	1945	1977
8	2000	1984	1942	1992	1935	1936
9	1949	1919	1941	1989	1977	1940
10	1936	1937	2001	1988	1973	1961

** naturalized flows at international or interprovincial boundary*

economy through pest control costs and economic losses. As well, they threaten social values by altering the natural landscape, decreasing property values, or affecting our health. Some introductions, the European starling and the house sparrow, have been deliberate, while others such as the Norwegian rat were accidental. (Alberta has a program aimed at keeping rats out of the province.) Recent examples of invasive species in the basin include the mountain pine beetle and purple loosestrife.

The mountain pine beetle is a small flying insect that has a native range extending from Mexico to central British Columbia, with an eastern extent near the Alberta boundary. The beetles preferentially attack mature pine trees, leading to stands of trees with reddish needles that eventually turn grey. The lodgepole pine is the primary host for the mountain pine beetle in Alberta. There are concerns that the infestation may spread to jack pine or non-pine species such as spruce.

The infestation is having a significant effect on parts of the Saskatchewan River basin headwaters. The death of the trees or the preventive cutting being conducted on licensed Forest Management Areas will change the habitat and hydrology of involved areas.

Severe winter temperatures tend to kill the beetle larvae but several days of temperatures below -30°C are required. The mild winters of recent years, combined with the relatively mature Alberta forests, are considered important factors in the current infestation.

Purple loosestrife is an herbaceous wetland perennial introduced into eastern North America from Europe in the early 1800s, but its first occurrence in Alberta was at Medicine Hat in 1990. It is believed that purple loosestrife arrived in the ballast of cargo ships, or perhaps through deliberate introduction by horticulturalists. Purple Loosestrife has square, woody stalks over one metre in height and pink/purple flowering spikes. It is classified as a noxious weed in the basin and nursery owners have stopped selling it.

Purple loosestrife invades wetlands, reducing the size and diversity of natural plant communities. Once purple loosestrife invades an area and eliminates native flora, the wildlife that once depended upon the native flora are displaced and those that cannot move into new areas are lost. What remains is a biological desert, devoid of native plant and wildlife species. Purple loosestrife has no natural predators in North America. There are three options for control: chemical, mechanical and biological. Chemical control is difficult because herbicides should not be used in water bodies and should be used with care near water bodies.

Invasive species can be introduced through movement of goods or people, natural dispersal using winds or water movement, or by climate change effects on habitat. There are many potential threats to the aquatic systems of the basin, including zebra mussels and whirling disease, an infectious disease affecting trout.

INSTITUTIONAL DEVELOPMENT

Governments at all levels have developed a sophisticated web of legislation and programs that apply to various aspects of water management in the Saskatchewan River basin. The *Water for Life Strategy* in Alberta, *Long-term Safe Drinking Water Strategy* in Saskatchewan and *The Manitoba Water Strategy* are examples. At the same time municipal governments, agricultural producers, industries, and other organizations have developed, over time, their own programs in response to legislation, regulation and other perceived needs. Contemporary water management seeks to engage basin interests and the general public in meeting the needs of society, without degrading the natural environment. There is an underlying concept of shared governance, at least as it pertains to water planning.

Traditional water management emphasized problem solving, but the solution to one problem was often accompanied by unintended consequences. There is every expectation that water management will grow more complex as the ever-increasing population of the Saskatchewan River basin faces the vulnerabilities and threats identified earlier in this chapter. The water resources of the basin are finite. Meeting future challenges will depend not only on better scientific understanding and technological improvements, but also on institutional development that encourages integrated and adaptive approaches to water management. These approaches require legislative and policy support, appropriate science, monitoring and data, and a basin or sub-basin scale institutional framework that accommodates various interests.

Integrated water resources management cannot be achieved quickly or without difficulty. There is certainly no operations manual for engaging in integrated water resources management. Drawing a circle around water-related activity in a basin will inevitably result in a series of intersecting circles around water and other factors, such as land management, energy, wildlife, fisheries, and so on. Natural resources agencies and organizations tend to be organized along sectoral lines; thus, the challenge lies in integrating water resources activity across those sectors.

Turning to the Saskatchewan River basin, there is a significant body of legislation and policy relating to water management in this basin. Chapter Three of this report considers these matters in some depth.

As regards science, monitoring and data, while there are significant programs in operation in the basin, there are many knowledge gaps related to matters such as climate change effects on hydrology, hydrological processes themselves, sources and pathways of contaminants, aquatic and riparian habitat, and water conservation. Data gaps are also evident. Although there are excellent data available on water allocation, there are little data on actual water diversion or consumption, or on groundwater quantity or quality. Even when data are collected, they are sometimes difficult to obtain. The Alberta Water Portal is a recent example of water data made more accessible to the public. There is also a need to continue to build capacity in the various regional planning organizations in the Saskatchewan River basin. The Water Planning and Advisory Councils, Water Advisory Committees, or Conservation Districts of the basin need to be nurtured and supported so that they can reach a common understanding of key vulnerabilities and threats, and explore possibilities for effective measures to meet those challenges.

At present, there are only two multi-interest organizations with a mandate that covers the entire Canadian portion of the Saskatchewan River basin: the Prairie Provinces Water Board and the Partners FOR the Saskatchewan River basin. One is a federal-provincial board and the other a water stewardship organization. As organizations in the basin grapple with increasingly more difficult issues, not the least of which will be the deteriorating state of Lake Winnipeg, an enhanced state of institutional readiness will be needed. There will be an increasing need to engage governments at all levels, including First Nations, in determining a sustainable way forward for the basin.

This State of the Saskatchewan River Basin Report was based on existing information. It identifies water-related concerns that occur in all or in parts of the Saskatchewan River basin. Some of the challenges facing water managers and institutions at various levels throughout the basin in the future may include:

- Reaching consensus on key vulnerabilities
- Identifying notable knowledge and information gaps
- Integrating IWMP with land use planning
- Sharing available information across jurisdictions and between orders of government
- Integrating First Nations and Métis governments into IWMP initiatives
- Creating a sense of a Saskatchewan River basin community around the water management discussion
- Accommodating increasing complexity, while also broadening the base of decision-making related to watershed management

- Adapting institutions and management to accommodate new information
- Adapting policies and programs to enable decisions to be made more quickly, but with more rigour than may currently be the practice

This report should be taken, not as an end in itself, but as one step on the path to sustainable water management for the basin.

ENDNOTES

[1] Alberta Riparian Habitat Management Society – Cows and Fish 2008. *Overview of Riparian Health in Alberta – a Review of Cows and Fish Sites from 1997-2006*. Cows and Fish Report 035. Prepared for Alberta Environment. Lethbridge, AB.

[2] Gauthier, D.A. and J.D. Henry 1989. "Misunderstanding the Prairies" in *Endangered Spaces: The Future for Canada's Wilderness*, M. Hummel ed. Kay Porter Books. Toronto, ON.

[3] Statistics Canada. *Census of Agriculture 1981, 1986, 1991, 1996, 2001, 2006*. Accessed on-line.

[4] Prairie Farm Rehabilitation Administration 2000. *Prairie Agricultural Landscapes: A Land Resource Review*. Prairie Farm Rehabilitation Administration, Regina, SK.

[5] Couroux, D., N. Keough, B. Miller, J. Row 2006. *Toward Smart Growth in Calgary*. A Discussion Paper Prepared for the Calgary Citizens Forum.

[6] Martz, L., J. Bruneau, and J.T. Rolfe (eds) 2007. *Climate Change and Water, South Saskatchewan River Basin*. University of Saskatchewan, Saskatoon, SK.

[7] Cutforth, H.W. and D. Judiesch 2007. "Long-term Changes to Incoming Solar Energy on the Canadian Prairies." *Agricultural and Forest Meteorology,* 145: 167-175

[8] Prowse, T.D., F.W. Wrona and G. Power 2004. "Dams, Reservoirs and Flow Regulation." Chapter 2 in *Threats to Water Availability in Canada*. National Water Research Institute, Environment Canada, Burlington, ON.

[9] Prowse et al. 2004, *supra.*

[10] Berg, A.A. and J.M. Byrne 1998. "Water Table Development Due to Household and Park Irrigation in Lethbridge, Alberta." *Canadian Water Resources Journal*, 23(1):61-75

[11] Infraguide (undated). *Securing Calgary's Water Supply in the Face of Explosive Population Growth*. Canadian Public Works Association.

[12] Health Canada 1996. *Guidelines for Canadian Drinking Water Quality*. Sixth Edition. Ministry of Supply and Services, Ottawa, ON.

[13] Corkal, D.R., W.C. Schutzman and C.R. Hilliard 2004. "Rural Water Safety from the Source to the On-farm Tap." *Journal of Toxicology and Environmental Health*, Part A. 67:1619-1642

[14] Canadian Council of Ministers of the Environment (CCME) 2006. *Municipal Wastewater Effluent in Canada*. CCME, Winnipeg, MB.

[15] Servos, M., P. Chambers, R. Macdonald, and G. Van Der Kraak 2001. "Municipal Wastewater Effluents." Chapter 9 in *Threats to Sources of Drinking Water and Aquatic System Health in Canada*. National Water Research Institute, Environment Canada, Burlington, ON

[16] Wilhite, D.A. and Margie Buchanan-Smith 2005. "Drought as Hazard: Understanding the Natural and Social Context" in *Drought and Water Crises, Science Technology and Management Issues*, D. A. Wilhite, Ed. Taylor & Francis Group, Boca Raton, Florida.

[17] Wheaton, E., S. Kulshreshtha, V. Wittrock, B.R. Bonsal, A. Chipanshi, C. Grant, and G. Koshida 2005. *Canadian Droughts of 2001 and 2002: Climatology, Impacts, and Adaptations*. Volumes I and II. Prepared for Agriculture and Agri-Food Canada. Saskatchewan Research Council, Saskatoon, SK.

[18] Sauchyn, D.J. and W.R. Skinner, 2001. "A Proxy Record of Drought Severity for the Southwestern Canadian Plains". *Canadian Water Resources Journal,* 26:2 253-272

[19] Case, R.A. and G.M. MacDonald 2003. "Tree Ring Reconstruction of Streamflow for Three Canadian Prairie Rivers." *Journal of the American Water Resources Association*, June 2003, 703-716.

[20] Sauchyn, D.J., J. Stroich and A. Beriault 2003. "A Paleoclimate Context for the Drought of 1999-2001 in the Northern Great Plains of North America". *The Geographical Journal,* 169:2 158-167.Publishing Ltd

[21] Wheaton, E., S. Kulshreshtha, V. Wittrock, and G. Koshida 2008. "Hard Times: Hard Lessons from the Canadian Drought of 2001 and 2002." *The Canadian Geographer,* 52:2 241-262.

ACKNOWLEDGEMENTS

Documents used in the preparation of this report are identified in endnotes in each chapter. Five publications were used extensively:

Ecological Stratification Working Group 1996. *A National Ecological Framework for Canada*. Canadian Soil Information System (CanSIS), Agriculture and Agri-Food Canada, Ottawa, ON.

Alberta Environment 2007. *Current and Future Water Use in Alberta*. Prepared by AMEC Earth & Environmental. Alberta Environment. Edmonton, AB.

Alberta Environment 2007. *Information Synthesis and Initial Assessment of the Status and Health of Aquatic Ecosystems in Alberta*. Technical Report 278/279-01. Alberta Environment, Edmonton, AB.

Saskatchewan Watershed Authority 2007. *Preliminary Background Report: North Saskatchewan River Watershed*. Saskatchewan Watershed Authority, Moose Jaw, SK.

Saskatchewan Watershed Authority 2007. *Background Report, South Saskatchewan River Watershed*. Saskatchewan Watershed Authority. Regina, SK.

The report also benefited from discussions with a large number of persons who graciously gave their time in providing information and clarifying many details. Any errors in this report are, of course, the sole responsibility of the authors. The contributions of the following persons are gratefully acknowledged:

Max Abraham, Norine Ambrose, Beverly Anderson, Don Anderson, Kristina Anderson, Dave Bartesko, Dan Benoit, Mark Bennett, Barb Bosh, Norman Brandson, Amanda Burke, Brett Calverly, Les Carriere, Kevin Cash, Patricia Chambers, Jim Chen, Malcolm Conly, Darrell Corkal, Sarah Coughlin, Ken Crutchfield, John-Mark Davies, Michael Demuth, Patrick DeRocher, Don Dill, Dave Dobson, David Donald, Wayne Dybvig, Craig Emmerton, Sal Figliuzzi, Katherine Finn, Allan Gaudry, Jim Gerhart, Bryce Haimila, Denise Hammel, Bob Harrison, Robert Harrison, Ron Harrison, Tom Harrison, Thorston Hebben, Lorna Hendrickson, Wayne Hildebrand, Scott Hill, Dale Hjertaas, Melissa Hotain, Kathyrn Hull, Emily Humphrey, Shelley Humphries, Amanda Karst, Mark Kornder, Marilena Kowalchuk, Gabe Lafond, Rod Leniuk, Chelsey Lumb, Greg MacCulloch, Lis Mack, Chandra Mahabir, Harold Martens, Fred Martin, Brian Matheson, Sam Matheson, Rob Matthews, Rhonda McDougal, Billie Milholland, Jennifer Nelson, Marshall Netherwood, Dave Neufeld, Robert Newbury, Bart Oemega, Barry Oswald, Stephanie Palechek, Rhonda Pankratz, Ian Pengelly, Merrell-Ann Phare, Rick Pickering, John Pomeroy, Robin Reader, Rick Rickwood, Harry Rohde, Petra Rowell, David Samm, Elwood Scott, Tracy Scott, Shawn Sexsmith, Patricia Stevenson, Harvey Thorleifson, Gordon Thompson, Jonathan Thompson, Jane Thornton, Brenda Toth, David Trew, Garth van der Kamp, Bert Van Duin, Douwe Vanderwel, Graham Watt-Gremm, John Whitaker, Gord Will, Jim Yarotski, Brian Yee.

Photographs used in the report were provided by:

Robert Berdan Photography – *page 1, 7, 9, 32, 53, 55, 61, 63, 99 and 148.*

Ducks Unlimited Canada – *page 8, 31, 49, 65, 88, 125, 147 and 149.*

Philip K. Gregory – *page i (b, c) and 115.*

Robert Halliday – *page i (a, b).*

Istockphoto.com – *page 2, 4, 91, 93, 113 and 127.*

Bob Lee – *page ii.*

Dr. Diane F. Malley – *page 137, 139 and 146.*

Mike Murray – *page 101.*

PFRA – *page 67, 77 and 79.*

This report was prepared by R. Halliday & Associates Ltd. and SLM McLeod Consulting. Inkpot Editing Services provided the editorial work and Philip K. Gregory the graphic design.

ABBREVIATIONS, ACRONYMS AND SYMBOLS

BMP – Best Management Practice

CCME – Canadian Council of Ministers of the Environment

CD – Conservation District (Manitoba)

ENGO – Environmental Non-government Organization

dam^3 – One thousand cubic metres

DDT – Dichloro-Diphenyl-Trichloroethane

DUC – Ducks Unlimited Canada

FMA – Forest Management Agreement (Alberta and Saskatchewan)

FML – Forest Management Licence (Manitoba)

FMP – Forest Management Plan

FMU – Forest Management Unit (Alberta and Manitoba)

HBC – Hudson's Bay Company

IJC – International Joint Commission

INAC – Indian and Northern Affairs Canada

IWMP – Integrated Water Management Process

km^2 – square kilometre

LNID – Lethbridge Northern Irrigation District

m^3/s – cubic metres a second

NGO – Non-government Organization

NWC – Northwest Company

PAH – Polycyclic Aromatic Hydrocarbon

PCB – Polychlorinated Biphenyl

PDSI – Palmer Drought Severity Index

PFRA – Prairie Farm Rehabilitation Administration

PPWB – Prairie Provinces Water Board

SSEWS – Saskatoon Southeast Water Supply System

WAC – Water Advisory Committee (Saskatchewan)

WPAC – Watershed Planning Advisory Council (Alberta)

WQI – Water Quality Index

GLOSSARY

Avulsion – A break-through of the banks of a stream thus forming a new channel or a cut-off.

Baseflow – The portion of streamflow entering the river channel from groundwater sources.

Benthic Invertebrates – Animals lacking a backbone, such as insects, worms or snails, that live on or within the bottom materials of streams, lakes or wetlands.

Chain Lakes – A series of relatively long and narrow lakes found in a valley containing a stream. The lakes may have been shaped by erosion from the stream itself or, in some cases, by outwash flows following the last ice age.

Drainage Area, Gross and Effective – The entire drainage basin having a common outlet for it surface runoff. The effective drainage area is that portion of a drainage basin that contributes runoff to the main stream in a median flow year.

Ecological Land Classification – A process of delineating and classifying ecologically distinctive areas of the surface, including geology, landform, soil, vegetation, climate, wildlife, water, and human factors. These areas, known as ecozones, can be further subdivided into ecoregions and ecodistricts.

Ecosystem – A community of dependent plants, animals and microorganisms together with the physical environment that they inhabit and with which they interact.

Ecosystem Service – The benefits people obtain from ecosystems. These include provisioning services such as food and water; regulating services such as flood and disease control; cultural services such as spiritual, recreational, and cultural benefits; and supporting services such as nutrient cycling that maintain the conditions for life on earth.

Ecotone – The transition region or boundary between two ecozones.

Ecozone – See ecological land classification.

Effluent – Any outflow from a natural body of water or engineered structure. More commonly used for the liquid waste or sewage discharged into a stream or other body of water. These latter effluents may be treated before discharge to reduce harm to the environment.

Eutrophic – Refers to water bodies that are rich in nutrients and very productive in terms of aquatic plant and animal life.

Eutrophication – The process by which waters become richer in dissolved nutrients through erosion and runoff that stimulate growth of aquatic plants. Eutrophication may be a natural process in the maturation of a water body or artificially induced by fertilization. Eutrophication can cause seasonal deficiencies in dissolved oxygen.

Glacier Wastage – Refers to the loss of glacier volume due to melting of ice. That is, the annual volume of glacier ice melt that exceeds the annual volume of snow accumulation into the glacier system, causing an annual net loss of glacier volume.

Hummocky – A landscape characterized by hills, knolls or mounds.

Hydrology – The science that deals with the waters of the earth, their occurrence, circulation and distribution, their chemical and physical properties, and their reaction with their environment, including their relation to living beings.

Kettle – A depression left in glacial drift formed by the melting of an isolated block of glacial ice.

Lacustrine – Of or pertaining to lakes.

Leachate – Water that has percolated through a solid mass such as a landfill and removed some of the constituents.

Macrophyte – A rooted vascular plant. Aquatic macrophytes are commonly associated with wetlands and riparian zones.

Mainstem – The principal part of a river, excluding its tributaries.

Major Ions – These are the positively charged ions or cations, (such as calcium, magnesium, sodium and potassium) and negatively charged ions or anions, (such as chloride, bicarbonate, sulfate and bromide) that help define the quality of a stream or lake. Concentrations of major ion determine characteristics such as hardness. Major ion chemistry is routinely monitored for many streams or lakes.

Mesotrophic – Refers to water bodies that contain moderate quantities of nutrients and are moderately productive in terms of aquatic plant and animal life.

Oligotrophic – Refers to water bodies that are nutrient poor and contain little aquatic plant or animal life.

Physicals (water quality) – The physical characteristics of a water body such as concentrations of dissolved oxygen, temperature, acidity (pH), conductivity, and fluorescence. Physicals are routinely monitored in many water bodies.

Phytoplankton – The diverse community of microscopic suspended single-celled algae that forms part of the aquatic food web. Phytoplankton may form a significant part of aquatic biomass. Phytoplankton production responds to nutrient loadings. Chlorophyl a concentrations are a measure of phytoplankton.

Reach – A section of a stream channel between two defining cross-sections. Reaches are often selected on the basis of exhibiting relatively uniform characteristics.

Riparian – Of, or relating to, the banks of a stream. The riparian zone is the transition zone between the land surface and flowing water.

Seismic Survey – A means of geophysical survey that uses the reflections from a controlled source of energy, such as explosives or vibrators, to determine the characteristics of sub-surface features. Such surveys are widely used in mining and petroleum exploration.

Sublimate – Change in phase directly from solid to gaseous state, as in loss of winter snowpack.

Surficial geology – The study of unconsolidated geologic material covering bedrock. These surface materials tend to be geologically young, having been deposited during or after glacial periods. Surficial deposits include glacial till, sand and gravel, and clays and silts.

Trophic Status – A measure of biological productivity of streams, lakes an wetlands.

Water Allocation – Under western water law, a specified annual quantity of water set aside for the beneficial use of an identified user. Allocations are subject to provincial licensing requirements.

Water Use – Consumptive – Water put to beneficial use that is consumed or lost in that use and does not return to the aquatic system. Water used in irrigated agriculture, for example.

Water Use – Non-Consumptive – Water put to beneficial use that returns to the aquatic system. Cooling water for a thermal power plant, for example.